A-Level Year 2
Biology

The Complete Course for OCR A

Let's face it, Biology is a tough subject. You'll need to get to grips with a lot of difficult concepts, and have plenty of practical skills up your lab-coat sleeve.

But don't worry — this brilliant CGP book covers everything you'll need for the new OCR A course. It's packed with clear explanations, exam practice, advice on maths skills and practical investigations... and much more!

It even includes a free Online Edition to read on your PC, Mac or tablet.

How to get your free Online Edition

Go to **cgpbooks.co.uk/extras** and enter this code...

This code will only work once. If someone has used this book before you, they may have already claimed the Online Edition.

Contents

Module 6

How to use this book

Learning Objectives
- These tell you exactly what you need to learn, or be able to do, for the exam.
- There's a specification reference at the bottom that links to the OCR A specification.

Tips
These are here to help you understand the theory.

Examples
These are here to help you understand the theory.

Exam Tips
There are tips throughout the book to help with all sorts of things to do with answering exam questions.

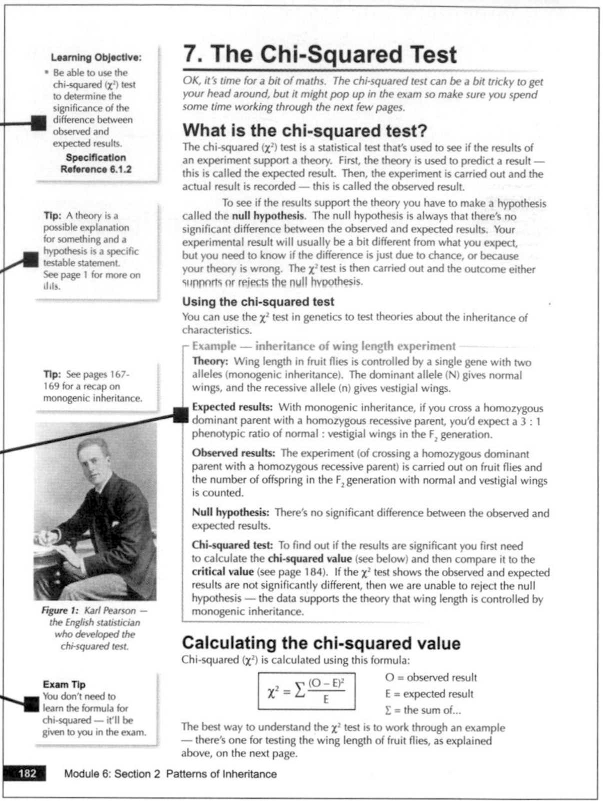

Learning Objective:
- Be able to use the chi-squared (χ^2) test to determine the significance of the difference between observed and expected results.
  Specification Reference 6.1.2

7. The Chi-Squared Test

OK, it's time for a bit of maths. The chi-squared test can be a bit tricky to get your head around, but it might pop up in the exam so make sure you spend some time working through the next few pages.

What is the chi-squared test?
The chi-squared (χ^2) test is a statistical test that's used to see if the results of an experiment support a theory. First, the theory is used to predict a result — this is called the expected result. Then, the experiment is carried out and the actual result is recorded — this is called the observed result.

To see if the results support the theory you have to make a hypothesis called the **null hypothesis**. The null hypothesis is always that there's no significant difference between the observed and expected results. Your experimental result will usually be a bit different from what you expect, but you need to know if the difference is just due to chance, or because your theory is wrong. The χ^2 test is then carried out and the outcome either supports or rejects the null hypothesis.

Tip: A theory is a possible explanation for something and a hypothesis is a specific testable statement. See page 1 for more on this.

Using the chi-squared test
You can use the χ^2 test in genetics to test theories about the inheritance of characteristics.

┌─ Example — inheritance of wing length experiment ─
Theory: Wing length in fruit flies is controlled by a single gene with two alleles (monogenic inheritance). The dominant allele (N) gives normal wings, and the recessive allele (n) gives vestigial wings.

Tip: See pages 167-169 for a recap on monogenic inheritance.

Expected results: With monogenic inheritance, if you cross a homozygous dominant parent with a homozygous recessive parent, you'd expect a 3 : 1 phenotypic ratio of normal : vestigial wings in the F_2 generation.

Observed results: The experiment (of crossing a homozygous dominant parent with a homozygous recessive parent) is carried out on fruit flies and the number of offspring in the F_2 generation with normal and vestigial wings is counted.

Null hypothesis: There's no significant difference between the observed and expected results.

Chi-squared test: To find out if the results are significant you first need to calculate the **chi-squared value** (see below) and then compare it to the **critical value** (see page 184). If the χ^2 test shows the observed and expected results are not significantly different, then we are unable to reject the null hypothesis — the data supports the theory that wing length is controlled by monogenic inheritance.

Figure 1: Karl Pearson — the English statistician who developed the chi-squared test.

Calculating the chi-squared value
Chi-squared (χ^2) is calculated using this formula:

$$\chi^2 = \sum \frac{(O - E)^2}{E}$$

O = observed result
E = expected result
Σ = the sum of...

Exam Tip
You don't need to learn the formula for chi-squared — it'll be given to you in the exam.

The best way to understand the χ^2 test is to work through an example — there's one for testing the wing length of fruit flies, as explained above, on the next page.

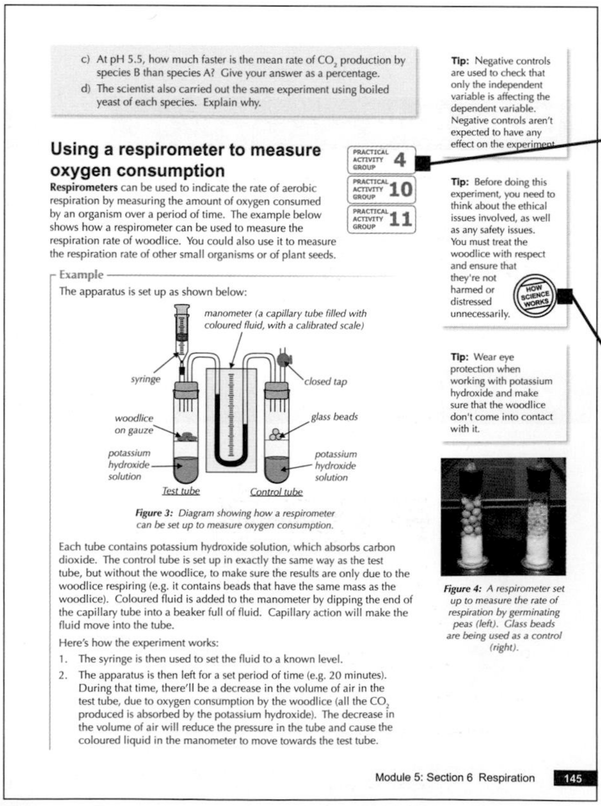

c) At pH 5.5, how much faster is the mean rate of CO_2 production by species B than species A? Give your answer as a percentage.
d) The scientist also carried out the same experiment using boiled yeast of each species. Explain why.

Tip: Negative controls are used to check that only the independent variable is affecting the dependent variable. Negative controls aren't expected to have any effect on the experiment.

Using a respirometer to measure oxygen consumption

PRACTICAL ACTIVITY GROUP 4
PRACTICAL ACTIVITY GROUP 10
PRACTICAL ACTIVITY GROUP 11

Respirometers can be used to indicate the rate of aerobic respiration by measuring the amount of oxygen consumed by an organism over a period of time. The example below shows how a respirometer can be used to measure the respiration rate of woodlice. You could also use it to measure the respiration rate of other small organisms or of plant seeds.

Tip: Before doing this experiment, you need to think about the ethical issues involved, as well as any safety issues. You must treat the woodlice with respect and ensure that they're not harmed or distressed unnecessarily.

┌─ Example ─
The apparatus is set up as shown below:

manometer (a capillary tube filled with coloured fluid, with a calibrated scale)
syringe
closed tap
woodlice on gauze
glass beads
potassium hydroxide solution
potassium hydroxide solution
Test tube
Control tube

Tip: Wear eye protection when working with potassium hydroxide and make sure that the woodlice don't come into contact with it.

Figure 3: Diagram showing how a respirometer can be set up to measure oxygen consumption.

Each tube contains potassium hydroxide solution, which absorbs carbon dioxide. The control tube is set up in exactly the same way as the test tube, but without the woodlice, to make sure the results are only due to the woodlice respiring (e.g. it contains beads that have the same mass as the woodlice). Coloured fluid is added to the manometer by dipping the end of the capillary tube into a beaker full of fluid. Capillary action will make the fluid move into the tube.

Here's how the experiment works:
1. The syringe is then used to set the fluid to a known level.
2. The apparatus is then left for a set period of time (e.g. 20 minutes). During that time, there'll be a decrease in the volume of air in the test tube, due to oxygen consumption by the woodlice (all the CO_2 produced is absorbed by the potassium hydroxide). The decrease in the volume of air will reduce the pressure in the tube and cause the coloured liquid in the manometer to move towards the test tube.

Figure 4: A respirometer set up to measure the rate of respiration by germinating peas (left). Glass beads are being used as a control (right).

Practical Activity Groups
You need to show you've mastered some key practical skills in your Practical Endorsement. Information on the skills you need and opportunities to apply them are marked up throughout the book.

How Science Works
- You need to know about How Science Works. There's a section on it at the front of the book.
- How Science Works is also covered throughout the book wherever you see this symbol.

HOW SCIENCE WORKS

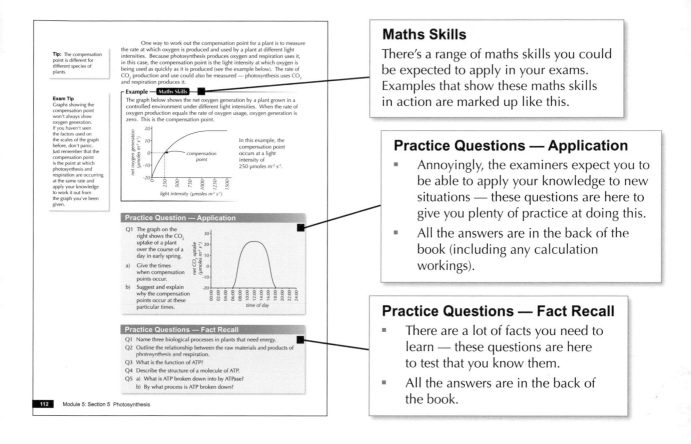

Maths Skills

There's a range of maths skills you could be expected to apply in your exams. Examples that show these maths skills in action are marked up like this.

Practice Questions — Application

- Annoyingly, the examiners expect you to be able to apply your knowledge to new situations — these questions are here to give you plenty of practice at doing this.

- All the answers are in the back of the book (including any calculation workings).

Practice Questions — Fact Recall

- There are a lot of facts you need to learn — these questions are here to test that you know them.

- All the answers are in the back of the book.

Exam-style Questions

- Practising exam-style questions is really important — you'll find some at the end of each section.

- They're the same style as the ones you'll get in the real exams — some will test your knowledge and understanding and some will test that you can apply your knowledge.

- All the answers are in the back of the book, along with a mark scheme to show you how you get the marks.

Exam Help

There's a section at the back of the book stuffed full of things to help with your exams.

Glossary

There's a glossary at the back of the book full of useful words — perfect for looking up key words and their meanings.

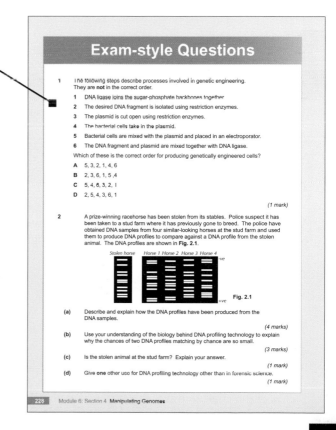

Published by CGP

Editors:
Charlotte Burrows, Katherine Faudemer, Rachel Kordan, Christopher Lindle, Rachael Marshall,
Christopher McGarry, Sarah Pattison, Claire Plowman, Rachael Rogers and Camilla Simson.

Contributors:
Gloria Barnett, James Foster, Derek Harvey and Adrian Schmit.

ISBN: 978 1 78294 325 9

With thanks to Lauren Burns, Janet Cruse-Sawyer, Glenn Rogers and Karen Wells for the proofreading.
With thanks to Laura Jakubowski for the copyright research.

Printed by Elanders Ltd, Newcastle upon Tyne.
Clipart from Corel®

The Scientific Process

Science tries to explain how and why things happen. It's all about seeking and gaining knowledge about the world around us. Scientists do this by asking questions and suggesting answers and then testing them to see if they're correct — this is the scientific process.

Developing theories

A **theory** is a possible explanation for something. Theories usually come about when scientists observe something and wonder why or how it happens. Scientists also sometimes form a **model** too — a simplified picture of what's physically going on.

┌ Examples ─────────────────────────────────

- Darwin came up with his theory of evolution by natural selection after observing wildlife (e.g. finches) and fossils during a trip around South America and the Galapagos Islands.

- The theory that smoking causes lung cancer was developed after it was observed that many people who contracted lung cancer also smoked.

- John Snow came up with the theory that cholera is transmitted in water, rather than air, after observing lots of cases of cholera clustered around a water pump.

- Edward Jenner came up with the idea that being infected with cowpox protected you from getting smallpox after observing that milkmaids didn't get smallpox.

> **Tip:** This stuff may look similar to what you learnt in Year 1, but that's because you need to understand How Science Works for Year 2 as well.

> **Tip:** A theory is only scientific if it can be tested.

Figure 1: *The doctor, John Snow.*

Testing theories

The next step is to make a **prediction** or **hypothesis** — a specific testable statement, based on the theory, about what will happen in a test situation. Then an experiment or study is carried out to provide evidence that will support the prediction (or help to disprove it). If it's disproved it's back to the drawing board — the theory is modified or a completely new one is developed.

┌ Examples ─────────────────────────────────

- Louis Pasteur designed an experiment to test his idea that 'germs' in the air caused disease and decomposition. He boiled two flasks of broth, both of which were left open to the air. One of the flasks had a curved neck (see Figure 2) to trap any airborne bacteria so they couldn't get into the broth. The broth in the flask with the curved neck stayed fresh, whereas the other broth went off. This provided evidence to support his theory. (After more evidence like this modern microbiology was born.)

- Edward Jenner tested his idea that getting cowpox protected people from getting smallpox by infecting a boy with cowpox, then exposing him to smallpox. The boy didn't get smallpox, which provided evidence to support his theory. (Eventually this led to the development of a smallpox vaccine.)

> **Tip:** The results of one experiment can't prove that a theory is true — they can only suggest that it's true. They can however disprove a theory — show that it's wrong.

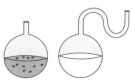

Figure 2: *Pasteur's experiment — the flask with the curved neck stayed fresh.*

Communicating results

The results are then published — scientists need to let others know about their work. Scientists publish their results in **scientific journals**. These are just like normal magazines, only they contain scientific reports (called papers) instead of the latest celebrity gossip.

Scientific reports are similar to the lab write-ups you do in school. And just as a lab write-up is reviewed (marked) by your teacher, reports in scientific journals undergo **peer review** before they're published. The report is sent out to peers — other scientists who are experts in the same area. They examine the data and results, and if they think that the conclusion is reasonable it's published. This makes sure that work published in scientific journals is of a good standard.

But peer review can't guarantee the science is correct — other scientists still need to reproduce it. Sometimes mistakes are made and flawed work is published. Peer review isn't perfect but it's probably the best way for scientists to self-regulate their work and to publish quality reports.

Validating theories

Other scientists read the published theories and results, and try to test the theory themselves in order to validate it (back it up). This involves:

- Repeating the exact same experiments.
- Using the theory to make new predictions and then testing them with new experiments.

Examples

- In 1998 a study was published that linked the MMR vaccine to autism (a developmental disorder). Other scientists then conducted different studies to try to find the same link, but their results didn't back up (validate) the theory.
- In the 1940s a study was published linking smoking and lung cancer. After this many more studies were conducted all over the world that validated the conclusion of the first study.

How do theories evolve?

If multiple experiments show a theory to be incorrect then scientists either have to modify the theory or develop a new one, and start the testing again. If all the experiments in all the world provide good evidence to back a theory up, the theory is thought of as scientific 'fact' (for now) — see Figure 3. But it will never become totally indisputable fact. Scientific breakthroughs or advances could provide new ways to question and test the theory, which could lead to new evidence that conflicts with the current evidence. Then the testing starts all over again... And this, my friend, is the tentative nature of scientific knowledge — it's always changing and evolving.

Tip: Some well known biological journals are Nature, The Lancet and the British Medical Journal.

Tip: Scientific findings are also communicated at conferences around the world.

Tip: Even negative results are communicated — knowing that something is wrong improves scientific knowledge.

Tip: Once an experimental method is found that gives good evidence it becomes a protocol — an accepted method to test that particular thing that all scientists can use.

Tip: Sometimes data from one experiment can be the starting point for developing a new theory.

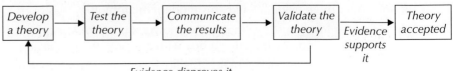

Figure 3: Flow diagram summarising the scientific process.

Figure 4: *Redi's experiment — the meat in the sealed flask (that flies couldn't enter) didn't produce maggots.*

Example

For many years, many people (including scientists) believed in spontaneous generation — the theory that life can arise from non-living organic matter. This theory was supported by observations such as maggots arising from rotting meat, and sterilised broth becoming cloudy with bacteria.

Over time, the theory was disproved by scientists such as Francesco Redi, whose experiments showed that maggots only arose from meat if flies laid their eggs on it (see Figure 4), and Louis Pasteur, whose experiment with a curved-neck flask (see page 1) showed that there were bacteria in the air that could cause decomposition.

Collecting evidence

1. Evidence from lab experiments

Results from controlled experiments in laboratories are great. A lab is the easiest place to control **variables** (quantities that have the potential to change) so that they're all kept constant (except for the one you're investigating). This means you can draw meaningful conclusions.

Tip: Pages 5-13 are all about carrying out lab experiments.

Example

If you're investigating how temperature affects the rate of photosynthesis, you need to keep everything but the temperature constant. This means controlling things like the light intensity, the concentration of CO_2, etc. Otherwise there's no way of knowing if it's the change in temperature that's affecting the rate, or some other changing variable.

Tip: Remember, the variable that you change is the called the independent variable and the variable that you measure is called the dependent variable.

2. Designing studies

There are things you can't investigate in a lab — you have to do a study instead. You still need to try and make the study as controlled as possible to make it valid. But in reality it's very hard to control all the variables that might be having an effect. You can do things to help, but you can't easily rule out every possibility.

Examples

- You can't investigate whether stress causes heart attacks in the lab, so you have to do a study. You could compare the number of heart attacks suffered by a group of people with a high amount of stress to the number suffered by a group with a low amount of stress. But there are always differences between groups of people. The best you can do is to have a well-designed study using matched groups — choose two equally-sized groups of people (those who have quite stressful jobs and those who don't) who are as similar as possible (same mix of ages, same mix of diets etc.) apart from the amount of stress they suffer. But you still can't rule out every possibility.

- It's also tricky to investigate whether adding fertiliser to farmland causes an increase in algal growth in nearby rivers, in the lab. You'd have to do a study on a river that's next to a fertilised field. However, there are variables other than the amount of fertiliser which may have an effect on the amount of algae, such as water temperature and amount of sunlight. You can't easily rule out every possibility. In this case, using a **negative control** too, e.g. a river next to an unfertilised field, can be a useful method for accounting for the effects of variables beyond your control — the results for the negative control could be used as a comparison, so any difference in the results could be attributed to the fertiliser.

Tip: In fieldwork, the effect of variables beyond your control can be reduced by methods such as random sampling (see p. 269).

Tip: Negative controls are used to check that only the independent variable is affecting the dependent variable.

Science and decision making

Scientific knowledge is used by society (that's you, me and everyone else) to make decisions — about the way we live, what we eat, what we drive, etc. All sections of society use scientific evidence to make decisions, e.g. politicians use it to devise policies and individuals use science to make decisions about their own lives.

Tip: Don't get mixed up — it's not the scientists who make the decisions, it's society. Scientists just produce evidence to help society make the decisions.

Examples

- The maximum amount of salt people are advised to eat per day was reduced in government guidelines in 2004, due to the results of a study which showed that reducing salt intake could significantly reduce heart disease.
- Leaded petrol in cars was phased out in many countries after it was found to cause air pollution that damaged the brain.

Factors affecting decision making

Other factors can influence decisions about science or the way science is used:

Economic factors

Society has to consider the cost of implementing changes based on scientific conclusions. Sometimes it decides the cost outweighs the benefits.

Tip: Economic factors just mean anything to do with money, and social factors just mean anything to do with people.

Example

The NHS can't afford the most expensive drugs without sacrificing something else. Sometimes they decide to use a less effective, but less expensive drug, despite evidence showing there's a more effective one.

Social factors

Decisions affect people's lives — sometimes people don't want to follow advice, or are strongly against some recommendations.

Tip: The people making the decisions can be affected by lots of other things too, e.g. public opinion, the media and whether they might benefit from a particular decision.

Examples

- Scientists may suggest banning smoking and alcohol to prevent health problems, but shouldn't we be able to choose whether we want to smoke and drink or not?
- Scientists may be able to cure many diseases using stem cells, but some people are strongly against the idea of embryonic stem cell research.

Environmental factors

Some scientific research and breakthroughs might affect the environment. Not everyone thinks the benefits are worth the possible environmental damage.

Figure 5: *Man protesting against the production of genetically modified organisms (GMOs).*

Examples

- Scientists believe unexplored regions like remote parts of rainforests might contain untapped drug resources. But some people think we shouldn't exploit these regions because any interesting finds may lead to deforestation and reduced biodiversity in these areas.
- Scientists have developed genetically modified (GM) crops (e.g. with frost resistance, or high nutrient content), but some people think the possible environmental harm they could do outweighs their benefits.

What is the Practical Endorsement?

The Practical Endorsement is assessed slightly differently to the rest of your course. Unlike the exams, you don't get a mark for the Practical Endorsement — you just have to get a pass grade. The Practical Endorsement is split into twelve categories, called Practical Activity Groups (PAGs). Each PAG covers a variety of practical techniques, for example, using a light microscope or separating biological compounds. All the PAGs you need to do are listed on page 12 and the practical techniques are listed on pages 12-13. In order to pass the Practical Endorsement, you'll have to carry out at least one experiment for each PAG, and demonstrate that you can carry out each of the required techniques. You'll do the experiments in class, and your teacher will assess you as you're doing them.

You'll need to keep a record of all your assessed practical activities. You may have already done some experiments that count towards the Practical Endorsement in Year 1 of the course. For example, dissections (PAG2) and using a colorimeter or potometer (PAG5) fit in with the material you learned in Year 1, so it's quite likely you carried out these practical activities then. You'll also meet some of the PAGs in this book.

> **Tip:** Throughout this book, experiments and skills that you could use for your Practical Endorsement are marked with a big PAG stamp, like this one:
>
> PRACTICAL
> ACTIVITY   **7**
> GROUP

1. General Practical Skills

The way you do an experiment is important. You may be given a method, or you may have to plan it yourself. It's important that you follow all the steps in a method — this ensures that you work safely, and also makes your results more likely to be precise.

Solving problems in a practical context

Practical experiments are used to solve problems or test whether a theoretical model works in a practical setting. If you're given a method to follow for an experiment, you should carry out each step, as described, in the correct order.

It's possible you'll be given a problem and asked to solve it using your own knowledge. In Module 1, there's loads of information about how to plan and carry out experiments correctly. Have a look back at your Year 1 book if it's all a bit hazy. Here's a quick round-up of some of the things you'll need to think about when you plan an experiment:

- First, identify the aim of your experiment.
- Next, work out how to achieve the aim. You'll often need to identify a variable that you'll change (the independent variable) and the variable you'll measure (the dependent variable) in order to gather data that meets the aim of your experiment.
- Identify all the variables that will need to be controlled during your experiment, and how to control them.
- Think about how to make your data as precise and accurate as possible. This could include repeating your experiment a number of times, or choosing equipment with a scale that has the right sensitivity for the data you're trying to collect.

> **Tip:** Experiments are often used to test scientific theories to see if they are true in a practical context.

> **Tip:** Variables include things like temperature, time, mass, volume and colour.

> **Tip:** Precise results are results that don't vary much from the mean. Accurate results are close to the true value.

Recording and analysing data

Once your experiment is planned, you can carry it out, working carefully to make sure your results are precise. Relevant practical techniques will be covered in this book as they come up during the course. You'll have already come across some techniques in Year 1. All of these techniques should be carried out safely (see pages 8-9) and correctly.

Recording data

As you carry out your experiment, you should record your results in a well laid-out table, leaving space for any data analysis you might want to do later. Your table should include a heading for each column. The units for any measurements should be included in the heading, not in the table itself (see Figure 1).

Shoot	Growth (mm)
A	6
B	5
C	1

Figure 1: *Table showing the amount of growth for three different plant shoots.*

Processing data

There are several different ways that you can analyse and process your data. When you've got results from several repeats of an experiment, you should calculate the **mean**. The **mode** and **median** are other types of averages that you could work out for your results. You can also work out the **range** and **standard deviation** of your results in order to analyse how spread out they are (and you can use the standard deviation to comment on their precision). **Percentages** are useful when you want to compare sample sets of different sizes. **Ratios** are another way you can compare quantities.

You can use statistical tests to analyse your data mathematically. You can be more confident in your conclusions if they're based on data that's been analysed in this way. The statistical tests you should be able to use are:

- **Spearman's rank correlation coefficient** — Spearman's rank correlation coefficient allows you to work out the degree to which two sets of data are correlated.

- **Student's t-test** — You can use this test when you have two sets of data that you want to compare. It tests whether there is a significant difference in the means of the two data sets. There's more about the Student's t-test on pages 79-81.

- **Chi-squared test** —You can use the Chi-squared test when you have categorical (grouped) data and you want to know whether your observed results are statistically different from your expected results. There's more on Chi-squared on pages 182-184.

Presenting data

Presenting your data can make it easier for you to understand your results and spot any trends. There are several different ways to do it though, and you need to be able to choose the best way for the data you've got.

Ways to present data include:

- Drawing **bar charts** or **pie charts** for **qualitative** data (non-numerical data, e.g. blood group, hair colour) or **discrete** data (numerical data that can only take certain values in a range, e.g. shoe size, number of patients).

Tip: Any recorded results that don't fit in with the rest of the data are called anomalous results. If you can work out that they were due to a mistake when carrying out your experiment, you can leave them out of your data analysis.

Tip: Processing data is useful because you're summarising your results — it's a lot quicker and easier to understand figures like the mean and range than a lot of raw data.

Tip: If you need more information about analysing data, including the maths you'll need to know, have a look back at your Year 1 notes — you should have covered it in Module 1.

Tip: Qualitative data can also be called categorical data — all the data can be sorted into categories and values between categories don't exist.

- Drawing **line graphs** or **histograms** for **continuous** data (data that can take any value in a range, e.g. height or weight) — see Figures 2 and 3.

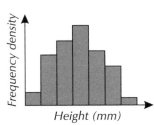

Figure 2: *A histogram showing frequency for a continuous variable (height).*

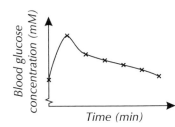

Figure 3: *A line graph showing how a variable (blood glucose concentration) changes over time.*

Tip: Take a look back at your Year 1 notes for more information about how to draw and interpret graphs.

Tip: You need to be able to find the rate of reaction from a graph. This includes using a tangent if the graph line is a curve.

- Drawing **scattergrams** to show how two variables are related (or correlated). You can draw a **line** (or curve) **of best fit** on the scattergram to help show the trend in your results. The trend is called the **correlation** — see Figure 4.

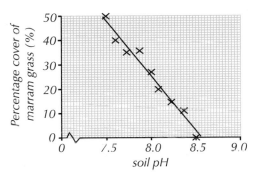

Figure 4: *Scattergram showing a negative correlation between soil pH and percentage cover of marram grass.*

Tip: A correlation between two variables can be positive (as one variable increases, the other increases), negative (as one variable increases, the other decreases), or there may be no correlation present.

Conclusions and evaluations

When you've collected and analysed your data, it's time to wrap up your experiment with some conclusions and an evaluation. Conclusions explain what your results showed. They need to be supported by the data you collected, and shouldn't make sweeping generalisations. If you've found a correlation between two variables, you should be cautious about claiming that the change in one has caused the change in the other — there may be another factor that is causing both variables to change.

An evaluation is a chance for you to look at what you did and think about how you could have improved your method to improve the validity, accuracy and precision of your results. You should consider how well your results address the original aim of your experiment, how you could reduce errors in your results, and whether you need to repeat your experiment further to show your results can be reproduced.

Tip: You may be able to use software to process your data and generate graphs for you, especially if you've used a data logger in your experiment.

Tip: When evaluating your experiment, you could comment on the uncertainty of your measurements and work out the margin of error or percentage error. The smaller these values are, the more precise your results will be. Look back at your Module 1 notes for how to work them out.

2. Working Safely

When you do an experiment, you need to carry out a risk assessment and work safely at all times. This reduces the risk of anyone being hurt.

Risks and hazards

Many biology experiments have risks associated with them. These can include risks associated with the equipment you're using, as well as risks associated with chemicals or biological material. When you're planning an experiment, you need to identify all the hazards and what the risk is from each hazard — this is a risk assessment. A risk assessment includes working out how likely it is that something could go wrong, and how serious it would be if it did go wrong. You then need to think of ways to reduce these risks.

Chemicals

Any hazardous chemicals you use should come with a list of dangers associated with them — this can be found on the bottle they come in, or looked up on something called a Material Safety Data Sheet. The table below shows some common hazard words that you may come across:

Hazard word	Potential harm	Example chemicals	Examples of how to reduce the risk
Corrosive	May cause chemical burns to tissues such as skin and eyes.	Potassium hydroxide	Use as little of the substance as possible. If the chemical is a solution, use it in low concentrations. Wear a lab coat, goggles and gloves when handling the chemical.
Irritant	May cause inflammation and discomfort.	Hydrochloric acid (2-6.5 M), hydrogen peroxide (1.5-2.3 M), Biuret reagent	Use as little of the substance as possible. If the chemical is a solution, use it in low concentrations. Wear a lab coat, goggles and gloves when handling the chemical.
Flammable	May catch fire.	Ethanol, propanone, some chromatography solvents, ninhydrin spray	Keep the chemical away from any naked flames. If you have to heat it, use an electric water bath instead of a Bunsen burner.
Harmful	May cause damage to health when breathed in, swallowed or absorbed via the skin.	Enzymes (as powders), ninhydrin spray	Use as little of the substance as possible. If the chemical is a solution, use it in low concentrations. Wear a lab coat, goggles and gloves when handling the chemical.

You may come across some volatile chemicals during your course (e.g. ninhydrin spray, some chromatography solvents). Volatile chemicals easily evaporate at room temperature and the vapours they produce may be hazardous — for example, they may be flammable or harmful if inhaled. Because of this, volatile substances should be used in a fume cupboard and you should take additional precautions based on the hazards associated with the vapour. Hazardous powders that may be inhaled (e.g. enzyme powders) should also be used in a fume cupboard.

Tip: A hazard is anything that has the potential to cause harm or damage. The risk associated with that hazard is the probability of someone (or something) being harmed if they are exposed to the hazard.

Tip: The CLEAPSS® website has a database with details of the potential harm lots of the hazardous chemicals you're likely to come across could cause. It also has student safety sheets, and your school or college may have CLEAPSS® Hazcards® you can use. These are all good sources of information if you're writing a risk assessment.

Tip: This isn't a comprehensive list of all the types of chemical hazards you may encounter — just some of the more common ones.

Figure 1: The hazard symbols for flammable (left), and corrosive (right).

Tip: Hazard symbols like the ones above are gradually replacing the older orange symbols. 'Harmful' and 'irritant' are being replaced by 'moderate hazard'. Its symbol looks like this: ➤

Heating substances

Some of the experiments that you are expected to do during your course may involve heating a solution. You should only heat a solution in a boiling tube directly over a Bunsen burner if it is not flammable. Solutions heated over a Bunsen burner can boil, so there is a risk of hot liquid splashing out of the tube. There is also a risk of burns from a hot boiling tube. You can reduce these risks by using a test tube holder to hold the boiling tube, with the open end pointing away from you and others, not filling more than one tenth of the tube with liquid and by wearing safety goggles to protect your eyes.

A water bath (Figure 2) is a more controlled way to heat substances, as it can be heated to a specific temperature and there is less risk of a flammable substance catching fire. Test tubes placed in the water bath are warmed to the same temperature as the water. You should move test tubes in and out of the water bath using a test tube holder to reduce the risk of scalding. You should also leave test tubes to cool down after being removed from the water, as the glassware can become hot (depending on the temperature of the water bath).

Figure 2: *A water bath.*

Tip: If the mixture you're heating contains hazardous chemicals (e.g. hydrochloric acid), it makes sense to use a water bath so there is less chance of the mixture splashing on to your skin.

Using dissection tools

The tools used for dissection include scalpels, dissecting scissors, tweezers and pins. You need to take precautions to reduce the risk of injuring yourself or others with these tools, e.g. by cutting in a direction away from yourself and carrying the tools in a tray when moving through the classroom, so that any blades or sharp points are not exposed. Blunt tools are more likely to slip while you are cutting, so you should make sure that your equipment is sharp before you start the dissection. You should also make sure all the tools you are using are free from rust, to reduce the likelihood of them breaking.

Tip: When dissecting, you should take care to position your fingers away from where you're cutting.

Biohazards

Some of the experiments that you are expected to do during your course may include possible biohazards (biological material that presents a risk to human health). You need to take appropriate precautions to reduce the risk of pathogenic (disease-causing) microorganisms spreading between objects or people, e.g. wash your hands after dissecting animal tissue, change and disinfect a spirometer mouthpiece between users. If you're culturing microorganisms, the microorganisms that you will be expected to work with should not be pathogenic. However, you need to take care that your cultures do not become contaminated with pathogenic bacteria. When you are culturing microorganisms, it is important to use aseptic techniques — see page 246 for more.

In experiments using insects, you need to be careful — some people are allergic to insects and/or their droppings, so gloves should be worn when handling live insects if you're in doubt as to whether a reaction could occur.

Tip: Although any microorganisms you use in the lab should be safe, you should always treat them as though they are pathogenic in case the samples have become contaminated.

Tip: Enzyme powders may also cause allergic reactions. If you're using them, make sure you're wearing safety goggles and gloves.

Glassware

Many pieces of equipment that you may use during your course are made of glass (e.g. test tubes, potometers, microscope slides). Broken glass can cause serious injury, so you should take care to transport glass items safely and check them for cracks and flaws before you use them. Any broken pieces of glass should be moved away from the work area immediately and disposed of in an appropriate container (not the normal waste bin).

Tip: Don't try to pick up broken glass with your hands — it's a lot safer to use a dustpan and brush.

Appropriate clothing

When working in the lab, you should make sure that you are wearing sensible clothing to reduce the risk of injury, e.g. open shoes or sandals won't protect your feet against spillages. You should also wear a lab coat to protect your skin and clothing. It's all about using your common sense really.

Tip: If you have long hair, it should be tied back if you're working near an open flame.

3. Keeping Scientific Records

When you carry out experiments, it's important to keep records of everything you do. The records should be detailed and clear enough that a complete stranger would be able to read them and understand what you did.

Records of scientific experiments

Throughout your A-Level Biology course, you should keep a record of all the experiments you carry out, the results you obtain and the solutions to any data analysis you do. This could be done in a physical lab book, or kept in folders on a computer. However you choose to keep your records, the information for each experiment should include:

- The aim of the experiment.
- A detailed method for how you carried out the experiment, including the quantities of all the chemicals and any safety precautions you had to take.
- The results of your experiment, clearly set out in a table. The results may be hand-written, or a print-out of data collected by a data logger.
- Any other important observations you made whilst carrying out your experiment, for example, anything that went wrong or anything you did slightly differently from how it was described in the method.
- The solutions to any analysis you did on your results, or any graphs drawn using your results. These should be clearly labelled to show what analysis has been done or what graph has been drawn.
- Citations of any references you used.

Sources of information

PRACTICAL ACTIVITY GROUP **12**

It's possible you'll have to do some research to find out information before you get started with an experiment. Useful sources of information include:

Websites

Using the Internet for research is really convenient, but you have to be slightly wary as not all the information you find will be true. It's hard to know where information comes from on forums, blogs and websites that can be edited by the general public, so you should avoid using these. Websites of organisations such as the Nuffield Foundation and the National Health Service (NHS) provide lots of information that comes from reliable scientific sources. To decide whether a website gives reliable information, think about the following things:

- Who has written the information — was it a scientist, a teacher, or just a member of the public?
- Whether or not anyone will have checked the source — articles on websites for scientific organisations will have people reading through the information and checking all the facts. Information on forums or blogs is likely to have been written by an individual, and won't necessarily have been thoroughly checked.
- What the purpose of the website is — if it's a website all about Biology, then it's likely whoever has written it will know quite a lot. If it's a website where you can also find out how to make a plant pot from an old teacup and some PVA glue, then the depth and quality of the information may not be enough.

Tip: Try to keep all your lab reports in the same place — write them in the same book, or keep them in the same folder on your computer. That way you'll know where everything is.

Tip: A clear and detailed method is important, as it could be used by another scientist who is trying to reproduce your results.

Tip: There's loads more detail about making observations, recording data and analysing your results in Module 1.

Tip: If you're unsure whether the information on a website is true or not, try and find the same piece of information in a different place. The more sources you can find for the information, the more likely it is to be correct.

Textbooks

Your school or public library is likely to have textbooks covering specific areas of Biology in a lot of detail.

Scientific papers

You can find papers in online catalogues, such as SciFinder or PubMed, as well as in journals that are often available in public libraries.

The source you do your research from needs to give the right level of information. It's no good trawling through a scientific paper if you're just looking for the boiling point of a compound — the information will be far too detailed, and you'll probably end up wading through lots of complicated information that you don't need to understand. Equally, if you're researching the theory behind an experiment, you want a source that gives enough detail. A GCSE textbook will probably be too simplistic — you're better off finding a book that deals specifically with the subject in a library instead.

Tip: Scientific papers are checked by other scientists who are experts in the subject of the paper. This is called peer review (see page 2).

Using references and making citations

It sounds obvious, but when you're using the information that you've found during your research, you can't just copy it down word for word. Any data you're looking up should be copied accurately, but you should rewrite everything else in your own words.

PRACTICAL ACTIVITY GROUP **12**

When you've used information from a source, you need to cite the reference properly. Citations allow someone else to go back and find the source of your information. This means they can check your information and see you're not making things up out of thin air. Citations also mean you've properly credited other people's data that you've used in your work.

Citations are included in the main text of a report and are usually written in brackets after the relevant piece of information. They can either include the entire reference or link the information to a list of references at the end of the report (e.g. using a number — see Figure 1). References for each piece of information may include the title of the book, paper or website where you found the information, the author and/or the publisher of the document and the date the document was published.

Tip: There are lots of slightly different ways of referencing sources, but the important thing is that it's clear where you found the information.

Tip: You should include page numbers with your citation if you quote directly from the text or copy a diagram.

Report

90% of people with diabetes have Type II diabetes (2, p. 434)...

References

1. http://www.diabetes.co.uk/diabetes_care/ blood-sugar-level-ranges.html [Accessed 06 June 2015]

2. McConnell T.H.; The Nature of Disease: Pathology for the Health Professions; 2007

3. King H., Aubert R.E., Herman W.H.; 1998. Global burden of diabetes, 1995-2025: prevalence, numerical estimates, and projections. Diabetes Care. 21: 1414-1431

Referencing a website: include the URL and the date accessed.

Referencing a book: include the author, book title and publication year.

Referencing a paper: include the authors, publication year, title of the paper, the journal it was published in, the volume number and page numbers.

Figure 1: *Example of a citation in the main text of a report and the corresponding references document.*

4. Practical Activity Groups

This section tells you all the Practical Activity Groups you'll be expected to have carried out for A-Level Biology, as well as the techniques included in them. You'll have met many of them before, and others will be covered in more detail as they crop up throughout the book.

PAGs

There are 12 Practical Activity Groups (PAGs) that you should have covered by the end of your A-Level course. These are shown in the table below, along with an example of the type of activity you could carry out for each one.

	PAG	Example activity
1	Microscopy	Examining cells in a blood smear.
2	Dissection	Dissection of a kidney (see p. 59).
3	Sampling techniques	Investigating biodiversity in a habitat.
4	Rates of enzyme controlled reactions	Investigating the effect of temperature on the rate of an enzyme-controlled reaction.
5	Colorimeter / Potometer	Determining the concentration of glucose in a solution. / Estimating transpiration rate.
6	Chromatography / Electrophoresis	Separating the pigments from leaves (see pages 126-127).
7	Microbiological techniques	Investigating the effect of temperature on the growth of a microorganism (see p. 247).
8	Transport in and out of cells	Investigating the effect of temperature on the rate of diffusion using model cells.
9	Qualitative testing	The iodine test for starch.
10	Investigation using a data logger / Computer modelling	Recording data from a spirometer using a data logger.
11	Investigation into the measurement of plant or animal responses	Investigating how exercise affects heart rate (see pages 78-79).
12	Research skills	Researching online for further information on a topic.

Tip: Research skills include being able to cite sources of information. There's more about citations on p. 11.

Practical techniques

As part of each PAG you'll be expected to show that you can carry out certain techniques, such as:

Tip: Quantitative measurements include measurements of mass, time, volume, temperature, length and pH.

- using appropriate apparatus and instrumentation (e.g. a potometer) to record quantitative measurements
- using lab glassware for different techniques, such as making serial dilutions
- using a light microscope and a graticule
- making scientific drawings of observations with labels
- identifying biological molecules using qualitative reagents

- separating biological compounds, using thin layer or paper chromatography or electrophoresis
- using organisms safely and ethically to measure plant or animal responses, or physiological functions
- using microbiological aseptic techniques, including using nutrient broth and agar plates
- using instruments safely in dissections
- using sampling techniques when carrying out fieldwork
- using ICT to collect data (e.g. via a data logger) · or software to process data

All of these techniques should be covered across all of the PAGs.

Tip: Each individual PAG won't cover every single one of these techniques, but you should have covered all the techniques you need to know by the end of your course.

Ethical issues

One of the practical techniques is knowing how to use any organisms involved in your experiments safely and ethically. This means that when you're planning an experiment involving animals or humans, you need to take any ethical issues into account.

Animals need to be treated humanely — they should be handled carefully and any wild animals captured for studying (e.g. during a biodiversity investigation) should be returned to their original habitat. Any animals (e.g. insects) being raised for dissection should be cared for in a humane way, e.g. they should not be kept in overcrowded conditions, and they should be killed humanely to minimise suffering.

If you are carrying out an experiment involving other students (e.g. investigating the effect of exercise on heart rate), the participants should not be forced to undergo testing against their will, or feel pressured to participate.

Tip: Animals kept in the lab should be kept in a safe environment (away from any chemicals or other hazards), have a clean enclosure, access to food and water, and they should not be subjected to extreme temperatures.

Tip: Many PAGs involve the use of organisms, e.g. PAG2, PAG3 and PAG11.

Learning Objectives:

- Be able to outline the need for communication systems in multicellular organisms, including the need for animals and plants to respond to changes in the internal and external environment and to coordinate the activities of different organs.

- Know that cells communicate with each other by a process called cell signalling and that this occurs between adjacent cells and between distant cells.

Specification Reference 5.1.1

1. Communication Basics

In order to survive, organisms need to respond to what's going on around them. Communication systems make sure information gets passed on from one part of the organism to another.

Responding to the environment

Animals increase their chances of survival by responding to changes in their external environment, e.g. by avoiding harmful environments such as places that are too hot or too cold. They also respond to changes in their internal environment to make sure that the conditions are always optimal for their metabolism (all the chemical reactions that go on inside them). Plants also increase their chances of survival by responding to changes in their environment. Any change in the internal or external environment, e.g. a change in temperature, light intensity or pressure, is called a **stimulus**.

Receptors and effectors

Receptors detect stimuli. They are specific — they only detect one particular stimulus, e.g. pressure, light or glucose concentration. There are many different types of receptor that each detect a different type of stimulus, e.g. pressure receptors only detect pressure. Some receptors are cells, e.g. photoreceptors are receptor cells that connect to the nervous system. Some receptors are proteins on cell surface membranes, e.g. glucose receptors are proteins found in the cell membranes of some pancreatic cells.

Effectors are cells that bring about a response to a stimulus, to produce an effect. Effectors include muscle cells and cells found in glands, e.g. the pancreas. Receptors and effectors play an important role in communicating information from one part of an organism to another. This makes sure that the activities of different organs are coordinated to keep the organism working effectively.

Tip: There's much more about how receptors work on pages 16-17.

Cell signalling

To produce a response, receptors need to communicate with effectors and effectors may need to communicate with other cells. This happens via cell signalling. Cell signalling can occur between adjacent (nearby) cells or between distant cells. For example, cells in the nervous system communicate by secreting chemicals called neurotransmitters, which send signals to adjacent cells, such as other nerve cells or muscle cells. The hormonal system works by cells releasing chemicals called hormones, which travel in the blood and act as signals to distant cells. Cell-surface receptors allow cells to recognise the chemicals involved in cell signalling.

Tip: The nervous system and hormonal system are 'communication systems'.

Practice Questions — Fact Recall

Q1 Why is it important that organisms respond to stimuli?

Q2 Give one reason why communication systems are needed in multicellular organisms.

Q3 What is cell signalling?

2. The Nervous System

The nervous system passes on information from one part of an organism to another using nerve impulses. It's a very fast form of communication.

Neurones

The nervous system is made up of a complex network of cells called neurones. There are three main types of neurone:

1. **Sensory neurones** transmit nerve impulses from receptors to the central nervous system (CNS) — the brain and spinal cord.
2. **Motor neurones** transmit nerve impulses from the CNS to effectors.
3. **Relay neurones** transmit nerve impulses between sensory neurones and motor neurones.

Structure of neurones

All neurones have a cell body with a nucleus (plus cytoplasm and all the other organelles you usually get in a cell). The cell body has extensions that connect to other neurones — dendrites and dendrons carry nerve impulses towards the cell body (dendrites are smaller branches of a dendron), and axons carry nerve impulses away from the cell body. You need to learn the structures of sensory, motor and relay neurones:

- Sensory neurones have short dendrites and one long dendron to carry nerve impulses from receptor cells to the cell body, and one short axon that carries nerve impulses from the cell body to the CNS.

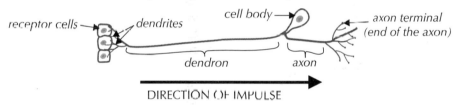

- Motor neurones have many short dendrites that carry nerve impulses from the CNS to the cell body, and one long axon that carries nerve impulses from the cell body to effector cells.

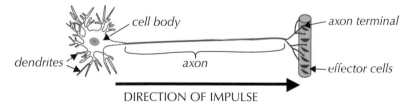

- Relay neurones have many short dendrites that carry nerve impulses from sensory neurones to the cell body, and one axon that carries nerve impulses from the cell body to motor neurones.

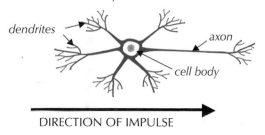

Learning Objectives:

- Know the structures and functions of sensory, motor and relay neurones.
- Understand the roles of mammalian sensory receptors in converting different types of stimuli into nerve impulses.
- Be able to outline the roles of sensory receptors (e.g. Pacinian corpuscle) in responding to specific types of stimuli and their roles as transducers.

Specification Reference 5.1.3

Tip: Dendrites and dendrons carry information towards the cell body, axons carry it away from the cell body.

Tip: This is a non-myelinated motor neurone — see page 22 for the structure of a myelinated one.

Figure 1: *A light micrograph of a motor neurone — many dendrites can be seen extending from the cell body.*

Tip: Relay neurones transmit nerve impulses through the CNS.

Nervous communication

A stimulus is detected by receptor cells and a nerve impulse is sent along a sensory neurone. When a nerve impulse reaches the end of a neurone chemicals called neurotransmitters take the information across the gap (called a synapse) to the next neurone, which then sends a nerve impulse (see pages 24-25). The CNS processes the information, decides what to do about it and sends impulses along motor neurones to an effector (see Figure 2).

$$\text{Stimulus} \Rightarrow \text{Receptors} \xrightarrow{\text{sensory neurone}} \text{CNS} \xrightarrow{\text{motor neurone}} \text{Effectors} \Rightarrow \text{Response}$$

Figure 2: *The pathway of nervous communication.*

Example

A real-life example of nervous communication is when you see a friend waving to you and you wave back in response:

- **Stimulus** — you see a friend waving.
- **Receptors** — light receptors (photoreceptors) in your eyes detect the wave. The electrical impulse is carried by a sensory neurone to the CNS.
- **CNS** — processes information and decides what to do about it. An electrical impulse is sent along a motor neurone.
- **Effectors** — muscle cells are stimulated by the motor neurone.
- **Response** — muscles contract to make your arm wave.

Sensory receptors

Different stimuli have different forms of energy, e.g. light energy or chemical energy. But your nervous system only sends information in the form of nerve impulses (electrical impulses). Sensory receptors convert the energy of a stimulus into electrical energy. They act as **transducers** — something that converts one form of energy into another.

Here's a bit more about how receptor cells that communicate information via the nervous system work...

The resting potential

When a nervous system receptor is in its resting state (not being stimulated), there's a difference in charge between the inside and the outside of the cell — the inside is negatively charged relative to the outside (see Figure 3). This means there's a **voltage** across the membrane. Voltage is also known as the **potential difference**. The potential difference when a cell is at rest is called its **resting potential**. The resting potential is generated by ion pumps and ion channels (see p. 19).

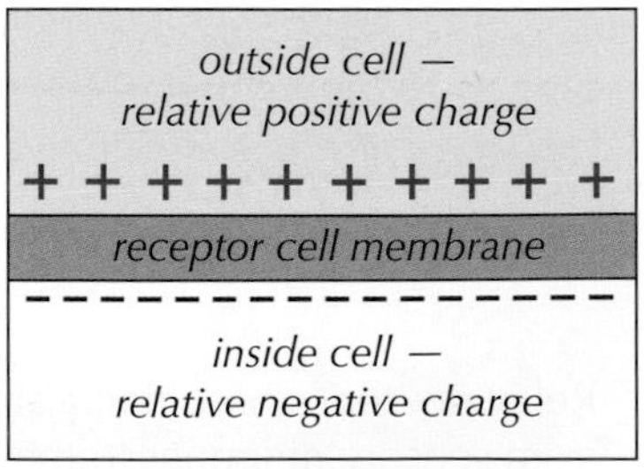

outside cell —
relative positive charge

+ + + + + + + + + +

receptor cell membrane

- - - - - - - - - -

inside cell —
relative negative charge

Figure 3: *Relative charges either side of a receptor cell membrane at rest.*

The generator potential

When a stimulus is detected, the cell membrane is excited and becomes more permeable, allowing more ions to move in and out of the cell — altering the potential difference. The change in potential difference due to a stimulus is called the **generator potential**.

A bigger stimulus excites the membrane more, causing a bigger movement of ions and a bigger change in potential difference — so a bigger generator potential is produced (see Figure 4).

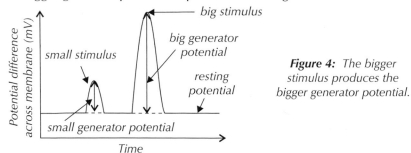

Figure 4: The bigger stimulus produces the bigger generator potential.

Tip: Potential difference across a cell membrane is usually measured in millivolts (mV).

The action potential

If the generator potential is big enough it'll trigger an action potential (nerve impulse) along a neurone. An action potential is only triggered if the generator potential reaches a certain level called the **threshold level**. If the stimulus is too weak the generator potential won't reach the threshold, so there's no action potential (see Figure 5).

Tip: There's much more on action potentials on pages 20-21.

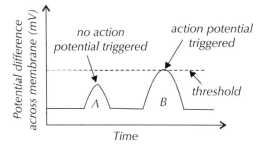

Figure 5: Generator potential not reaching the threshold (A) and reaching the threshold (B).

Tip: Pacinian corpuscles only respond to mechanical stimuli, not to any other type of stimulus — this is a good example of how receptors only respond to specific stimuli.

--- Example ---

Pacinian corpuscles are mechanoreceptors — they detect mechanical stimuli, e.g. pressure and vibrations. They're found in your skin. They contain the end of a sensory neurone, called a sensory nerve ending. The sensory nerve ending is wrapped in lots of layers of connective tissue called lamellae.

When a Pacinian corpuscle is stimulated, e.g. by a tap on the arm, the lamellae are deformed and press on the sensory nerve ending. This causes deformation of stretch-mediated sodium channels in the sensory neurone's cell membrane. The sodium ion channels open and sodium ions diffuse into the cell (see Figure 6), creating a generator potential. If the generator potential reaches the threshold, it triggers an action potential.

Tip: <u>Stretch-mediated</u> sodium ion channels get their name because they only open and let sodium ions pass through when they're <u>stretched</u>.

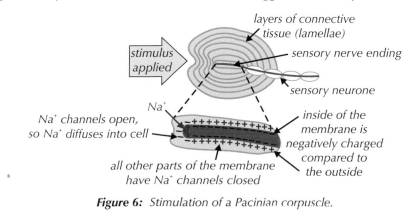

Figure 6: Stimulation of a Pacinian corpuscle.

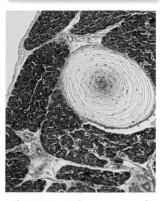

Figure 7: Light micrograph showing a section of a Pacinian corpuscle at rest.

Practice Questions — Application

For a particular receptor cell, an action potential is triggered when the generator potential reaches –60 mV.

Q1 What name is given to the value at which an action potential will be triggered?

Q2 The graph below shows generator potentials in the receptor cell.

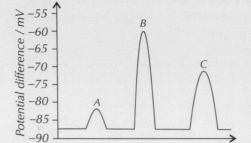

a) Which curve shows a generator potential that would trigger an action potential? Give a reason for your answer.

b) What is the resting potential of this receptor cell?

Practice Questions — Fact Recall

Q1 What is the function of:
  a) a sensory neurone?
  b) a motor neurone?
  c) a relay neurone?

Q2 The diagram on the right shows a non-myelinated motor neurone. Name the structures labelled A-D.

Q3 Give two structural differences between a sensory neurone and a motor neurone.

Q4 Describe the pathway of nervous communication from stimulus to response.

Q5 Why are sensory receptors described as 'transducers'?

Q6 Explain how a generator potential is produced.

Q7 Explain how a bigger stimulus causes a bigger generator potential than a smaller stimulus.

Q8 Describe the response of a Pacinian corpuscle stimulated by a tap on the arm.

Exam Tip
Questions on the structure of neurones are easy marks, so make sure you learn the structures of each type of neurone really well.

3. The Nervous Impulse

Nervous impulses are the electrical charges transmitted along a neurone. They're created by the movement of sodium and potassium ions across a neurone cell membrane.

The resting membrane potential

In a neurone's resting state (when it's not being stimulated), the outside of the membrane is positively charged compared to the inside. This is because there are more positive ions outside the cell than inside. So the membrane is polarised — there's a difference in charge. The voltage across the membrane when it's at rest is called the resting potential — it's about –70 mV.

Movement of sodium and potassium ions

The resting potential is created and maintained by **sodium-potassium pumps** and **potassium ion channels** in a neurone's membrane (see Figure 1).

- Sodium-potassium pumps use **active transport** to move three sodium ions (Na⁺) out of the neurone for every two potassium ions (K⁺) moved in. ATP is needed to do this.

- Potassium ion channels allow **facilitated diffusion** of potassium ions (K⁺) out of the neurone, down their concentration gradient.

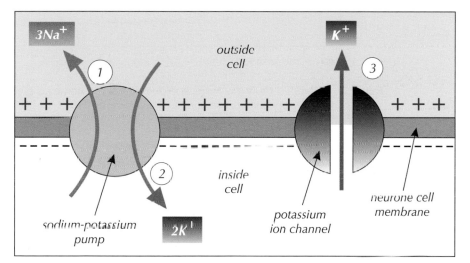

Figure 1: *Movement of sodium and potassium ions across a resting cell membrane.*

1. The sodium-potassium pumps move sodium ions out of the neurone, but the membrane isn't permeable to sodium ions, so they can't diffuse back in. This creates a sodium ion **electrochemical gradient** (a concentration gradient of ions) because there are more positive sodium ions outside the cell than inside.

2. The sodium-potassium pumps also move potassium ions in to the neurone.

3. When the cell's at rest, most potassium ion channels are open. This means that the membrane is permeable to potassium ions, so some diffuse back out through potassium ion channels.

Even though positive ions are moving in and out of the cell, in total more positive ions move out of the cell than enter. This makes the outside of the cell positively charged compared to the inside.

Learning Objectives:

- Understand how the resting potential is established and maintained.

- Understand the generation and transmission of nerve impulses in mammals, including how an action potential is generated (with reference to positive feedback) and transmitted in a myelinated neurone.

- Understand the significance of the frequency of impulse transmission.

- Understand the differences in structure and function of myelinated and non-myelinated neurones.

Specification Reference 5.1.3

Tip: The neurone cell membrane also has sodium ion channels (see next page), but these are closed when the cell's at rest.

Tip: Remember, sodium-potassium pumps are SOPI — Sodium Out, Potassium In.

Action potentials

When a neurone is stimulated, sodium ion channels in the cell membrane open. If the stimulus is big enough, it'll trigger a rapid change in potential difference. This causes the cell membrane to become **depolarised** (it's no longer polarised). The sequence of events that happens is known as an action potential — see Figure 2.

Tip: Voltage-gated ion channels are channels that only open at a certain voltage.

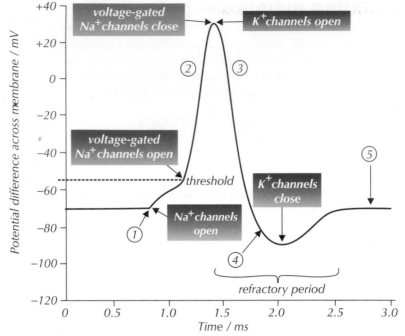

Figure 2: A graph to show the changes in potential difference across a neurone cell membrane during an action potential.

Tip: The graph below shows when the sodium ion channels (orange) are open during an action potential (dotted line):

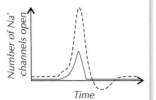

And this graph shows when the potassium ion channels (blue) are open:

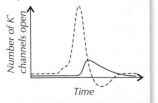

1. **Stimulus** — this excites the neurone cell membrane, causing sodium ion channels to open. The membrane becomes more permeable to sodium, so sodium ions diffuse into the neurone down the sodium ion electrochemical gradient. This makes the inside of the neurone less negative.

2. **Depolarisation** — if the potential difference reaches the threshold (around −55 mV), voltage-gated sodium ion channels open and more sodium ions diffuse into the neurone. This is positive feedback (see page 35).

3. **Repolarisation** — at a potential difference of around +30 mV the sodium ion channels close and voltage-gated potassium ion channels open. The membrane is more permeable to potassium so potassium ions diffuse out of the neurone down the potassium ion concentration gradient. This starts to get the membrane back to its resting potential. This is negative feedback (see pages 34-35).

4. **Hyperpolarisation** — potassium ion channels are slow to close so there's a slight 'overshoot' where too many potassium ions diffuse out of the neurone. The potential difference becomes more negative than the resting potential (i.e. less than −70 mV).

5. **Resting potential** — the ion channels are reset. The sodium-potassium pump returns the membrane to its resting potential by pumping sodium ions out and potassium ions in, and maintains the resting potential until the membrane's excited by another stimulus.

The refractory period

After an action potential, the neurone cell membrane can't be excited again straight away. This is because the ion channels are recovering and they can't be made to open — sodium ion channels are closed during repolarisation and potassium ion channels are closed during hyperpolarisation. This period of recovery is called the refractory period (see Figure 3).

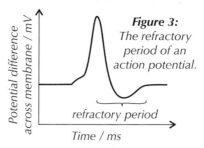

Figure 3: The refractory period of an action potential.

The refractory period acts as a time delay between one action potential and the next. This makes sure that action potentials don't overlap but pass along as discrete (separate) impulses. The refractory period also makes sure action potentials are unidirectional (they only travel in one direction).

Waves of depolarisation

When an action potential happens, some of the sodium ions that enter the neurone diffuse sideways. This causes sodium ion channels in the next region of the neurone to open and sodium ions diffuse into that part. This causes a wave of depolarisation to travel along the neurone. The wave moves away from the parts of the membrane in the refractory period because these parts can't fire an action potential.

Tip: A wave of depolarisation is like a Mexican wave travelling through a crowd — sodium ions rushing inwards causes a wave of activity along the membrane.

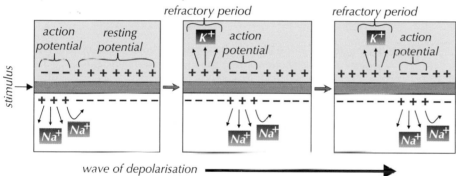

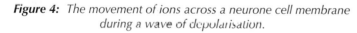

Figure 4: The movement of ions across a neurone cell membrane during a wave of depolarisation.

Tip: The electrical impulse can be said to 'propagate' along the neurone. This just describes the wave-like movement of the action potential.

Frequency of impulses

Once the threshold is reached, an action potential will always fire with the same change in voltage, no matter how big the stimulus is. If the threshold isn't reached, an action potential won't fire (see Figure 5). This is the **all-or-nothing** nature of action potentials.

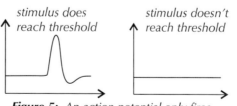

Figure 5: An action potential only fires if the stimulus reaches the threshold.

A bigger stimulus won't cause a bigger action potential but it will cause them to fire more frequently (see Figure 6). So if the brain receives a high frequency of action potentials, it interprets this as a big stimulus and responds accordingly.

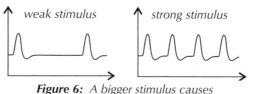

Figure 6: A bigger stimulus causes more frequent action potentials.

Tip: The all-or-nothing principle stops the brain from getting over-stimulated by not responding to very small stimuli.

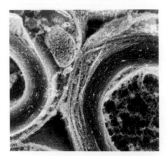

Figure 7: A cross-section through a myelinated neurone. The myelin sheath (orange/brown) surrounds the axon (dark brown).

Exam Tip
You need to know the structure and function of neurones — both the myelinated ones (like those in Figure 8) and the non-myelinated ones (see page 15).

Tip: In the central nervous system, the myelin sheath is formed from cells called oligodendrocytes.

Tip: Long neurones, like a motor neurone from your spinal cord to your foot, are myelinated to speed up the conduction of action potentials.

Tip: If you imagine a Mexican wave travelling through a crowd, then saltatory conduction is like every tenth person doing the wave instead of everyone doing the wave — so it travels much faster.

Tip: The pumps and channels that move ions across the membrane are proteins, so these will denature at high temperatures.

Speed of conduction

Three factors affect the speed of conduction of action potentials:

1. Myelination

Some neurones are myelinated — they have a **myelin sheath** (see Figure 8). The myelin sheath is an electrical insulator. In the peripheral nervous system (see p. 72), the myelin sheath is made of a type of cell called a **Schwann cell**, which is wrapped around the axon (and/or dendron). Between the Schwann cells are tiny patches of bare membrane called the **nodes of Ranvier**. Sodium ion channels are concentrated at the nodes of Ranvier.

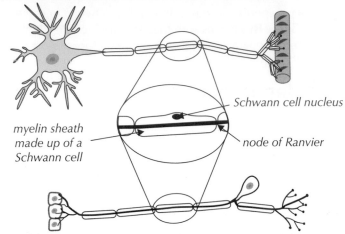

Schwann cell nucleus

myelin sheath made up of a Schwann cell

node of Ranvier

Figure 8: Structure of a myelinated motor neurone (top) and a myelinated sensory neurone (bottom), with the myelin sheath enlarged.

Saltatory conduction

In a myelinated neurone, depolarisation only happens at the nodes of Ranvier (where sodium ions can get through the membrane). The neurone's cytoplasm conducts enough electrical charge to depolarise the next node, so the impulse 'jumps' from node to node. This is called saltatory conduction and it's really fast — see Figure 9.

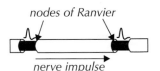

nodes of Ranvier

nerve impulse

Figure 9: Saltatory conduction along a myelinated neurone.

In a non-myelinated neurone, the impulse travels as a wave along the whole length of the axon membrane (see Figure 10). This is slower than saltatory conduction (although it's still pretty quick).

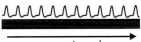

nerve impulse

Figure 10: Conduction along a non-myelinated neurone.

2. Axon diameter

Action potentials are conducted quicker along axons with bigger diameters because there's less resistance to the flow of ions than in the cytoplasm of a smaller axon. With less resistance, depolarisation reaches other parts of the neurone cell membrane quicker.

3. Temperature

The speed of conduction increases as the temperature increases too, because ions diffuse faster. The speed only increases up to around 40 °C though — after that the proteins begin to denature and the speed decreases.

Practice Questions — Application

Tip: Remember, the potential difference is the voltage across the membrane.

The graph below shows the changes in potential difference across a neurone cell membrane during an action potential.

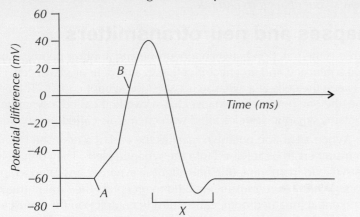

Q1 Describe the different events occurring at points A and B.

Q2 What is the threshold level for this action potential?

Q3 What is the resting potential of this neurone cell membrane?

Q4 a) Explain the shape of the curve during the period marked X.

    b) What name is given to the period marked X?

Q5 How would the graph look if a bigger stimulus triggered the action potential? Explain your answer.

Exam Tip
Always be clear in your exam answers as to whether you're talking about sodium ions (Na^+) or potassium ions (K^+) — don't just write 'sodium', 'potassium' or 'ions'.

Practice Questions — Fact Recall

Q1 Which two proteins in a neurone's cell membrane are responsible for creating and maintaining the resting membrane potential?

Q2 Following a stimulus, explain how the opening of sodium ion channels affects the potential difference across a neurone cell membrane.

Q3 a) Describe and explain the movement of sodium ions if the potential difference across a neurone cell membrane reaches the threshold level.

    b) What type of feedback is this an example of?

Q4 a) After an action potential, why can't the neurone cell membrane be excited again straight away?

    b) What two effects does this have on the conduction of action potentials along a neurone?

Q5 Explain how waves of depolarisation are produced.

Q6 Describe the structure of a myelinated neurone in the peripheral nervous system.

Q7 How does conduction along a myelinated neurone differ compared to conduction along a non-myelinated neurone?

Q8 Give two factors, other than myelination, that affect the conduction of action potentials.

Exam Tip
In your exam, be careful not to use phrases like 'ions move across the membrane' — you need to make it clear whether they're moving into or out of the cell.

- Know the structure of synapses, including the structure of a cholinergic synapse.
- Understand the role of synapses in neurotransmission, including the action of neurotransmitters at the synapse, the effect of excitatory and inhibitory synapses, and the importance of synapses in summation and control.

Specification Reference 5.1.3

4. Synapses

If you've ever wondered how information passes from one neurone to the next, now's your chance to find out...

Synapses and neurotransmitters

A synapse is the junction between a neurone and another neurone, or between a neurone and an effector cell, e.g. a muscle or gland cell. The tiny gap between the cells at a synapse is called the synaptic cleft. The presynaptic neurone (the one before the synapse) has a swelling called a synaptic knob. This contains synaptic vesicles filled with chemicals called neurotransmitters.

When an action potential reaches the end of a neurone it causes neurotransmitters to be released into the synaptic cleft. They diffuse across to the postsynaptic membrane (the one after the synapse) and bind to specific receptors. When neurotransmitters bind to receptors they might trigger an action potential (in a neurone), cause muscle contraction (in a muscle cell), or cause a hormone to be secreted (from a gland cell).

Neurotransmitters are removed from the cleft so the response doesn't keep happening, e.g. they're taken back into the presynaptic neurone or they're broken down by enzymes (and the products are taken into the neurone).

Cholinergic synapses

There are different types of synapses, each with a slightly different structure that relates to their function. You need to learn the structure of a **cholinergic synapse** — see Figure 2. A cholinergic synapse uses the neurotransmitter **acetylcholine** (**ACh**) which binds to receptors called cholinergic receptors.

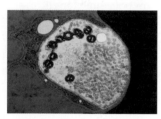

Figure 1: *A synaptic knob (yellow) containing vesicles (large red circles).*

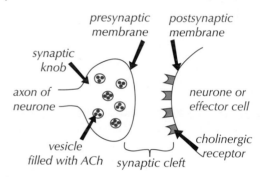

Figure 2: *The structure of a cholinergic synapse.*

Synaptic transmission

This is how a nerve impulse is transmitted across a cholinergic synapse:

1. Arrival of an action potential

An action potential arrives at the synaptic knob of the presynaptic neurone. The action potential stimulates voltage-gated calcium ion channels in the presynaptic neurone to open. Calcium ions (Ca^{2+}) diffuse into the synaptic knob. (They're pumped out afterwards by active transport.)

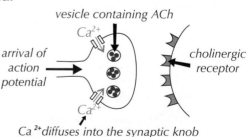

Ca^{2+} diffuses into the synaptic knob

2. Fusion of the vesicles

The influx of calcium ions into the synaptic knob causes the synaptic vesicles to move to the presynaptic membrane. They then fuse with the presynaptic membrane. The vesicles release ACh into the synaptic cleft by **exocytosis**.

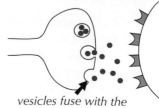

vesicles fuse with the membrane and release ACh

3. Diffusion of ACh

ACh diffuses across the synaptic cleft and binds to specific cholinergic receptors on the postsynaptic membrane. This causes sodium ion channels in the postsynaptic neurone to open. The influx of sodium ions into the postsynaptic neurone causes depolarisation. An action potential on the postsynaptic membrane is generated if the threshold is reached. ACh is removed from the synaptic cleft so the response doesn't keep happening. It's broken down by an enzyme called acetylcholinesterase (AChE) and the products are re-absorbed by the presynaptic neurone and used to make more ACh.

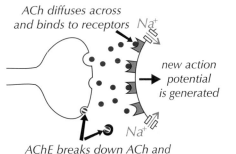

ACh diffuses across and binds to receptors

Na^+

new action potential is generated

Na^+

AChE breaks down ACh and the products are re-absorbed

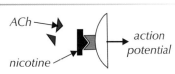

Tip: Look back at page 20 if you need a reminder of how action potentials are generated.

Disruption of synaptic transmission

Because synapses use chemical communication, they can be affected by chemicals like drugs, toxins or poisons. For example, some chemicals are the same shape as neurotransmitters so they mimic their action at receptors (these drugs are called agonists). This means more receptors are activated.

Exam Tip
Don't worry, you don't have to learn the action of any specific drug or toxin for your exam. But examiners like to test your knowledge of synapses, e.g. by asking about how drugs or toxins would affect their activity, so make sure you understand these examples.

┌─ Example ─────────────────────

Nicotine mimics acetylcholine. It binds to certain types of cholinergic receptors in the brain.

ACh

action potential

nicotine

Some chemicals block receptors so they can't be activated by neurotransmitters. This means fewer receptors (if any) can be activated.

┌─ Example ─────────────────────

Curare blocks the effects of acetylcholine by blocking certain cholinergic receptors at neuromuscular junctions, so muscle cells can't be stimulated. This results in the muscle being paralysed.

ACh

no action potential

curare

Some chemicals inhibit the enzyme that breaks down neurotransmitters (they stop it from working). This means there are more neurotransmitters in the synaptic cleft to bind to receptors and they're there for longer.

┌─ Example ─────────────────────

Nerve gases stop acetylcholine from being broken down in the synaptic cleft. This can lead to loss of muscle control.

ACh

enzyme (AChE) inhibitor

action potential

enzyme (AChE)

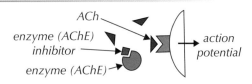

Tip: The nervous system uses lots of different neurotransmitters, not just acetylcholine. You'll come across ones called dopamine and noradrenaline too.

Some chemicals inhibit the release of neurotransmitters from the presynaptic neurone so fewer receptors are activated.

┌─ Example ─────────────────────

Opioids block calcium ion channels in the presynaptic neurone. This means fewer vesicles fuse with the presynaptic membrane so less neurotransmitter is released.

Ca^{2+} *channel*

no action potential

opioid

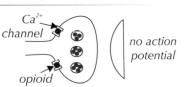

Roles of synapses

Synapses play vital roles in the nervous system. The way they work affects how information is passed on throughout the body.

Excitatory and inhibitory synapses

Neurotransmitters can be excitatory, inhibitory or both. Excitatory neurotransmitters depolarise the postsynaptic membrane, making it fire an action potential if the threshold is reached (see pages 24-25). Inhibitory neurotransmitters hyperpolarise the postsynaptic membrane (make the potential difference more negative), preventing it from firing an action potential. A synapse where excitatory neurotransmitters are released from the presynaptic membrane following an action potential is called an **excitatory synapse**. A synapse where inhibitory neurotransmitters are released is an **inhibitory synapse**.

Tip: Acetylcholine is an excitatory neurotransmitter at cholinergic synapses in the CNS and at neuromuscular junctions (see p. 90). But it's an inhibitory neurotransmitter at cholinergic synapses in the heart. When it binds to receptors here, it can cause potassium ion channels to open on the postsynaptic membrane, hyperpolarising it.

Divergence and convergence

When one neurone connects to many neurones information can be dispersed to different parts of the body. This is called **synaptic divergence** (see Figure 3). When many neurones connect to one neurone information can be amplified (made stronger). This is called **synaptic convergence** (see Figure 4).

Tip: Synaptic <u>d</u>ivergence is when information from one neurone <u>d</u>ivides, and synaptic <u>c</u>onvergence is when information from many neurones <u>c</u>omes together.

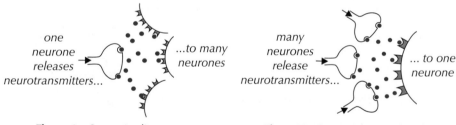

one neurone releases neurotransmitters... *...to many neurones*

many neurones release neurotransmitters... *... to one neurone*

Figure 3: Synaptic divergence.   **Figure 4:** Synaptic convergence.

Summation

If a stimulus is weak, only a small amount of neurotransmitter will be released from a neurone into the synaptic cleft. This might not be enough to excite the postsynaptic membrane to the threshold level and stimulate an action potential. Summation is where the effect of neurotransmitters released from many neurones (or one neurone that's stimulated a lot in a short period of time) is added together. It means synapses accurately process information, finely tuning the response. There are two types of summation:

Tip: <u>Sum</u>mation is where the <u>sum</u> total of lots of smaller impulses triggers an action potential.

1. **Spatial summation** is where two or more presynaptic neurones converge and release their neurotransmitters at the same time onto the same postsynaptic neurone. The small amount of neurotransmitter released from each of these neurones can be enough altogether to reach the threshold in the postsynaptic neurone and trigger an action potential — see Figure 5 on the next page. Stimuli might arrive from different sources, but spatial summation allows signals from multiple stimuli to be coordinated into a single response.

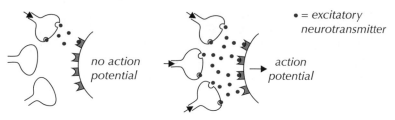

Tip: Remember, only excitatory neurotransmitters can trigger an action potential (see previous page).

Figure 5: *One presynaptic neurone only releases a few neurotransmitters (left) but three presynaptic neurones release enough to trigger an action potential (right).*

If some neurones release an inhibitory neurotransmitter then the total effect of all the neurotransmitters might be no action potential — see Figure 6.

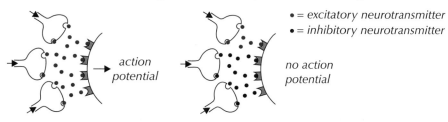

Figure 6: *If some presynaptic neurones release inhibitory neurotransmitters, it might prevent an action potential from being triggered (right).*

2. **Temporal summation** is where two or more nerve impulses arrive in quick succession from the same presynaptic neurone. This makes an action potential more likely because more neurotransmitter is released into the synaptic cleft — see Figure 7.

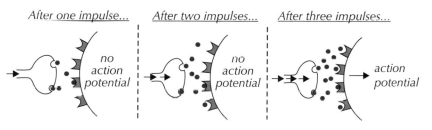

Figure 7: *The effects of temporal summation at a synapse.*

Tip: Impulses have to follow each other very quickly, otherwise the neurotransmitter will be removed from the cleft before it's reached a level high enough to trigger an action potential.

Unidirectional transmission

Synapses make sure impulses are unidirectional — the nervous impulse can only travel in one direction. This is because neurotransmitters are only released from presynaptic neurones and receptors for neurotransmitters are only on the postsynaptic membranes.

Practice Questions — Fact Recall

Q1 At a cholinergic synapse in the CNS:
   a) Describe and explain the movement of calcium ions following the arrival of an action potential at a presynaptic neurone.
   b) Explain how acetylcholine (ACh) leaves the presynaptic neurone and can cause an action potential in the postsynaptic neurone.

Q2 Explain the purpose of:
   a) synaptic divergence,   b) synaptic convergence.

Q3 Explain how an action potential may be more likely as a result of:
   a) spatial summation,   b) temporal summation.

Tip: Don't get the presynaptic and postsynaptic neurones mixed up — remember 'pre' means before and 'post' means after.

Exam-style Questions

1   **Fig 1.1** shows five action potentials recorded across the membrane of a myelinated axon.

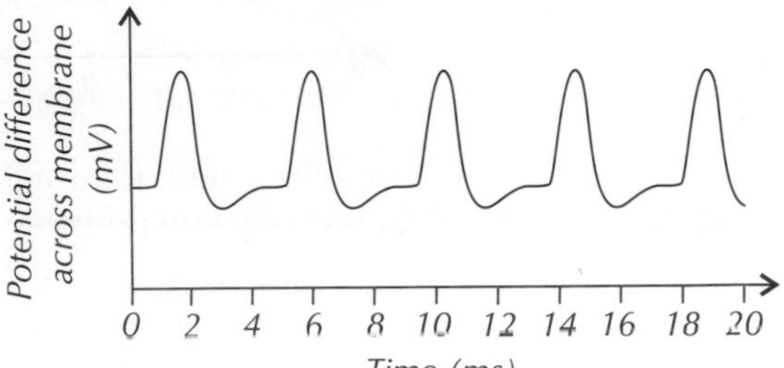

(a) (i) Explain why the action potentials don't overlap.

(3 marks)

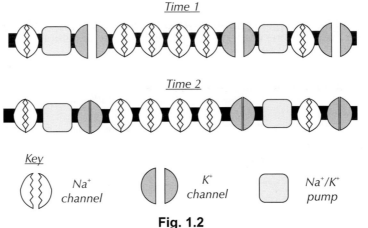

Fig. 1.1

(ii) If the action potentials continue at the same frequency, calculate the number of action potentials along the axon in 500 ms.

(2 marks)

(b)   **Fig. 1.2** shows the neurone cell membrane at two different times during one action potential.

Time 1

Time 2

Key

| | Na$^+$ channel | | K$^+$ channel | | Na$^+$/K$^+$ pump |

Fig. 1.2

(i)* Describe the stages of the action potential that are occurring at Times 1 and 2. Use evidence from **Fig. 1.2** to support your answer.

(6 marks)

The neurone cell membrane shows **sodium-potassium (Na$^+$/K$^+$) pumps**.

(ii) Describe the movement of sodium and potassium ions across a sodium-potassium pump.

(3 marks)

(iii) Explain why a sodium-potassium pump is needed by the neurone cell membrane after Time 2.

(2 marks)

(c)   Saxitoxin is a chemical that blocks **voltage-gated sodium ion channels**.

Use your knowledge of action potentials to explain the effect that saxitoxin is likely to have upon the nervous system.

(2 marks)

* The quality of your response will be assessed in this question.

2   **Fig. 2.1** shows the structure of a myelinated motor neurone.

Fig. 2.1

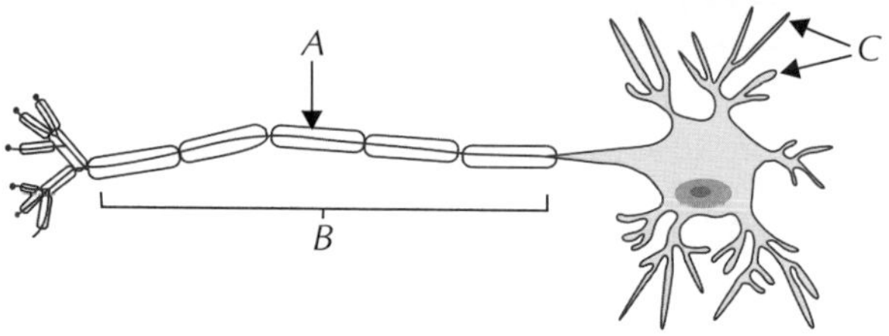

(a) (i)   Name the type of cell that forms structure **A**.

(1 mark)

(ii)   Complete the table to give the names of the structures labelled **B** and **C** and their functions.

	Structure	Function
B		
C		

(4 marks)

(b)   Sensory and relay neurones differ in structure and function to motor neurones.

(i)   Give the **function** of a sensory neurone.

(1 mark)

(ii)   Give the **function** of a relay neurone.

(1 mark)

(c)   Guillain-Barré syndrome is an auto-immune disease whereby the myelin sheath around certain neurones is damaged.

Use your knowledge of myelination to explain how Guillain-Barré syndrome can result in muscle weakness and paralysis.

(2 marks)

3   A neuromuscular junction is a specialised synapse between a motor neurone and a muscle cell. It uses **acetylcholine** as a neurotransmitter.

(a)   Explain how an action potential along a motor neurone results in acetylcholine being released at the neuromuscular junction.

(4 marks)

(b)   An action potential is more likely if two or more nerve impulses arrive in quick succession from the same presynaptic neurone.

(i)   What is the name given to this effect?

(1 mark)

(ii)   Explain why this effect makes an action potential in the muscle cell more likely.

(5 marks)

(c)   The drug tubocurarine blocks receptors at neuromuscular junctions.

Doctors use this drug as an anaesthetic as it temporarily paralyses muscles. Suggest how tubocurarine works.

(4 marks)

Learning Objectives:

- Understand endocrine communication by hormones, including the secretion of hormones into the blood, transport by the blood and detection by target cells or tissues.

- Know the action of hormones in cell signalling, including adrenaline (first messenger), activation of adenylyl cyclase, and cyclic AMP (second messenger).

- Know the structure and functions of the adrenal glands, including the hormones secreted by the cortex and medulla and their functions.

- Understand the histology of the pancreas, including the endocrine tissues.

- Be able to examine and draw stained sections of the pancreas to show the histology of the endocrine tissues (PAG1).

Specification References 5.1.4, 5.1.5

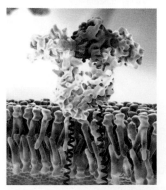

Figure 2: A growth hormone molecule (pink) bound to a growth hormone receptor (yellow and beige) in the membrane of the target cell.

5. The Hormonal System and Glands

Like the nervous system, the hormonal system is a form of cell signalling that helps us to respond to our environment.

What is the hormonal system?

The hormonal system sends information as chemical signals. It's made up of glands (called endocrine glands) and hormones. **Endocrine glands** are groups of cells that are specialised to secrete hormones, e.g. the pancreas secretes insulin. **Hormones** are 'chemical messengers'. Many hormones are proteins or peptides, e.g. insulin. Some hormones are steroids, e.g. progesterone.

Hormones are secreted when an endocrine gland is stimulated. Glands can be stimulated by a change in concentration of a specific substance (sometimes another hormone). They can also be stimulated by electrical impulses.

Hormonal communication

Hormones diffuse directly into the blood, then they're taken around the body by the circulatory system. They diffuse out of the blood all over the body but each hormone will only bind to specific receptors for that hormone, found on the membranes of some cells, called **target cells**. Tissue that contains target cells is called **target tissue**. The hormones trigger a response in the target cells (the effectors).

Stimulus ➡ *Receptors* ➡ *Hormone* ➡ *Effectors* ➡ *Response*

Figure 1: *The pathway of hormonal communication.*

Example

A real-life example of hormonal communication is the process the body uses to increase blood glucose concentration when it's lower than normal:

- **Stimulus** — low blood glucose concentration.

- **Receptors** — receptors on pancreas cells detect the low blood glucose concentration.

- **Hormone** — the pancreas releases the hormone glucagon into the blood.

- **Effectors** — target cells in the liver detect glucagon and convert glycogen into glucose.

- **Response** — glucose is released into the blood, so glucose concentration increases.

Action of hormones

A hormone is called a **first messenger** because it carries the chemical message the first part of the way, from the endocrine gland to the receptor on the target cells. When a hormone binds to its receptor it activates an enzyme in the cell membrane. The enzyme catalyses the production of a molecule inside the cell called a signalling molecule — this molecule signals to other parts of the cell to change how the cell works.

The signalling molecule is called a **second messenger** because it carries the chemical message the second part of the way, from the receptor to other parts of the cell. Second messengers activate a cascade (a chain of reactions) inside the cell.

Adrenaline

Adrenaline is a hormone that's secreted from your adrenal glands (see below). It's secreted when there's a low concentration of glucose in your blood, when you're stressed and when you're exercising. Adrenaline gets the body ready for action by making more glucose available for muscles to respire, e.g. by activating glycogenolysis (the breakdown of glycogen to glucose — see p. 41).

Adrenaline is a first messenger. It binds to specific receptors in the cell membranes of many cells, e.g. liver cells. When adrenaline binds it activates an enzyme in the membrane called adenylyl cyclase. Activated adenylyl cyclase catalyses the production of a second messenger called cyclic AMP (cAMP) from ATP. cAMP activates a cascade, e.g. a cascade of enzyme reactions makes more glucose available to the cell by catalysing the breakdown of glycogen into glucose — see Figure 3.

Tip: The release of adrenaline also has an effect on heart rate — there's more about this on page 76.

Tip: Lots of cells in the body have receptors for adrenaline. The cascade that's activated is not the same in every type of cell and the second messenger isn't always cAMP, so adrenaline affects different tissues in different ways.

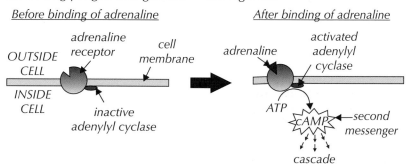

Figure 3: *Diagram showing the action of adrenaline as a first messenger and cAMP as a second messenger.*

Adrenal glands

The adrenal glands are endocrine glands that are found just above your kidneys. Each adrenal gland has an outer part called the cortex and an inner part called the medulla (see Figure 4). The cortex and the medulla have different functions and the hormones they secrete produce different responses. For example, they play different roles in our response to stress, producing effects which help to prepare the body for the **'fight or flight'** response (see page 76).

Tip: The <u>m</u>edulla is the name given to the <u>m</u>iddle of an organ. The c<u>o</u>rtex is the <u>o</u>uter layer.

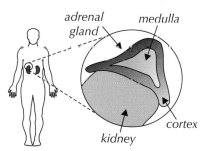

Figure 4: *The location and structure of an adrenal gland.*

The cortex

The cortex secretes **steroid hormones**, e.g. it secretes cortisol and aldosterone when you're stressed. These hormones have a role in both the short-term and the long-term responses to stress. Their effects include:

- stimulating the breakdown of proteins and fats into glucose. This increases the amount of energy available so the brain and muscles can respond to the situation.

- increasing blood volume and pressure by increasing the uptake of sodium ions and water by the kidneys.

- suppressing the immune system.

Tip: Cortisol, aldosterone, adrenaline and noradrenaline work together to control your response to stress. See the next page for more on the roles of adrenaline and noradrenaline.

The medulla

The medulla secretes **catecholamine hormones** (modified amino acids), e.g. it secretes adrenaline and noradrenaline when you're stressed. These act to make more energy available in the short-term by increasing heart and breathing rate, causing cells to break down glycogen into glucose and constricting some blood vessels so that blood is diverted to the brain and muscles.

The pancreas

The pancreas is a gland that's found below the stomach. You need to know about its endocrine function. The areas of the pancreas that contain endocrine tissue are called the **islets of Langerhans**. They're found in clusters around blood capillaries and they secrete hormones directly into the blood. They're made up of two types of cell, alpha (α) cells and beta (β) cells (see Figure 5). α cells secrete a hormone called glucagon and β cells secrete a hormone called insulin. Glucagon and insulin help to control blood glucose concentration (see p. 41).

Tip: One of the learning objectives is to understand the histology of the pancreas — this just means its structure as seen under a microscope.

Tip: See page 43 for more detail on the structure of beta cells.

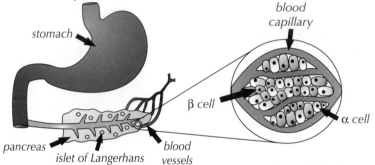

Figure 5: The location of α and β cells in the islets of Langerhans.

Figure 6 shows what you might see if you looked at a stained section of pancreatic tissue under a light microscope.

PRACTICAL ACTIVITY GROUP **1**

Tip: You will have covered how to use a light microscope to examine and draw a section in Year 1 of your course.

The purple stained cells are the β cells.

If you look closely you can see pink stained cells — these are α cells.

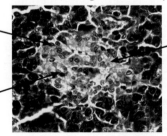

The islets of Langerhans (endocrine tissue) appear as paler patches in amongst all the other cells.

Figure 6: Light micrograph of a section of pancreatic tissue.

Tip: You can only differentiate between α and β cells if a special stain has been used to make them different colours, e.g. chrome haematoxylin and phloxine.

Practice Questions — Application

Read the passage below and then answer the questions that follow on the next page.

When a baby sucks on its mother's nipple, electrical impulses are sent from the nipple via the central nervous system to the mother's posterior pituitary gland, which is stimulated to secrete oxytocin into the blood. Oxytocin binds to specific receptors on myoepithelial cells, found in the epithelial tissue of mammary glands in the mother's breast. This causes contraction of the myoepithelial cells, which in turn causes milk to be secreted via milk ducts, out of the mother's nipple.

Q1 Copy and complete the table below by naming the molecules and structures involved in the pathway of communication described on the previous page.

Molecule / Structure	Name
Hormone	
Target cells	
Target tissue	
Endocrine gland	

Q2 It can take several minutes from when the baby starts sucking its mother's nipple to when milk is released. Suggest why this is.

Practice Questions — Fact Recall

Q1 What is an endocrine gland?

Q2 Give two types of stimuli that trigger hormone secretion.

Q3 Once a hormone is in the bloodstream, why doesn't it affect every cell in the body?

Q4 When adrenaline binds to receptors in the cell membrane of liver cells, it activates the enzyme adenylyl cyclase. This then catalyses the production of a second messenger inside the cell.

   a) What is the name of the second messenger produced?

   b) What effect does the second messenger have inside the cell?

   c) What is the first messenger in this example?

Q5 The adrenal glands have an inner part and an outer part.

   a) Name both parts.

   b) Explain the role that the inner part plays when the body is stressed.

Q6 The image below shows a light micrograph of a section through the pancreas. The yellow tissue contains α and β cells.

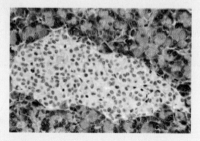

   a) What is the name of the yellow tissue shown in the micrograph?

   b) Name the hormone secreted by:

     i) α cells,

     ii) β cells.

Exam Tip
Make sure you read questions in the exam carefully — e.g. if you're asked to give <u>two</u> examples of something make sure you give two. You'll miss out on marks if you only give one and waste time if you give more than two.

Learning Objectives:

- Understand the principles of homeostasis.
- Know the differences between receptors and effectors in homeostasis.
- Know the differences between negative feedback and positive feedback.

Specification Reference 5.1.1

6. Homeostasis Basics

The body has some pretty clever systems to control its internal environment...

What is homeostasis?

Changes in your external environment can affect your internal environment — the blood and tissue fluid that surrounds your cells. Homeostasis is the maintenance of a constant internal environment. It involves control systems that keep your internal environment roughly constant (within certain limits). Keeping your internal environment constant is vital for cells to function normally and to stop them being damaged.

It's particularly important to maintain the right core body temperature. This is because temperature affects enzyme activity, and enzymes control the rate of metabolic reactions (chemical reactions in living cells).

Temperature

The rate of metabolic reactions increases when the temperature's increased. More heat means more kinetic energy, so molecules move faster. This makes the substrate molecules more likely to collide with the enzymes' active sites. The energy of these collisions also increases, which means each collision is more likely to result in a reaction.

But, if the temperature gets too high (e.g. over 40 °C), the reaction essentially stops. The rise in temperature makes the enzyme's molecules vibrate more. If the temperature goes above a certain level, this vibration breaks some of the hydrogen bonds that hold the enzyme in its 3D shape. The active site changes shape and the enzyme and substrate no longer fit together. At this point, the enzyme is denatured — it no longer functions as a catalyst (see Figure 1).

If body temperature is too low enzyme activity is reduced, slowing the rate of metabolic reactions. The highest rate of enzyme activity happens at their optimum temperature — about 37 °C in humans (see Figure 1).

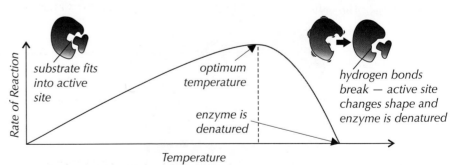

Figure 1: *Effect of temperature on the rate of a metabolic reaction.*

Negative feedback

Homeostatic systems involve receptors, a communication system and effectors. Receptors detect when a level is too high or too low, and the information's communicated via the nervous system or the hormonal system to effectors. The effectors respond to counteract the change — bringing the level back to normal. The mechanism that restores the level to normal is called a **negative feedback mechanism** — see Figure 2 (on the next page).

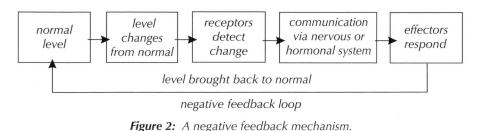

level brought back to normal

negative feedback loop

Figure 2: *A negative feedback mechanism.*

Tip: The 'level' in Figure 2 refers to something inside the body that needs to be controlled, e.g. temperature level, blood glucose level.

Negative feedback keeps things around the normal level.

Example

Body temperature is usually kept within 0.5 °C above or below 37 °C.

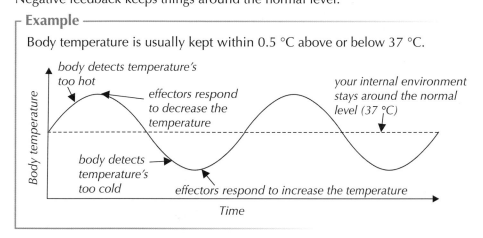

Tip: There are various ways in which effectors respond to change body temperature in mammals — see pages 38-39 for more.

Negative feedback only works within certain limits though — if the change is too big then the effectors may not be able to counteract it, e.g. a huge drop in body temperature caused by prolonged exposure to cold weather may be too large to counteract.

Positive feedback

Some changes trigger a positive feedback mechanism, which amplifies the change. The effectors respond to further increase the level away from the normal level. The mechanism that amplifies a change away from the normal level is called a **positive feedback mechanism** — see Figure 3.

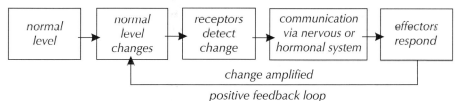

change amplified

positive feedback loop

Figure 3: *A positive feedback mechanism.*

Positive feedback isn't involved in homeostasis because it doesn't keep your internal environment constant. Positive feedback is useful to rapidly activate processes in the body.

Example

During the formation of a blood clot after an injury, platelets become activated and release a chemical — this triggers more platelets to be activated, and so on. This means platelets very quickly form a blood clot at the injury site. (The process ends with negative feedback, when the body detects the blood clot has been formed.)

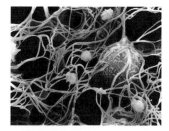

Figure 4: *At a site of injury, more and more platelets (shown above as small, green balls) are produced to form a clot as part of a positive feedback mechanism.*

Practice Questions — Application

Q1 Read the following two passages about control systems in the body:

Passage A	Passage B
A high blood concentration of carbon dioxide lowers the pH of the blood. Chemoreceptors in the blood vessels detect this change and send signals to the brain to increase the respiration rate.	When oestrogen concentration is high it stimulates the anterior pituitary gland to release LH. LH stimulates the ovaries to release more oestrogen.

For each passage, state whether it's an example of negative or positive feedback and explain your answer.

Tip: Oestrogen and LH are both hormones — you don't need to know anything about their effects in the body to answer the question.

Q2 When low blood calcium concentration is detected, the secretion of parathyroid hormone (PTH) from the parathyroid gland is stimulated. When high blood calcium concentration is detected, the secretion of the hormone calcitonin, from the thyroid gland, is stimulated. These two hormones work via negative feedback mechanisms to control the blood calcium concentration. Their effects are shown on the graph.

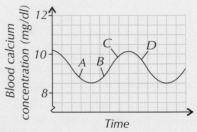

Tip: Parathyroid and thyroid glands are found in the neck.

a) Suggest an explanation for the shape of the graph between:

   i) A and B.   ii) C and D.

b) Suggest what could happen to the blood calcium concentration of someone who has had a parathyroid gland removed. Explain your answer.

Practice Questions — Fact Recall

Q1 What is homeostasis?

Q2 Explain why it is important for the body to maintain its internal temperature within normal limits.

Q3 The diagram below shows a negative feedback loop. Describe what happens in the missing labels, A-C.

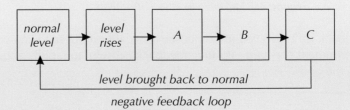

negative feedback loop

Q4 Describe how positive feedback mechanisms differ from negative feedback mechanisms.

7. Control of Body Temperature

Some organisms can control their body temperature internally. Many different mechanisms allow them to do this and they're controlled by the brain.

Temperature control in ectotherms and endotherms

Animals are classed as either ectotherms (e.g. reptiles, fish) or endotherms (e.g. mammals, birds), depending on how they control their body temperature.

Ectotherms

Ectotherms can't control their body temperature internally — they control their temperature by changing their behaviour.

> **Example**
>
> A lizard is an ectotherm. When its internal temperature drops, a lizard will move to find a warmer area such as a place in the sunshine. When its internal temperature gets too high, it will move to somewhere cooler such as a burrow beneath the sand.

This means the internal temperature of ectotherms depends on the external temperature (their surroundings).

Ectotherms have a variable metabolic rate because they can't keep their internal temperature constant. They generate very little heat themselves. This means the activity level of ectotherms depends on the external temperature too — they're more active at higher temperatures and less active at lower temperatures.

Endotherms

Endotherms control their body temperature internally by homeostasis, as well as by altering their behaviour.

> **Example**
>
> An elephant is an endotherm. Its temperature is mainly controlled internally by homeostasis, but it may also change its behaviour to control its temperature. For example, it may wallow in mud or flap its ears to help it cool down

This means that, compared to ectotherms, the internal temperature of endotherms is less affected by the external temperature (within certain limits).

Endotherms have a constantly high metabolic rate because they can keep their internal temperature constant. They generate a lot of heat from metabolic reactions. This means the activity level of endotherms is largely independent of the external temperature — they can be active at any temperature (within certain limits).

Learning Objectives:

- Understand the behavioural responses involved in temperature control in ectotherms.
- Understand the physiological and behavioural responses involved in temperature control in endotherms, including peripheral temperature receptors, the role of the hypothalamus and effectors in skin and muscles.

Specification Reference 5.1.1

Figure 1: *A lizard basking in the sun to warm up.*

Tip: In ectotherms, respiration and other metabolic reactions happen faster in warmer weather. This means in warmer weather more energy is available for faster movement, etc., so ectotherms are more active in warmer weather.

Practice Questions — Application

Q1 On a thermal image, areas of heat radiation appear brightly coloured. On the right is a thermal image of a mouse and a snake.

a) What can you conclude about the temperature of the external environment when the image was taken? Explain your answer.

b) Would you expect the mouse or the snake to be more active at the time the image was taken? Explain your answer.

Q2 In an experiment, the internal temperatures of a chuckwalla and a hoatzin were recorded over a range of external temperatures controlled by a heat source. The organisms were kept in enclosed environments with a heat source. The results are shown in the table below.

	Temperature (°C)				
External	20	24	28	32	38
Chuckwalla	26.7	30.4	37.7	40.1	43.2
Hoatzin	38.5	38.7	38.8	39.0	38.9

a) Use information from the table to explain which organism is an ectotherm and which is an endotherm.

b) Will the metabolic reactions of the chuckwalla or the hoatzin be most affected during this investigation? Explain your answer.

Mechanisms to change body temperature

Mammals use different mechanisms to reduce or increase their body temperature.

Mechanisms to reduce body temperature

1. **Sweating** — more sweat is secreted from sweat glands when the body's too hot. The water in sweat evaporates from the surface of the skin and takes heat from the body. The skin is cooled.

2. **Hairs lie flat** — mammals have a layer of hair that provides insulation by trapping air (air is a poor conductor of heat). When it's hot, erector pili muscles relax so the hairs lie flat. Less air is trapped, so the skin is less insulated and heat can be lost more easily.

3. **Vasodilation** — when it's hot, arterioles near the surface of the skin dilate (this is called vasodilation). More blood flows through the capillaries in the surface layers of the dermis. This means more heat is lost from the skin by radiation and the temperature is lowered.

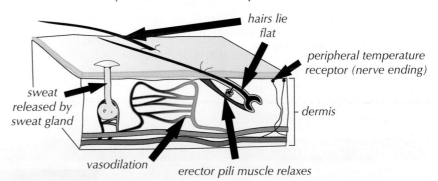

Figure 2: *Mechanisms to reduce body temperature in a mammal.*

Mechanisms to increase body temperature

1. **Shivering** — when it's cold, muscles contract in spasms. This makes the body shiver and more heat is produced from increased respiration.

2. **Hormones** — the body releases adrenaline and thyroxine. These increase metabolism and so more heat is produced.

3. **Much less sweat** — less sweat is secreted from sweat glands when it's cold, reducing the amount of heat loss.
4. **Hairs stand up** — erector pili muscles contract when it's cold, which makes the hairs stand up. This traps more air and so prevents heat loss.
5. **Vasoconstriction** — when it's cold, arterioles near the surface of the skin constrict (this is called vasoconstriction) so less blood flows through the capillaries in the surface layers of the dermis. This reduces heat loss.

Tip: These three mechanisms are all ways to conserve heat, whereas the previous two mechanisms (shivering and hormones) actually produce heat.

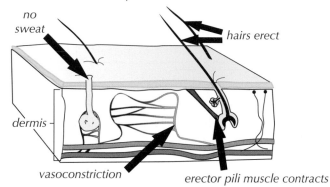

Figure 3: *Mechanisms to increase body temperature in a mammal.*

Control of body temperature by the hypothalamus

Body temperature in mammals is maintained at a constant level by a part of the brain called the **hypothalamus**. The hypothalamus receives information about both internal and external temperature from **thermoreceptors** (temperature receptors):

Tip: Control of body temperature is called thermoregulation.

- Thermoreceptors in the hypothalamus detect internal temperature (the temperature of the blood).
- Thermoreceptors in the skin (called peripheral temperature receptors) detect external temperature (the temperature of the skin).

Thermoreceptors send impulses along sensory neurones to the hypothalamus, which sends impulses along motor neurones to effectors (e.g. skeletal muscles, or sweat glands and erector pili muscles in the skin). The effectors respond to restore the body temperature back to normal.

Tip: The levels of some things in our body are controlled by the nervous system (like body temperature here) and others are controlled by the hormonal system.

Rise in body temperature

When thermoreceptors detect body temperature is too high, they send impulses to the hypothalamus, which sends impulses to effectors. Effectors respond to increase heat loss from the body (e.g. sweat glands produce sweat) and to reduce the amount of heat that's produced by the body. Body temperature then returns to normal — see Figure 4.

Tip: When you feel hot (e.g. when you exercise) you might find yourself sweaty and red-faced — this is just your body's (unattractive) response to the rise in internal body temperature.

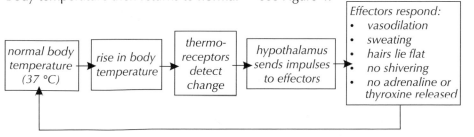

Figure 4: *Negative feedback mechanism activated by a rise in body temperature.*

Fall in body temperature

When thermoreceptors detect body temperature is too low, they send impulses to the hypothalamus, which sends impulses to effectors. Effectors respond to produce more heat (e.g. adrenaline and thyroxine are released to increase metabolism) and to conserve it. Body temperature then returns to normal — see Figure 5 below.

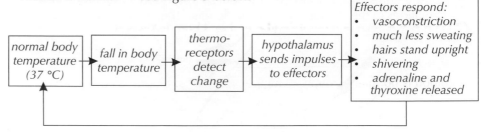

Figure 5: Negative feedback mechanism activated by a fall in body temperature.

Practice Questions — Application

Q1 If a person spends a long time in a hot bath, their skin might appear pink when they get out. Explain the role of the nervous system in this response.

Q2 When blood glucose concentration gets low, the brain receives signals which stimulate feelings of hunger. Assuming activity levels are the same, is a person likely to feel hungry more quickly in a hot or cold external environment? Explain your answer.

Q3 The effects of some sympathomimetic drugs, such as cocaine, include vasoconstriction and an increase in muscular activity. In hot weather people who have taken cocaine are at risk of hyperthermia (their internal body temperature becomes dangerously high). Suggest why this occurs.

Practice Questions — Fact Recall

Q1 How is body temperature controlled in:
   a) an ectotherm?
   b) an endotherm?

Q2 How do the metabolic rates of an ectotherm and an endotherm differ?

Q3 Explain how sweat glands are important for controlling body temperature.

Q4 Describe two mechanisms that the body uses to increase heat production and explain how they work.

Q5 Describe how arterioles near the skin surface respond when low temperatures are detected by thermoreceptors.

Q6 What part of a mammal's brain controls body temperature?

Q7 Describe how the brain receives information about the external temperature of the body.

Q8 Briefly describe how the nervous system returns internal body temperature to normal following a fall in body temperature.

8. Control of Blood Glucose Concentration

Blood glucose concentration is under tight control by a hormonal system. If this control system doesn't work properly it may result in diabetes.

Glucose concentration in the blood

All cells need a constant energy supply to work — so blood glucose concentration must be carefully controlled. The concentration of glucose in the blood is normally around 90 mg per 100 cm^3 of blood. It's monitored by cells in the **pancreas**. Blood glucose concentration rises after eating food containing carbohydrate. It falls after exercise, as more glucose is used in respiration to release energy.

Hormonal control of blood glucose concentration

The hormonal system (see p. 30) controls blood glucose concentration using two hormones called insulin and glucagon. They're both secreted by clusters of cells in the pancreas called the **islets of Langerhans** (see page 32). The islets of Langerhans contain **beta (β) cells** and **alpha (α) cells**. β cells secrete insulin into the blood. α cells secrete glucagon into the blood. Insulin and glucagon act on effectors, which respond to restore the blood glucose concentration to the normal level.

Insulin

Insulin lowers blood glucose concentration when it's too high. It binds to specific receptors on the cell membranes of liver cells and muscle cells and increases the permeability of cell membranes to glucose, so the cells take up more glucose.

Insulin also activates enzymes that convert glucose into glycogen. Liver and muscle cells are able to store glycogen in their cytoplasm, as an energy source. The process of forming glycogen from glucose is called **glycogenesis** (see Figure 1). Insulin also increases the rate of respiration of glucose, especially in muscle cells.

activated by insulin

GLUCOSE →(glycogenesis)→ GLYCOGEN

Figure 1: The process of glycogenesis.

Glucagon

Glucagon raises blood glucose concentration when it's too low. It binds to specific receptors on the cell membranes of liver cells and activates enzymes that break down glycogen into glucose. The process of breaking down glycogen is called **glycogenolysis**.

Glucagon also promotes the formation of glucose from glycerol and amino acids. The process of forming glucose from non-carbohydrates is called **gluconeogenesis** (see Figure 2). Glucagon also decreases the rate of respiration of glucose in cells.

GLYCEROL AMINO ACIDS →(gluconeogenesis)→ GLUCOSE ←(glycogenolysis)← GLYCOGEN

activated by glucagon

Figure 2: The processes of glycogenolysis and gluconeogenesis.

Learning Objectives:

- Understand how blood glucose concentration is regulated, including the action of insulin and glucagon as an example of negative feedback, and the role of the liver.

- Know how insulin secretion is controlled, with reference to potassium channels and calcium channels in the beta cells of the pancreas.

- Know the differences between Type 1 and Type 2 diabetes mellitus, including their causes and the treatments used for each.

- Know the potential treatments for diabetes mellitus, including the use of insulin produced by genetically modified bacteria and the potential use of stem cells.

Specification Reference 5.1.4

Tip: Liver cells are also called hepatocytes.

Tip: You learnt about glycogen in Year 1 — it's a polysaccharide made up of branched chains of α–glucose.

Exam Tip
Take care not to write 'a cells' and 'b cells' instead of 'α cells' and 'β cells'. Read through your answers before the end of the exam to catch easy mistakes like this.

Negative feedback mechanisms and glucose concentration

Negative feedback mechanisms keep blood glucose concentration normal.

Rise in blood glucose concentration

When the pancreas detects blood glucose concentration is too high, the β cells secrete insulin and the α cells stop secreting glucagon. Insulin then binds to receptors on liver and muscle cells (the effectors). The liver and muscle cells respond to decrease the blood glucose concentration, e.g. glycogenesis is activated (see previous page). Blood glucose concentration then returns to normal.

Tip: 'Genesis' means 'making' — so glyc**ogenesis** means making glycogen.

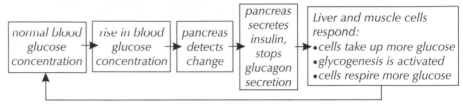

blood glucose concentration falls

Figure 3: *Negative feedback mechanism activated by a rise in blood glucose.*

Fall in blood glucose concentration

When the pancreas detects blood glucose is too low, the α cells secrete glucagon and the β cells stop secreting insulin. Glucagon then binds to receptors on liver cells (the effectors). The liver cells respond to increase the blood glucose concentration, e.g. glycogenolysis is activated (see previous page). Blood glucose concentration then returns to normal.

Tip: 'Lysis' means 'splitting' — so glycogeno**lysis** means splitting glycogen.

Tip: 'Neo' means 'new' — so gluco**neo**genesis means making new glucose.

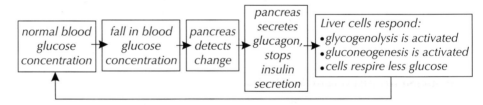

blood glucose concentration rises

Figure 4: *Negative feedback mechanism activated by a fall in blood glucose.*

Practice Questions — Application

Q1 Adrenaline activates glycogenolysis. What effect will adrenaline have on blood glucose concentration?

Q2 After eating a big bowl of pasta describe how a person's blood glucose concentration will change and explain how their body returns it back to normal.

Q3 Von Gierke's disease is a glycogen storage disease. It's caused by an enzyme deficiency, which means the processes of glycogenolysis and gluconeogenesis can't work properly. Explain why someone with von Gierke's disease might suffer from hypoglycaemia if they don't eat regularly.

Tip: Hypoglycaemia is a condition where blood glucose concentration is abnormally low. (And hyperglycaemia is a condition where blood glucose concentration is abnormally high.)

Control of insulin secretion by beta cells

β cells contain insulin stored in vesicles. They have potassium ion (K⁺) channels and calcium ion (Ca²⁺) channels in their membrane (see Figure 5). When the blood glucose concentration is around the normal level (or lower), the K⁺ channels are open and the Ca²⁺ channels are closed. Potassium ions diffuse out of the cell through the open K⁺ channels, which makes the inside of the cell membrane more negatively charged compared to the outside. This is because there are more positive ions outside the cell than inside — the membrane is polarised.

Tip: The β cell is similar to a sensory receptor cell. When it's at rest (not being stimulated) its membrane is polarised — see page 16.

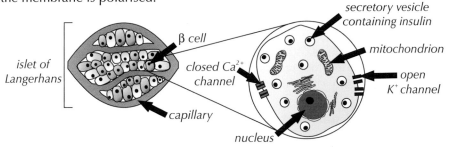

Tip: You should be familiar with the functions of the organelles inside an animal cell from Year 1.

Figure 5: *Diagram showing location of β cells in the islets of Langerhans, with the structure of a β cell enlarged.*

When the β cell detects a high blood glucose concentration, changes within the cell result in the secretion of insulin. Here's how it happens:

1. High blood glucose concentration detected

When blood glucose concentration is high, more glucose enters the β cells by facilitated diffusion. More glucose in a β cell causes the rate of respiration to increase, making more ATP.

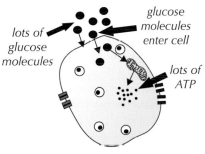

Tip: Facilitated diffusion means particles (e.g. glucose molecules) diffuse across a membrane with the help of carrier proteins or channel proteins in the plasma membrane.

2. Potassium ion channels close

The rise in ATP triggers the potassium ion channels in the β cell plasma membrane to close. This means potassium ions (K⁺) can't get through the membrane — so they build up inside the cell. This makes the inside of the β cell less negative because there are more positively-charged potassium ions inside the cell — so the plasma membrane of the β cell is depolarised.

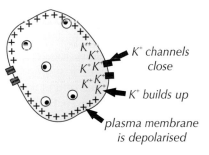

3. Calcium ion channels open

Depolarisation triggers calcium ion channels in the membrane to open, so calcium ions diffuse into the β cell. This causes the vesicles to move to and fuse with the β cell plasma membrane, releasing insulin by exocytosis.

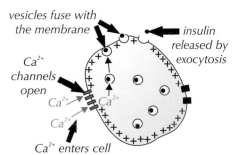

Tip: The calcium ion channels are voltage-gated — they open at a certain voltage.

Diabetes

Diabetes mellitus is a condition where blood glucose concentration can't be controlled properly. There are two types: Type 1 diabetes and Type 2 diabetes.

Type 1 diabetes

Type 1 diabetes is an auto-immune disease, in which the body attacks and destroys the β cells in the islets of Langerhans. This means people with Type 1 diabetes don't produce any insulin. After eating, the blood glucose concentration rises and stays high, which can result in death if left untreated. The kidneys can't reabsorb all this glucose, so some of it's excreted in the urine.

Type 1 diabetes usually develops in children or young adults. A person's risk of developing Type 1 diabetes is slightly increased if there's a close family history of the disease.

Tip: An auto-immune disease is where a person's immune system mistakes their own cells for pathogens, so it starts to attack them.

Treating Type 1 diabetes

Type 1 diabetes is treated with insulin therapy. For most people with Type 1 diabetes this involves having regular insulin injections throughout the day. For some people it involves using an insulin pump — a machine that continuously delivers insulin into the body via a tube inserted beneath the skin.

Some people have been successfully treated by having islet cell transplantation — they receive healthy islet cells from a donor so their pancreas can produce some insulin (although they usually still need some additional insulin therapy).

Whatever type of treatment they have, people with Type 1 diabetes need to regularly monitor their blood glucose concentration and think carefully about their diet and level of activity. Eating a healthy, balanced diet reduces the amount of insulin that needs to be injected, so people with Type 1 diabetes often have a carefully planned diet so that they can manage the amount of glucose they are taking in. Doing regular exercise reduces the amount of insulin that needs to be injected by using up blood glucose.

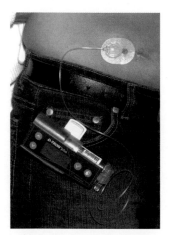

Figure 6: An insulin pump attached to a person's abdomen.

Type 2 diabetes

Type 2 diabetes occurs when the β cells don't produce enough insulin or when the body's cells don't respond properly to insulin. Cells don't respond properly because the insulin receptors on their membranes don't work properly, so the cells don't take up enough glucose. This means the blood glucose concentration is higher than normal.

Type 2 diabetes is usually acquired later in life than Type 1, and it's often linked with obesity. The risk of developing Type 2 diabetes is also increased in people from certain ethnic groups, e.g. African or Asian, and in people with a close family history of the disease.

Tip: Type 2 diabetes is becoming increasingly common in the UK. This has been linked to increasing levels of obesity, a move towards more unhealthy diets and low levels of physical activity.

Treating Type 2 diabetes

Type 2 diabetes is initially managed through lifestyle changes. Eating a healthy, balanced diet, getting regular exercise and losing weight if needed can help prevent the onset of Type 2 diabetes as well as control the effects.

If blood glucose concentration can't be controlled through lifestyle changes alone, then medication may be prescribed. There are some examples of this medication on the next page.

- Metformin — This is usually the first medicine to be prescribed. Metformin acts on liver cells to reduce the amount of glucose that they release into the blood. It also acts to increase the sensitivity of cells to insulin so more glucose can be taken up with the same amount of insulin.

- Sulfonylureas (e.g. gliclazide) — These stimulate the pancreas to produce more insulin.

- Thiazolidinediones (e.g. pioglitazone) — These also make the body cells more sensitive to insulin.

In some people with Type 2 diabetes, these types of medication are not enough to control blood glucose concentration so insulin therapy is used in addition or instead.

Practice Questions — Application

In an experiment, the blood glucose concentrations of a person with Type 2 diabetes and a person without diabetes were recorded at regular intervals in a 150 minute time period. 15 minutes into the experiment a glucose drink was given. The normal range for blood glucose concentration in a healthy individual is between 82 and 110 mg per 100 cm^3. The results of the experiment are shown on the graph below.

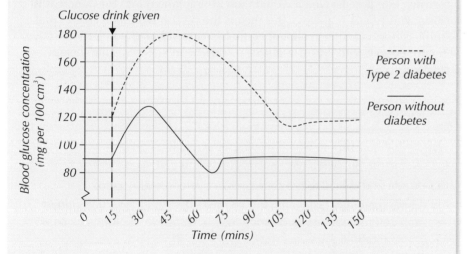

Exam Tip
If you get given a graph in the exam it's a good idea to look at it carefully and try and work out what it is showing before you start answering the questions. It sounds obvious, but if you just jump straight in you might miss something important.

Q1 Explain why the blood glucose concentration of the person with Type 2 diabetes takes longer to decrease after they take the glucose drink than the person without diabetes.

Q2 Suggest how the blood glucose concentration of a person with Type 1 diabetes would differ from the person with Type 2 diabetes after having the glucose drink.

Tip: Think about the causes of the two different types of diabetes for Q2.

Q3 Suggest what time insulin is released in the person without diabetes. Explain your answer.

Q4 Blood glucose concentration continues to rise after the release of insulin. Why is this?

Q5 Explain how negative feedback works to increase the blood glucose concentration in the person without diabetes between 65 and 75 minutes.

Insulin from GM bacteria

Tip: GM bacteria have had a gene from another organism inserted into them, so that they'll produce the protein coded for by that gene.

Insulin used to be extracted from animal pancreases (e.g. pigs and cattle), to treat people with Type 1 diabetes. But nowadays, human insulin can be made by genetically modified (GM) bacteria (see p. 239). Using GM bacteria to produce insulin is much better for many reasons, for example:

- Producing insulin using GM bacteria is cheaper than extracting it from animal pancreases.
- Larger quantities of insulin can be produced using GM bacteria.
- GM bacteria make human insulin. This is more effective than using pig or cattle insulin (which is slightly different to human insulin) and it's less likely to trigger an allergic response or be rejected by the immune system.
- Some people prefer insulin from GM bacteria for ethical or religious reasons. E.g. some vegetarians may object to the use of animals, and some religious people object to using insulin from pigs.

Curing diabetes

Tip: Look back at Module 2 if you need to remind yourself about stem cells.

Your body is made up of many different types of cells that are specialised for their function, e.g. liver cells, β cells. All specialised cells originally came from stem cells. Stem cells are unspecialised cells — they have the ability to develop into any type of cell.

Using stem cells could potentially cure diabetes. Stem cells could be grown into β cells, which would then be implanted into the pancreas of a person with Type 1 diabetes. This means the person would be able to make insulin as normal. This treatment is still being developed but, if it's effective, it'll cure people with Type 1 diabetes — they won't need insulin therapy anymore.

Exam Tip
There are lots of similar sounding words in this section so you need to make sure you get your spelling spot on in the exam, e.g. if you write 'glycogon' the examiner won't know whether you mean glucagon or glycogen so you won't get the marks.

Practice Questions — Fact Recall

Q1 Give three ways in which insulin reduces blood glucose concentration.

Q2 Name the process that converts glucose to glycogen.

Q3 Name and describe two processes activated by glucagon.

Q4 In the pancreas, potassium ion channels and calcium ion channels in β cell membranes open and close in response to blood glucose concentration.

    a) State whether the channels are opened or closed when the blood glucose concentration is around the normal level.

    b) State what happens to the channels when the blood glucose concentration is high.

Q5 a) What is Type 1 diabetes?

    b) Describe how Type 1 diabetes can be treated with insulin therapy.

    c) Give another way that Type 1 diabetes can be treated and describe what this involves.

Q6 Describe the different ways that Type 2 diabetes can be treated.

Q7 Give three advantages of using genetically modified bacteria to produce insulin rather than using animal pancreases.

Q8 Describe how stem cells may be able to cure Type 1 diabetes.

Section Summary

Make sure you know...

- That multicellular organisms need communication systems to respond to changes in their internal and external environment and to coordinate the activities of different organs.

- That cell signalling allows communication between adjacent cells and distant cells.

- That sensory neurones have short dendrites, long dendrons and short axons, and transmit nerve impulses from receptors to the central nervous system (CNS).

- That motor neurones have short dendrites and long axons, and transmit nerve impulses from the CNS to effectors.

- That relay neurones have short dendrites and one axon, and transmit nerve impulses between sensory neurones and motor neurones.

- That sensory receptors act as transducers as they convert the energy of a stimulus into electrical energy, and that they respond to specific stimuli, e.g. Pacinian corpuscles respond to touch.

- How a resting membrane potential is established and maintained by sodium-potassium pumps and potassium ion channels in a neurone's cell membrane.

- That when sodium ion channels in a neurone's cell membrane open, the membrane becomes more permeable to sodium ions and that this causes depolarisation (the potential difference of the membrane becomes more positive), resulting in an action potential if the threshold level is reached.

- That voltage-gated sodium ion channels open when the potential difference reaches the threshold level in an example of positive feedback and that they close again as voltage-gated potassium ion channels open during repolarisation.

- That the slow closure of potassium ion channels allows too many potassium ions to leave the neurone, causing a period of 'hyperpolarisation', but that the sodium-potassium pump returns the membrane back to its resting potential.

- That an action potential is transmitted along a neurone in a wave of depolarisation.

- That if the threshold is reached, an action potential will always fire with the same change in voltage and if the threshold isn't reached there'll be no action potential.

- The structure of a myelinated neurone.

- That action potentials are passed more quickly along myelinated than unmyelinated neurones because impulses are only conducted at the nodes of Ranvier (where sodium channels are concentrated).

- The structure of a synapse, e.g. a cholinergic synapse includes a synaptic knob, vesicles filled with acetylcholine (ACh), a synaptic cleft and specific cholinergic receptors on the postsynaptic membrane.

- That the arrival of an action potential at the presynaptic neurone triggers voltage-gated calcium channels to open, so calcium ions diffuse into the synaptic knob causing vesicles to fuse with the presynaptic membrane. Neurotransmitters diffuse across the synaptic cleft to bind to receptors on the postsynaptic membrane. This causes sodium ion channels to open and the influx of sodium ions triggers an action potential if the threshold is reached.

- The roles of synapses in the nervous system, including excitatory synapses (in which neurotransmitters depolarise the postsynaptic membrane), inhibitory synapses (in which neurotransmitters hyperpolarise the postsynaptic membrane), synaptic divergence (one neurone connecting to many neurones), synaptic convergence (many neurones connecting to one neurone), spatial summation (two or more presynaptic neurones releasing their neurotransmitters at the same time onto the same postsynaptic neurone), temporal summation (two or more nerve impulses arriving in quick succession from the same presynaptic neurone) and unidirectional transmission (impulses only travelling in one direction).

- That communication by the hormonal system involves the secretion of hormones (chemical messengers) into the blood by endocrine glands (groups of cells that are specialised to secrete hormones), transport by the blood and detection by target cells (cells that contain receptors for certain hormones) or target tissues (tissues that contain target cells).

- That a first messenger (e.g. adrenaline) activates an enzyme (e.g. adenylyl cyclase) in a cell membrane and this catalyses the production of a second messenger inside a cell (e.g. cAMP) from ATP, which activates a cascade inside the cell (e.g. catalysing the breakdown of glycogen into glucose).

- That the cortex of an adrenal gland secretes steroid hormones, e.g. cortisol, which are involved in both the short-term and the long-term responses to stress and the medulla secretes catecholamine hormones, e.g. adrenaline, which are involved in the short-term response to stress.

- The histology of the pancreas — it contains endocrine tissue called the islets of Langerhans, which contains α and β cells.

- How to examine and draw a section of pancreatic tissue using a light microscope.

- That homeostasis is the maintenance of a constant internal environment and that homeostatic systems involve receptors, which detect when a level is too high or too low, and effectors, which respond to counteract the change.

- That negative feedback is a mechanism that restores a level to normal, whereas positive feedback is a mechanism that amplifies a change away from the normal level.

- That ectotherms control their body temperature by changing their behaviour, and endotherms control their body temperature internally by homeostasis, as well as by altering their behaviour.

- How endotherms control their body temperature internally with communication via peripheral temperature receptors, the hypothalamus and effectors in skin and muscles (e.g. thermoreceptors in the skin detect changes in temperature and send impulses to the hypothalamus, which sends impulses to effectors to respond in a negative feedback mechanism).

- That insulin lowers blood glucose concentration when it's too high by binding to receptors on liver and muscle cells, causing cells to take up and respire more glucose and activating glycogenesis (the process of forming glycogen from glucose).

- That glucagon raises blood glucose concentration when it's too low by binding to receptors on liver cells and activating glycogenolysis (the process of breaking down glycogen) and gluconeogenesis (the process of forming glucose from non-carbohydrates), and causing the cells to respire less glucose.

- That the actions of insulin and glucagon in regulating glucose concentration are examples of negative feedback.

- That insulin secretion from β cells in the pancreas happens when blood glucose concentration is high and more glucose molecules enter the β cells. This increases the rate of respiration and increases ATP production, which causes potassium ion channels to close, depolarising the β cell membranes. This causes calcium ion channels to open and allows calcium ions to enter the cells, which causes vesicles to move to and fuse with the cell membranes so that insulin is released by exocytosis.

- That Type 1 diabetes is an auto-immune disease that causes the body to be unable to produce insulin.

- That Type 1 diabetes can be treated with insulin therapy (regular insulin injections or attachment to an insulin pump) or islet cell transplantation (receiving healthy islet cells from a donor) alongside a healthy, balanced diet and exercise.

- That Type 2 diabetes occurs when the β cells in the pancreas don't produce enough insulin or the body's cells don't respond properly to insulin.

- That Type 2 diabetes can be managed through lifestyle changes (eating a healthy, balanced diet and getting regular exercise), medication and insulin therapy (if necessary).

- That insulin can nowadays be produced by genetically modified bacteria and this has many advantages over using insulin from animals (e.g. it's cheaper, larger quantities can be produced, it's more effective as it makes human insulin, people may prefer it for religious or ethical reasons).

- That it may be possible to grow stem cells into β cells and insert these into the pancreas of someone with Type 1 diabetes, as a potential way of curing the disease.

Exam-style Questions

1 Which of the following statements is **not** correct?

   A People with Type 1 diabetes don't produce insulin.

   B Type 1 diabetes can be controlled by eating a healthy, balanced diet.

   C Type 2 diabetes is usually acquired later in life than Type 1 diabetes.

   D People with Type 2 diabetes don't produce enough insulin
      or don't respond properly to insulin.

(1 mark)

2 The 'fight or flight' response is important for a person's survival.
Adrenaline is one hormone that is involved in this response.

(a) During times of danger, more adrenaline will be secreted into
a person's bloodstream from their adrenal glands.
Where in the adrenal glands is adrenaline released from?

(1 mark)

(b) Describe how adrenaline triggers a cascade inside a cell.

(3 marks)

(c) One effect of a cascade triggered by adrenaline is the breakdown of
glycogen into glucose.

   (i) What name is given to this process?

(1 mark)

   (ii) Which hormone also produces this response?

(1 mark)

3 β cells respond to changes in blood glucose concentration as part of a negative
feedback mechanism.

(a) What is a negative feedback mechanism?

(1 mark)

(b) **Fig. 3.1** shows a diagram of a cell in the body of someone who has recently eaten a
meal high in carbohydrates (which are broken down to glucose).

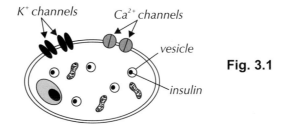

Fig. 3.1

   (i) Name the type of cell shown in **Fig. 3.1**.

(1 mark)

(ii) The potassium ion channels are **closed** in **Fig. 3.1**. Describe and explain the events that have caused these channels to close.

(3 marks)

(iii) When the potassium ion channels are closed, potassium ions can't diffuse through the membrane, which causes them to build up inside the cell. Explain how this leads to the release of insulin from the vesicle.

(4 marks)

(c) One of the effects of insulin release is **glycogenesis**. What is meant by glycogenesis?

(1 mark)

4 The activity levels of a squirrel and a tortoise living in the same area were recorded over a 20 hour period. The temperature of the external environment in the test period was also recorded. The results are shown in **Fig. 4.1**.

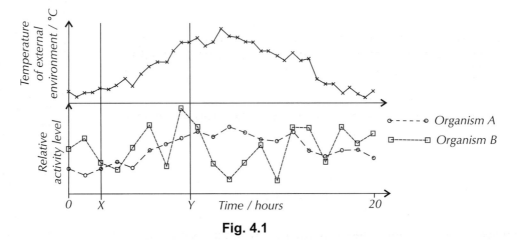

Fig. 4.1

(a) Describe the activity levels of the organisms in relation to temperature.

(2 marks)

(b) Tortoises are ectotherms, squirrels are endotherms.

   (i) Which organism, **A** or **B**, is the tortoise? Explain your answer.

(1 mark)

   (ii) Squirrels have a much wider geographical range than tortoises. Suggest why this is.

(2 marks)

(c) (i) It was observed that the hairs on the squirrel were standing up at point **X**. Explain how and why this response came about.

(4 marks)

   (ii) The squirrel has mechanisms that work to reduce its body temperature. Describe and explain **two** of these mechanisms that may occur at point **Y** in **Fig. 4.1**.

(4 marks)

1. The Liver and Excretion

Excretion is all about removing waste. Without it, the waste products our cells produce would build up inside us — not good. The main organs involved in excretion are the liver and the kidneys. Let's kick off with the liver...

What is excretion?

All the chemical reactions that happen in your cells make up your **metabolism**. Metabolism produces waste products — substances that aren't needed by the cells, such as carbon dioxide and nitrogenous (nitrogen-containing) waste. Many of these products are toxic, so if they were allowed to build up in the body they would cause damage, e.g. by affecting other metabolic reactions. This is where excretion comes in. Excretion is the removal of the waste products of metabolism from the body.

┌─ **Example** ─────────────────────────────

Carbon dioxide is a waste product of respiration. Too much in the blood is toxic, so it's removed from the body by the lungs (e.g. in mammals) or gills (e.g. in fish). The lungs and gills act as excretory organs.

Excreting waste products from the body maintains normal metabolism. It also maintains **homeostasis** (see page 34) by helping to keep the levels of certain substances in the blood roughly constant.

The liver

One of the functions of the liver is to break down metabolic waste products and other substances that can be harmful, like drugs and alcohol. They're broken down into less harmful products that can then be excreted.

You need to learn all the different veins, arteries and ducts connected to the liver. These are listed below and shown in Figure 1.

- The hepatic artery supplies the liver with oxygenated blood from the heart, so the liver has a good supply of oxygen for respiration, providing plenty of energy.

- The hepatic vein takes deoxygenated blood away from the liver.

- The hepatic portal vein brings blood from the duodenum and ileum (parts of the small intestine), so it's rich in the products of digestion. This means any ingested harmful substances are filtered out and broken down straight away.

- The bile duct takes bile (a substance produced by the liver to emulsify fats) to the gall bladder to be stored.

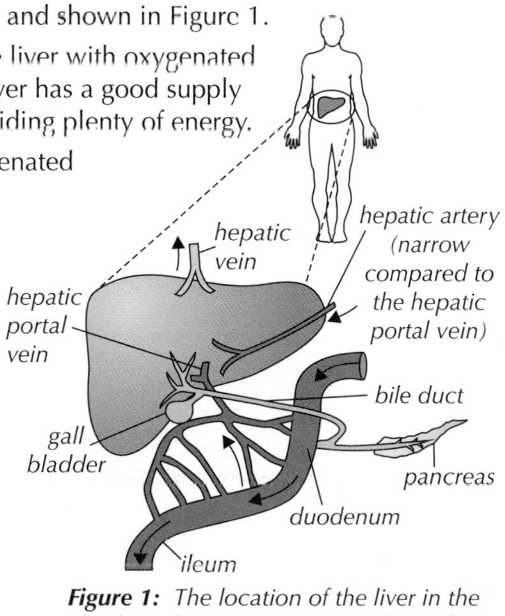

Figure 1: *The location of the liver in the body and its associated blood vessels.*

Learning Objectives:

- Know what is meant by excretion and its importance in maintaining metabolism and homeostasis, including the removal of metabolic wastes (such as carbon dioxide and nitrogenous waste) from the body.

- Know the gross structure and the histology of the mammalian liver.

- Be able to examine and draw stained sections to show the histology of liver tissue (PAG1).

- Know the functions of the mammalian liver, including its roles in:
  - the formation of urea (including an outline of the ornithine cycle),
  - detoxification,
  - the storage of glycogen.

Specification Reference 5.1.2

Tip: 'Hepatic' means anything to do with the liver. For example, the hepatic artery is the artery supplying the liver with blood.

Tip: Don't get the hepatic vein and hepatic portal vein mixed up — remember, the hepatic portal vein brings the products of digestion to the liver.

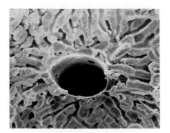

Figure 3: An electron micrograph of a liver lobule, showing the sinusoids (grey tracks) between the hepatocytes (pink), radiating out from the cental vein (the black hole).

Figure 4: An electron micrograph of a Kupffer cell attached to the wall of a sinusoid.

Liver histology

The liver is made up of liver lobules — cylindrical structures made of cells called hepatocytes that are arranged in rows radiating out from the centre (see Figure 2). Each lobule has a central vein in the middle that connects to the hepatic vein. Many branches of the hepatic artery, hepatic portal vein and bile duct are also found connected to each lobule (only one of each is shown in Figure 2).

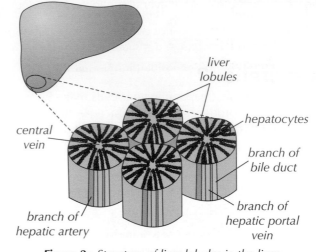

Figure 2: Structure of liver lobules in the liver.

The hepatic artery and the hepatic portal vein are connected to the central vein by capillaries called sinusoids (see Figure 5). Blood runs through the sinusoids, past the hepatocytes that remove harmful substances and oxygen from the blood. The harmful substances are broken down by the hepatocytes into less harmful substances that then re-enter the blood. The blood runs to the central vein, and the central veins from all the lobules connect up to form the hepatic vein. Cells called Kupffer cells are also attached to the walls of the sinusoids. They remove bacteria and break down old red blood cells. The bile duct is connected to the central vein by tubes called canaliculi.

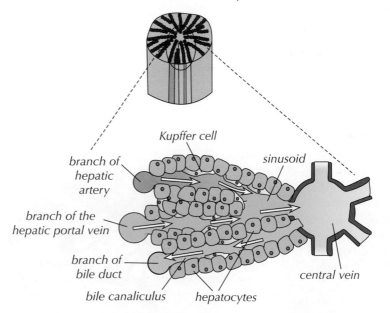

Figure 5: Enlarged diagram of a liver lobule, showing the sinusoid and hepatocytes radiating out from the central vein.

Examining liver tissue under a microscope

You need to know what liver tissue looks like under a light microscope and be able to identify and draw the different structures that you see. Before examination, a sample of liver tissue is placed on a microscope slide. The sample is stained so the cells are easier to see.

Tip: Be careful when handling slides — they can shatter very easily.

Example

Figure 6 shows an example of what liver tissue looks like under a light microscope — it shows a section through one of the liver's many lobules.

Tip: Tissue samples to be viewed under the microscope are commonly stained with haematoxylin and eosin.

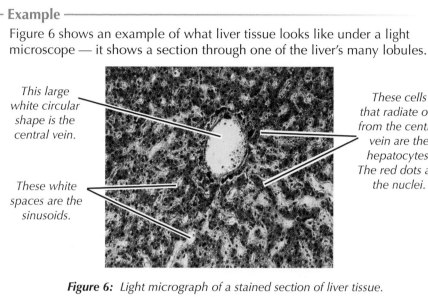

This large white circular shape is the central vein.

These cells that radiate out from the central vein are the hepatocytes. The red dots are the nuclei.

These white spaces are the sinusoids.

Tip: See page 52 for the functions of all these structures.

Figure 6: *Light micrograph of a stained section of liver tissue.*

Deamination and the ornithine cycle

One of the liver's most important roles is getting rid of excess amino acids produced by eating and digesting protein. Amino acids contain nitrogen in their amino groups. Nitrogenous substances can't usually be stored by the body. This means excess amino acids can be damaging to the body, so they must be used by the body (e.g. to make proteins) or be broken down and excreted. Here's how excess amino acids are broken down in the liver:

Tip: All amino acids share the same basic structure, shown below:

$$H_2N - \overset{\overset{\displaystyle R}{|}}{\underset{\underset{\displaystyle H}{|}}{C}} - COOH$$

Each amino acid has an amino group ($-NH_2$), containing nitrogen. The variable R group can be any hydrocarbon.

1. First, the nitrogen-containing amino groups ($-NH_2$) are removed from any excess amino acids, forming ammonia (NH_3) and organic acids — this process is called **deamination**.

amino acids $\xrightarrow{\text{deamination}}$ ammonia + organic acids

2. The organic acids can be respired to give ATP or converted to carbohydrate and stored as glycogen.

3. Ammonia is too toxic for mammals to excrete directly, so it's combined with CO_2 in the **ornithine cycle** to create urea and water (see next page).

ammonia + carbon dioxide $\longrightarrow$ urea + water

Tip: Glycogen stored in the liver is important in the control of blood glucose level (see page 41 for more).

4. The urea is released from the liver into the blood. The kidneys then filter the blood and remove the urea as urine (see pages 56-58), which is excreted from the body.

Tip: Figure 7 on the next page summarises the processes of deamination and the ornithine cycle.

Tip: You don't need to worry too much about the names of the chemicals involved in the process of converting ammonia to urea. The important thing to remember in the ornithine cycle is that ammonia from deamination is combined with carbon dioxide to produce urea and water.

Tip: Ornithine and citrulline are amino acids. These are too big to diffuse quickly through the mitochondrial membrane so require carrier proteins to move them across via facilitated diffusion or active transport.

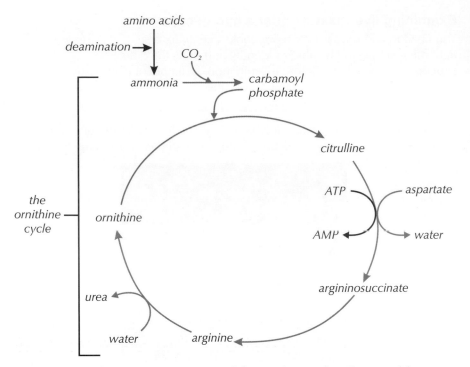

Figure 7: Deamination and the ornithine cycle. The part of the ornithine cycle in orange happens in the mitochondria of liver cells and the part in green happens in the cytoplasm.

Detoxification

The liver also breaks down other harmful substances, like alcohol, drugs and unwanted hormones. They're broken down into less harmful compounds that can then be excreted from the body — this process is called detoxification. Some of the harmful products broken down by the liver include:

Alcohol (ethanol)

Alcohol is a toxic substance that can damage cells. It's broken down by the liver into ethanal, which is then broken down into a less harmful substance called acetic acid. Excess alcohol over a long period can lead to cirrhosis of the liver — this is when the cells of the liver die and scar tissue blocks blood flow.

Paracetamol

Paracetamol is a common painkiller that's broken down by the liver. Excess paracetamol in the blood can lead to liver and kidney failure.

Insulin

Insulin is a hormone that controls blood glucose concentration (see page 41). Insulin is also broken down by the liver as excess insulin can cause problems with blood sugar levels.

Glycogen storage

The body needs glucose for energy. The liver converts excess glucose in the blood to glycogen in a process called glycogenesis (see p. 41). The glycogen is then stored as granules in the liver cells until the glucose is needed for energy.

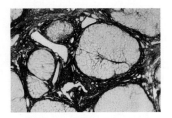

Figure 8: Light micrograph of a liver tissue with cirrhosis. The lobules (pale yellow circles) are surrounded by fibrous scar tissue (red).

Practice Questions — Application

Argininosuccinate synthetase (AS) is an enzyme which catalyses the conversion of citrulline to argininosuccinate in the ornithine cycle, as shown in the diagram below. If there's an AS deficiency then ammonia builds up in the blood, which can be fatal.

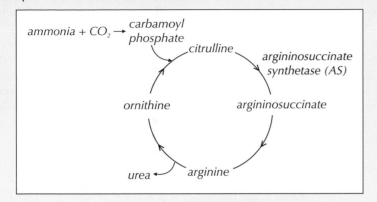

Q1 a) Predict whether there would be a high or a low level of argininosuccinate in the blood of a person with AS deficiency. Explain why.

b) Predict whether there would be a high or a low level of citrulline in the blood of a person with AS deficiency. Explain why.

Q2 AS deficiency can be treated by eating a low protein diet. Explain how this treatment works.

Exam Tip
Don't panic in the exam if you're given the name of something like an enzyme or a disease that you don't recognise. Just apply your knowledge of how the ornithine cycle works normally and you'll be able to work out the answer.

Tip: To answer Q2 think about where the ammonia entering the ornithine cycle is coming from.

Practice Questions — Fact Recall

Q1 Define the term 'excretion'.

Q2 Give two waste products of metabolism that need to be removed from the body.

Q3 Why is excretion important for homeostasis?

Q4 Where does blood from the hepatic portal vein come from?

Q5 Which blood vessel do the central veins in liver lobules connect to?

Q6 What are sinusoids?

Q7 Name the features labelled X and Y on the light micrograph of a cross-section through a liver lobule on the right.

Q8 Briefly describe how urea is formed, starting with the breakdown of excess amino acids.

Q9 What is detoxification?

Q10 Briefly describe how the liver processes excess glucose in the blood.

- Know the functions of the mammalian kidney.

- Know the gross structure and histology of the mammalian kidney, including the detailed structure of a nephron and its associated blood vessels.

- Know the mechanisms of action of the mammalian kidney, including the processes of ultrafiltration, selective reabsorption and the production of urine.

- Be able to examine and draw stained sections of kidney tissue to show the histology of nephrons (PAG1).

- Know how to dissect, examine and draw the external and internal structure of the kidney (PAG2).

Specification Reference 5.1.2

Tip: The kidneys also play a role in the control of the water potential of the blood (see p. 61-63).

Tip: 'Renal' means anything to do with the kidneys.

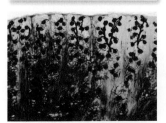

Figure 2: *Light micrograph of a section through the cortex, showing the glomeruli (tiny balls) and the vessels that supply them.*

2. The Kidneys and Excretion

One of the main functions of the kidneys is to excrete waste products, e.g. urea produced by the liver.

Excretion of waste products

Blood enters the kidney through the renal artery and then passes through capillaries in the cortex of the kidneys. As the blood passes through the capillaries, substances are filtered out of the blood and into long tubules that surround the capillaries. This process is called **ultrafiltration** (see below). Useful substances (e.g. glucose) are reabsorbed back into the blood from the tubules in the medulla and cortex — this is called **selective reabsorption** (see next page). The remaining unwanted substances (e.g. urea) pass along the tubules, then along the ureter to the bladder, where they're expelled as urine. The filtered blood passes out of the kidneys through the renal vein.

You need to learn the structure of the kidneys (see Figure 1).

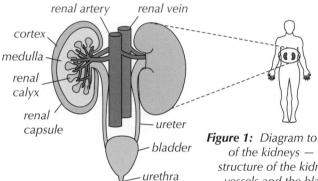

Figure 1: *Diagram to show the location of the kidneys — with the gross structure of the kidneys, their blood vessels and the bladder enlarged.*

The nephrons

The long tubules along with the bundle of capillaries where the blood is filtered are called nephrons — there are around one million nephrons in each kidney.

Ultrafiltration

Blood from the renal artery enters smaller arterioles in the cortex. Each arteriole splits into a structure called a glomerulus — a bundle of capillaries looped inside a hollow ball called a Bowman's capsule (see Figure 3). This is where ultrafiltration takes place.

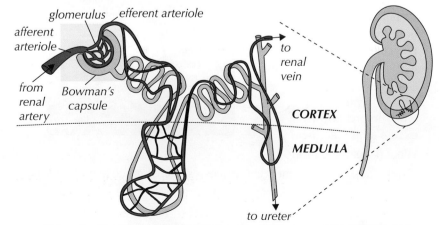

Figure 3: *The location and structure of one nephron. Ultrafiltration takes place in the glomerulus and Bowman's capsule (highlighted in blue).*

The arteriole that takes blood into each glomerulus is called the afferent arteriole, and the arteriole that takes the filtered blood away from the glomerulus is called the efferent arteriole (see Figure 3 on the previous page). The efferent arteriole is smaller in diameter than the afferent arteriole, so the blood in the glomerulus is under high pressure. The high pressure forces liquid and small molecules in the blood out of the capillary and into the Bowman's capsule.

The liquid and small molecules pass through three layers to get into the Bowman's capsule and enter the nephron tubule — the capillary endothelium, a membrane (called the basement membrane) and the epithelium of the Bowman's capsule (see Figure 4).

Tip: The kidneys are involved in removing toxic waste from the body — so they have an important role in homeostasis (see p. 34).

Figure 4: *Diagram to show the three layers separating the glomerular capillary and the Bowman's capsule.*

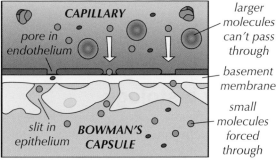

Tip: The cells that make up the epithelium of the Bowman's capsule are called podocytes.

Larger molecules like proteins and blood cells can't pass through and stay in the blood. The liquid and small molecules, now called **filtrate**, pass along the rest of the nephron and useful substances are reabsorbed along the way — see below. Finally, the filtrate flows through the collecting duct and passes out of the kidney along the ureter.

Tip: The filtrate can also be called the tubular fluid.

Selective reabsorption

Selective reabsorption of the useful substances takes place as the filtrate flows along the proximal convoluted tubule (PCT), through the loop of Henle, and along the distal convoluted tubule (DCT) — see Figure 5. Useful substances leave the tubules of the nephrons and enter the capillary network that's wrapped around them.

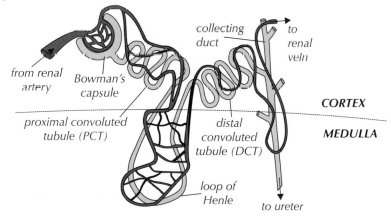

Figure 5: *Diagram to show the structure of one nephron. Selective reabsorption takes place in the areas highlighted in yellow.*

Figure 6: *Electron micrograph of a cross-section through the proximal convoluted tubule (PCT). Microvilli (shown in reddish-brown) line the inside of the tubule, increasing the surface area for reabsorption.*

The epithelium of the wall of the PCT has microvilli to provide a large surface area for the reabsorption of useful materials from the filtrate (in the tubules) into the blood (in the capillaries). Useful solutes like glucose, amino acids, vitamins and some salts are reabsorbed along the PCT by **active transport** and **facilitated diffusion**. Some urea is also reabsorbed by diffusion.

Water enters the blood by **osmosis** because the water potential of the blood is lower than that of the filtrate. Water is reabsorbed from the loop of Henle, DCT and the collecting duct (see p. 61). The filtrate that remains is urine, which passes along the ureter to the bladder.

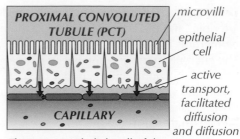

Figure 7: Epithelial wall of the proximal convoluted tubule (PCT).

Urine

Urine is usually made up of water and dissolved salts, urea and other substances such as hormones and excess vitamins. Urine doesn't usually contain proteins or blood cells as they're too big to be filtered out of the blood. Glucose, amino acids and vitamins are actively reabsorbed back into the blood (see previous page), so they're not usually found in the urine either.

Kidney histology

PRACTICAL ACTIVITY GROUP **1**

You need to be able to look at stained kidney tissue under a light microscope and identify and draw what you see. You'll see different parts of the nephron depending on whether you're looking at the cortex or the medulla region of the kidney.

┌─ **Examples** ─

▪ The light micrograph below shows a stained section of tissue from the **cortex** of the kidney.

This bundle of capillaries is the glomerulus.

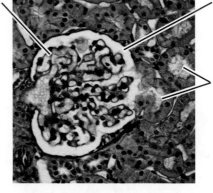

The white area around the glomerulus is the Bowman's capsule.

These circular areas are the PCTs and DCTs. They are surrounded by squamous epithelial cells — the purple blobs are the nuclei.

▪ The light micrograph below shows a stained section of tissue from the **medulla** of the kidney.

The loops of Henle are surrounded by capillaries — the red dots here are red blood cells in the capillaries.

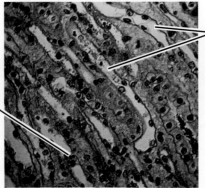

These white areas are the loops of Henle.

Kidney dissection

PRACTICAL ACTIVITY GROUP **2**

You need to know how to dissect a mammalian kidney and examine and draw the external and internal structure. For this dissection you'll need a mammal's kidney (e.g. from a sheep, pig or cow), a dissecting tray, a scalpel, an apron and lab gloves.

Tip: It's important to do a risk assessment before you start this practical. Be careful with sharp dissection instruments and make sure you wash your hands thoroughly once you have finished.

External examination

1. Look at the outside of the kidney — it's covered with a thin, strong membrane called the renal capsule.

2. Beneath the renal capsule is the outside of the cortex.

3. You'll notice that part of the kidney is indented — this is the renal hilum and you'll probably see tubes coming from here.

4. Have a look at the tubes and see if you can identify them as the renal vein, renal artery and ureter. You might need to look inside the blood vessels to identify them — the wall of the artery will be thicker than the wall of the vein. The ureter is likely to have the most adipose (fatty) tissue around it.

5. Draw a sketch of the outside of the kidney and add clear labels (see Figure 8).

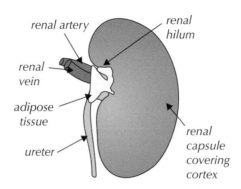

Figure 8: *A diagram showing the external features of a kidney.*

Tip: Make sure you use a sharp pencil when drawing your sketch and try to use one smooth line to draw the outline of features rather than lots of sketchy lines. You don't need to colour in or shade your diagrams.

Internal examination

1. Cut the kidney in half lengthways from one side. Split it open and have a look at the structures inside.

2. You should notice that the cortex appears dense and grainy and is a lighter shade than the medulla.

3. In the medulla you will find many cone-shaped structures — these are renal pyramids. They appear stripy because they contain straight sections of nephrons (loops of Henle and collecting ducts).

4. In-between the pyramids are renal columns.

5. You may see hollow cavities leading from the base of the renal pyramids — these are the renal calyces (singular is a renal calyx).

6. These lead to a larger hollow structure called the renal pelvis, which connects to the ureter.

7. Draw a sketch to show the structures you see inside the kidney (see Figure 10). Don't forget to add labels.

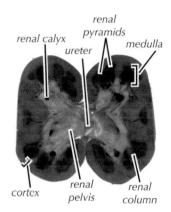

Figure 9: *A kidney cut in half lengthways to show the internal structures.*

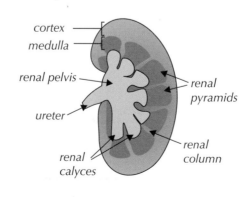

Figure 10: *A diagram showing the internal structures of a kidney.*

Tip: Your completed diagram should show the different structures in the correct proportions. It might be difficult to see the structures clearly — use Figures 9 and 10 to help you identify what you're looking at.

Practice Questions — Application

Q1 The kidneys filter the blood in order to produce urine.
The flow diagram below shows the sequence of urine production.
Name the missing structures, A to D.

| glomerulus | → | A | → | proximal convoluted tubule | → | B |

| bladder | ← | D | ← | collecting duct | ← | C |

Q2 The diagram below shows an electron micrograph of a cross-section of the barrier between the Bowman's capsule and the blood supply.

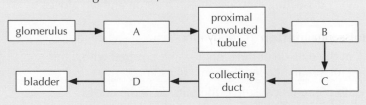

capillary endothelium

X

Y

a) Name the structures labelled X and Y.

b) Hereditary nephrotic syndrome is an inherited disease which affects the structure of the barrier shown above, resulting in the presence of large amounts of protein in the urine (proteinuria). Suggest why hereditary nephrotic syndrome causes proteinuria.

Exam Tip
Don't be put off by long words or unfamiliar diseases in your exams — the examiners just want you to apply what you know to an unfamiliar context.

Practice Questions — Fact Recall

Q1 The diagram below shows a glomerulus and surrounding structures.

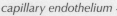

B

A

C

a) Name blood vessel A.

b) Name the structure labelled C.

c) Vessel A has a larger diameter than vessel B. Explain why this is important in the process of ultrafiltration.

Q2 Name three substances that are reabsorbed in the proximal convoluted tubule.

Q3 Name the structures labelled X, Y and Z on the diagram of a dissected kidney on the right.

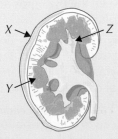

X *Z*

Y

Q4 If you were examining the internal structure of a kidney:

a) explain how you could differentiate between the renal vein, renal artery and ureter.

b) describe what you would expect to see in the medulla region.

3. The Kidneys and Water Potential

Learning Objectives:
- Know the functions of the mammalian kidney.
- Understand the control of the water potential of the blood, including the roles of:
  - osmoreceptors in the hypothalamus,
  - the posterior pituitary gland,
  - ADH and its effect on the walls of the collecting ducts.

Specification Reference 5.1.2

As well as helping out with excretion, the kidneys also play a major role in regulating the blood's water potential — they're pretty busy organs...

Regulation of water potential

Water is essential to keep the body functioning, so the amount of water in the blood (and so the water potential of the blood) needs to be kept constant. Mammals excrete urea (and other waste products) in solution, which means water is lost during excretion. Water is also lost in sweat. The kidneys regulate the water potential of the blood (and urine), so the body has just the right amount of water:

- If the water potential of the blood is too low (the body is dehydrated), more water is reabsorbed by osmosis into the blood from the tubules of the nephrons. This means the urine is more concentrated, so less water is lost during excretion.

- If the water potential of the blood is too high (the body is too hydrated), less water is reabsorbed by osmosis into the blood from the tubules of the nephrons. This means the urine is more dilute, so more water is lost during excretion (see next page).

Regulation of the water potential of the blood takes place in the middle and last parts of the nephron — the loop of Henle, the distal convoluted tubule (DCT) and the collecting duct (see below). The volume of water reabsorbed is controlled by hormones (see next page).

Tip: For more on reabsorption in the nephrons, see pages 57-58.

The loop of Henle

The loop of Henle is made up of two 'limbs' — the descending limb and the ascending limb. They help set up a mechanism called the countercurrent multiplier mechanism — see Figure 1. It's this mechanism that helps to reabsorb water back into the blood.

Tip: Figure 1 is explained in detail on the next page.

Tip: Na⁺ is a sodium ion and Cl⁻ is a chloride ion. These ions help establish the water potential that drives the reabsorption of water from the filtrate back into the blood.

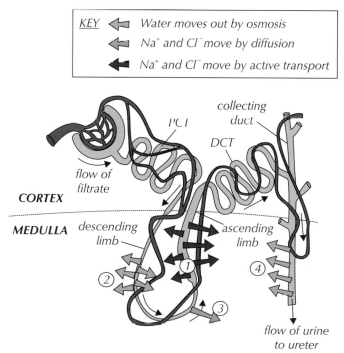

Figure 1: The countercurrent multiplier mechanism.

Here's how the countercurrent multiplier mechanism works:

1. Near the top of the ascending limb, Na⁺ and Cl⁻ ions are actively pumped out into the medulla. The ascending limb is impermeable to water, so the water stays inside the tubule. This creates a low water potential in the medulla, because there's a high concentration of ions.

2. Because there's a lower water potential in the medulla than in the descending limb, water moves out of the descending limb into the medulla by osmosis. This makes the filtrate more concentrated (the ions can't diffuse out — the descending limb isn't permeable to them). The water in the medulla is reabsorbed into the blood through the capillary network.

3. Near the bottom of the ascending limb Na⁺ and Cl⁻ ions diffuse out into the medulla, further lowering the water potential in the medulla. (The ascending limb is impermeable to water, so it stays in the tubule.)

4. The first three stages massively increase the ion concentration in the medulla, which lowers the water potential. This causes water to move out of the collecting duct by osmosis. As before, the water in the medulla is reabsorbed into the blood through the capillary network.

The volume of water reabsorbed from the collecting duct into the capillaries is controlled by changing the permeability of the collecting duct (see below).

Loop of Henle length in different animals

Different animals have different length loops of Henle. The longer an animal's loop of Henle, the more water they can reabsorb from the filtrate. When there's a longer ascending limb, more ions are actively pumped out into the medulla, which creates a really low water potential in the medulla. This means more water moves out of the nephron and collecting duct into the capillaries, giving very concentrated urine. Animals that live in areas where there's little water usually have long loops to save as much water as possible.

Figure 2: The fennec fox (top), desert kangaroo rat (middle) and camel (bottom) all have long loops of Henle.

Examples

- The fennec fox, desert kangaroo rat and camel (see Figure 2) live in hot, dry environments such as deserts. As a result they have evolved long loops of Henle, which enable them to produce small volumes of concentrated urine in order for them to conserve water.

- In contrast, frogs and toads don't have a loop of Henle at all, so they can't produce concentrated urine. This is because they live in a wet environment, so they don't have to conserve water.

Antidiuretic hormone (ADH)

The water potential of the blood is monitored by cells called **osmoreceptors** in a part of the brain called the **hypothalamus**. When the osmoreceptors are stimulated by a low water potential in the blood, the hypothalamus sends nerve impulses to the **posterior pituitary gland** to release a hormone called antidiuretic hormone (ADH) into the blood.

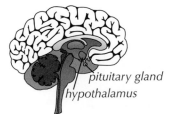

pituitary gland
hypothalamus

Figure 3: Location of the hypothalamus and the pituitary gland in the brain.

ADH molecules bind to receptors on the plasma membranes of cells in the DCT and the collecting duct. When this happens, protein channels called aquaporins are inserted into the plasma membrane. These channels allow water to pass through via osmosis, making the walls of the DCT and collecting duct more permeable to water. This means more water is reabsorbed from these tubules into the medulla and into the blood by osmosis. A small amount of concentrated urine is produced, which means less water is lost from the body.

ADH changes the water content of the blood when it's too low or too high:

Dehydration — blood water content is too low

Dehydration is what happens when you lose water, e.g. by sweating during exercise, so the water content of the blood needs to be increased:

- The water content of the blood drops, so its water potential drops.
- This is detected by osmoreceptors in the hypothalamus.
- The posterior pituitary gland is stimulated to release more ADH into the blood.
- More ADH means that the DCT and collecting duct are more permeable, so more water is reabsorbed into the blood by osmosis.
- A small amount of highly concentrated urine is produced and less water is lost.

Hydration — blood water content is too high

If you're hydrated, you've taken in lots of water, so the water content of the blood needs to be reduced:

- The water content of the blood rises, so its water potential rises.
- This is detected by the osmoreceptors in the hypothalamus.
- The posterior pituitary gland releases less ADH into the blood.
- Less ADH means that the DCT and collecting duct are less permeable, so less water is reabsorbed into the blood by osmosis.
- A large amount of dilute urine is produced and more water is lost.

Tip: Diuresis is when lots of dilute urine is produced. Antidiuretic hormone is so called because it causes a small amount of concentrated urine to be produced (the opposite of diuresis).

Tip: Like many hormones, ADH is a protein. Once it's had its effect, it travels in the bloodstream to the liver where it's broken down (see page 53).

Practice Questions — Application

Q1 A runner is dehydrated whilst running on a hot, sunny day. He left his drink at home and is producing a lot of sweat during his run.

a) Why is the runner dehydrated?

b) How does the runner's body detect that he is dehydrated?

c) The runner's posterior pituitary gland releases antidiuretic hormone (ADH). Explain what effect ADH has on the distal convoluted tubule and the collecting duct of the runner's kidneys.

d) When he returns home, he rehydrates by drinking a sports drink containing sodium and chloride ions. Explain how the presence of these ions helps the runner's kidneys to conserve water.

Q2 Exercise-associated hyponatremia (EAH) is a condition experienced by some athletes who drink excessive amounts of fluid when competing in endurance events like marathons. The condition affects the balance of fluid in cells and is potentially fatal if it affects the brain cells.

a) Explain what normally happens when a person consumes too much fluid.

b) Athletes who experience EAH are often unable to suppress their ADH production. Explain why this can cause problems if they have consumed too much fluid.

Practice Questions — Fact Recall

Q1 Which limb of the loop of Henle is impermeable to water?

Q2 Explain why a longer loop of Henle allows more concentrated urine to be produced.

4. Kidney Failure

If things start going wrong with the kidneys, it can cause big problems...

What is kidney failure?

Kidney failure is when the kidneys can't carry out their normal functions because they don't work properly. Kidney failure can be detected by measuring the **glomerular filtration rate** (**GFR**) — this is the rate at which blood is filtered from the glomerulus into the Bowman's capsule. A rate lower than the normal range indicates the kidneys aren't working properly. Kidney failure can be caused by many things, including kidney infections and high blood pressure.

Kidney infections

Kidney infections can cause inflammation (swelling) of the kidneys, which can damage the cells. This interferes with filtering in the Bowman's capsules, or with reabsorption in the other parts of the nephrons.

High blood pressure

High blood pressure can damage the glomeruli. The blood in the glomeruli is already under high pressure but the capillaries can be damaged if the blood pressure gets too high. This means larger molecules like proteins can get through the capillary walls and into the urine.

Problems arising from kidney failure

Kidney failure causes lots of problems:

┌─ **Examples** ─────────────────────────────

- Waste products that the kidneys would normally remove (e.g. urea) begin to build up in the blood. Too much urea in the blood causes weight loss and vomiting.
- Fluid starts to accumulate in the tissues because the kidneys can't remove excess water from the blood. This causes parts of the body to swell, e.g. the person's legs, face and abdomen can swell up.
- The balance of electrolytes (ions) in the body becomes, well, unbalanced. The blood may become too acidic, and an imbalance of calcium and phosphate can lead to brittle bones. Salt build-up may cause more water retention.
- Long-term kidney failure causes anaemia — a lack of haemoglobin in the blood.

If the problems caused by kidney failure can't be controlled, it can eventually lead to death.

Treating kidney failure

When the kidneys can no longer function (i.e. they've totally failed), a person is unable to survive without treatment. There are two main treatment options — renal dialysis or a kidney transplant (see the next page).

Renal dialysis

Renal dialysis is where a patient's blood is filtered. There are two types:

1. Haemodialysis

In haemodialysis the patient's blood is passed through a dialysis machine —
the blood flows on one side of a partially permeable membrane and dialysis
fluid flows on the other side (see Figure 2). The blood and dialysis fluid flow
in opposite directions in order to maintain a steep concentration gradient
between the two fluids, to increase the rate of diffusion.

During haemodialysis, waste products and excess water and ions
diffuse across the membrane into the dialysis fluid, removing them from the
blood. Blood cells and larger molecules like proteins are prevented from
leaving the blood.

One of the problems with haemodialysis is that patients can feel
increasingly unwell between haemodialysis sessions because waste products
and fluid starts to build up in their blood. Also, each session takes three to
five hours, and patients need two or three sessions a week, usually in hospital.
This is quite expensive and is pretty inconvenient for the patient.

Figure 1: *A haemodialysis
machine, which acts as
an artificial kidney.*

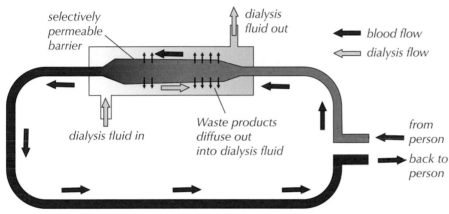

Figure 2: *A simplified diagram showing blood flow
and dialysis flow in a haemodialysis machine.*

Tip: During a
haemodialysis session,
an anticoagulant is
added to the blood
to prevent it from
clotting in the machine.
Towards the end of
the session no more
anticoagulant is added,
to allow the blood to
clot as normal once the
session has finished.

2. Peritoneal dialysis

Before a patient can have peritoneal dialysis for the first time, an operation
is needed to insert a tube that goes from outside the patient's body into their
abdominal cavity (the space in the body where the intestines, stomach,
kidneys, etc. are found). The abdominal cavity is lined with a membrane
called the peritoneum. During peritoneal dialysis, dialysis fluid is put through
the tube into the abdominal cavity (see Figure 3). The fluid remains in the
body while waste products from the patient's blood diffuse out of capillaries
and across the peritoneum into the dialysis fluid. After several hours, there's
an exchange — the fluid inside the body is drained out, and a fresh lot of
dialysis fluid is put in. This fluid is left there until the next exchange.

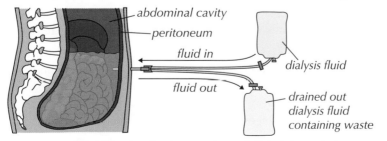

Figure 3: *Diagram showing how peritoneal dialysis is carried out.*

Peritoneal dialysis can be carried out by the patient at home — this either involves around four exchanges a day or else the dialysis can be carried out by a machine overnight. The main downsides of peritoneal dialysis compared to haemodialysis are that there's a risk of infection around the site of the tube and the patient doesn't have any dialysis-free days.

There are disadvantages to both types of renal dialysis, but dialysis can keep a person alive until a transplant is available (see below), and it's a lot less risky than having the major surgery involved in a transplant.

Kidney transplant

A kidney transplant is where a new kidney is implanted into a patient's body to replace a damaged kidney. The new kidney has to be from a person with the same blood and tissue type. They're often donated from a living relative, as people can survive with only one kidney. They can also come from other people who've recently died — organ donors.

Transplants have a lot of advantages over dialysis. For example, it's cheaper to give a person a transplant than keep them on dialysis for a long time. Having a kidney transplant is more convenient for a person than having regular dialysis sessions, and patients don't have the problem of feeling unwell between dialysis sessions.

However, there are also disadvantages to having a kidney transplant. These include the fact that the patient will have to undergo a major operation, which is risky. There's also the risk that the immune system may reject the transplant. This means that the patient has to take drugs to suppress it.

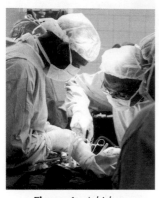

Figure 4: *A kidney transplant is a risky but potentially life saving operation for a patient with kidney failure.*

Exam Tip:
In your exams you might be asked to weigh up the positive and negative aspects of a treatment such as renal dialysis or a kidney transplant — so make sure you know both sides of the story.

Practice Questions — Application

Q1 A patient has kidney failure and is having haemodialysis while he waits for a transplant.

   a) In haemodialysis, why must the blood and the dialysis fluid flow in opposite directions?

   b) The patient is old and weak. Suggest one reason why his doctor may be concerned about him having a kidney transplant.

Q2 A hospital patient is found to have a GFR of 5200 cm^3 $hour^{-1}$, which is lower than the normal range. Tests revealed the patient had 0 mg of glucose in their urine and a blood glucose concentration of 0.9 mg cm^{-3}.

   a) Using the patient's GFR, calculate the rate at which glucose is reabsorbed back into their blood. Give your answer in mg min^{-1}.

   b) What could have caused a lower GFR than normal?

Practice Questions — Fact Recall

Q1 How can kidney failure be detected?

Q2 Explain how kidney infections can cause problems with reabsorption in the nephrons.

Q3 Give two problems that can result from kidney failure.

Q4 Explain how haemodialysis can help to restore the electrolyte balance of the blood.

Q5 Give two disadvantages of using peritoneal dialysis to treat kidney failure.

5. Detecting Chemicals

Urine is made by filtering the blood, so you can have a look at what's in a person's blood by testing their urine. Urine samples can be used for medical purposes such as testing for pregnancy and drug use.

Human chorionic gonadotropin (hCG)

Human chorionic gonadotropin (hCG) is a hormone that is only found in the urine of pregnant women. This means you can test if a woman is pregnant by looking for hCG.

Testing for pregnancy

- A stick is used with an application area that contains monoclonal antibodies for hCG bound to a coloured bead (blue). Monoclonal antibodies are all identical to each other.

- When urine is applied to the application area any hCG will bind to the antibody on the beads.

- The urine moves up to the test strip, carrying the beads with it.

- The test strip has antibodies to hCG stuck in place (immobilised).

- If there is hCG present the test strip turns blue because the immobilised antibody binds to any hCG attached to the blue beads, concentrating the blue beads in that area. If no hCG is present, the beads will pass through the test area without binding to anything, and so it won't go blue.

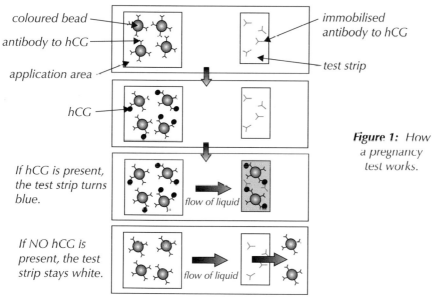

coloured bead
antibody to hCG
application area
hCG
immobilised antibody to hCG
test strip
If hCG is present, the test strip turns blue.
flow of liquid
If NO hCG is present, the test strip stays white.
flow of liquid

Figure 1: *How a pregnancy test works.*

Anabolic steroids

Anabolic steroids are drugs that build up muscle tissue. Testosterone is an anabolic steroid, and there are other common ones, such as Nandrolone. Some athletes are banned from taking anabolic steroids. This is to try to stop the misuse of steroids that can have dangerous side-effects, such as liver damage. Also, it's considered unfair for some athletes to use steroids.

However, there are some athletes who continue to take steroids, as there is an increasing pressure on elite athletes to perform well (e.g. for sponsorship deals, etc.). Taking steroids can have positive effects on performance, such as increased strength and power owing to the build up of athletes' muscle tissue.

Learning Objective:

- Know how excretory products can be used in medical diagnosis, including the use of urine samples in diagnostic tests, with reference to:
    - using monoclonal antibodies in pregnancy testing,
    - testing for anabolic steroids and drugs.

Specification Reference 5.1.2

Tip: Even though hCG is a protein hormone, it's small enough to pass from the blood into the filtrate at the Bowman's capsule (see page 57 for more).

Tip: Antibodies are proteins that bind to antigens (molecules found on the surface of cells) to form an antigen-antibody complex. In a pregnancy test, the hCG antibodies in the test strip will bind to the antigens on the hCG in the urine.

Figure 2: *A lab technician testing a urine sample for hCG.*

Figure 3: Gas chromatography/mass spectrometry machine used to test for the presence of steroids in an athlete's urine.

Testing for steroids

Steroids are removed from the blood in the urine, so athletes regularly have their urine tested for steroids (or the products made when they're broken down) by a technique called gas chromatography/mass spectrometry (GC/MS). In gas chromatography the urine sample is vaporised (turned into a gas) and passed through a column containing a polymer. Different substances move through the column at different speeds, so substances in the urine sample separate out.

Once the substances have separated out, a mass spectrometer converts them into ions, then separates the ions depending on their mass and charge. The results are analysed by a computer and by comparing them with the results of known substances it's possible to tell which substances were in the urine sample.

Recreational drugs

Sometimes people have their urine tested to see if they've been using recreational drugs such as cannabis, ecstasy or cocaine. For example, some employers can carry out drug tests on their employees. Testing for these drugs usually starts with test strips, which contain antibodies that the drug being tested for (or the products made when it's broken down) will bind to.

A sample of urine is applied to the test strip and if a certain amount of the drug (or its products) is present a colour change will occur, indicating a positive result. If this first test shows a positive result, a sample of the urine is usually sent for further testing to confirm which drugs have been used. This second test uses GC/MS (just like the test for steroids).

Practice Questions — Application

An employer carries out a five panel drug test on all potential employees before hiring them. The test screens for five different types of illegal drugs: amphetamines, cocaine, opiates, phencyclidine and marijuana. It consists of five test strips, one for each type of drug. The results are indicated by coloured lines appearing on the test strips.

Q1 Suggest why five different test strips are needed to screen for the five different types of drugs.

Q2 a) Some prescribed drugs, e.g. codeine, can produce a false positive on the opiates test strip. Suggest why this might be the case.

b) If a strip tests positive for opiates, suggest what else could be done with the sample to confirm whether the potential employee has taken illegal drugs.

Tip: A false positive occurs when a test produces a positive result, when in truth the result should be negative.

Practice Questions — Fact Recall

Q1 Which hormone is detected in a pregnancy test?

Q2 A pregnancy test uses antibodies bound to a blue bead. What colour will the test strip turn in a negative pregnancy test?

Q3 a) What technique is used to test a urine sample for the presence of anabolic steroids?

b) Briefly explain how this technique works.

Section Summary

Make sure you know...

- That excretion is the removal of waste products of metabolism (e.g. carbon dioxide and nitrogenous waste) from the body. This helps to maintain normal metabolism and homeostasis by keeping the levels of certain substances in the blood roughly constant.

- The gross structure of the liver, including the hepatic artery, hepatic vein, hepatic portal vein and bile duct.

- The histology of the liver, including the liver lobules, hepatocytes, sinusoids, central vein, Kupffer cells and canaliculi.

- How to examine and draw a stained section of liver tissue.

- The liver's role in the formation of urea — this process involves the deamination of excess amino acids, and the conversion of ammonia and carbon dioxide into urea and water via the ornithine cycle.

- That the liver breaks down substances such as alcohol, paracetamol and insulin into less harmful substances in a process known as detoxification.

- That the liver converts excess glucose into glycogen and stores it as granules in its cells until it is needed for energy.

- That one of the main functions of the kidney is to excrete waste products.

- The gross structure of the kidney, including the kidney cortex and medulla, renal calyx, renal capsule, renal artery, renal vein and ureter.

- The detailed structure of the nephron and its associated blood vessels, including the afferent arteriole, glomerulus, Bowman's capsule, efferent arteriole, proximal convoluted tubule (PCT), loop of Henle, distal convoluted tubule (DCT) and collecting duct.

- How urine is formed through the processes of ultrafiltration and selective reabsorption.

- How the kidney reabsorbs water as it travels through the loop of Henle, the distal convoluted tubule and the collecting duct.

- How to examine and draw a stained section of kidney tissue to show the histology of nephrons.

- How to dissect a mammalian kidney, and examine and draw its external and internal structure.

- That one of the functions of the kidney is to aid the control of the water potential of the blood.

- That the water potential of the blood is monitored by osmoreceptors in the hypothalamus, and how the release of antidiuretic hormone (ADH) from the posterior pituitary gland is used to control the reabsorption of water in the kidneys.

- The problems arising from kidney failure including the effect on glomerular filtration rate (GFR) and electrolyte balance.

- The potential treatment options available to patients with kidney failure (haemodialysis, peritoneal dialysis and kidney transplants).

- How monoclonal antibodies are used to test urine samples for the presence of human chorionic gonadotropin (hCG) and therefore pregnancy in women.

- How antibodies and gas chromatography/mass spectrometry are used to test urine samples for the presence of anabolic steroids and drugs.

Exam-style Questions

1   The following statements describe the development of a positive result in a pregnancy test. They are not in the correct order.

    1   hCG binds to mobile antibodies and coloured beads.

    2   Urine is applied to a test stick.

    3   A colour change is visible to the user.

    4   hCG binds to immobilised antibodies.

    5   Antibodies for hCG bound to coloured beads are applied to a test stick.

    Which is the correct order for the development of a positive result in a pregnancy test?

    A   2, 1, 3, 5, 4   **B**   2, 5, 4, 1, 3   **C**   5, 2, 3, 1, 4   **D**   5, 2, 1, 4, 3

(1 mark)

2 (a)   **Fig. 2.1** is an electron micrograph showing a section through a proximal convoluted tubule of a kidney.

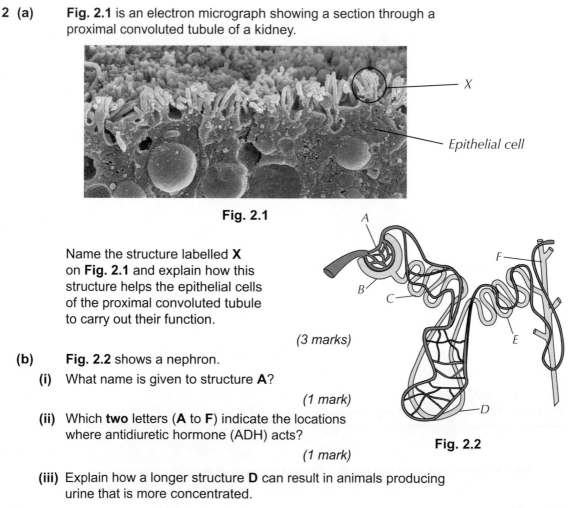

Fig. 2.1

Name the structure labelled **X** on **Fig. 2.1** and explain how this structure helps the epithelial cells of the proximal convoluted tubule to carry out their function.

(3 marks)

(b)   **Fig. 2.2** shows a nephron.

    (i)   What name is given to structure **A**?

(1 mark)

    (ii)   Which **two** letters (**A** to **F**) indicate the locations where antidiuretic hormone (ADH) acts?

(1 mark)

Fig. 2.2

    (iii) Explain how a longer structure **D** can result in animals producing urine that is more concentrated.

(4 marks)

3 (a) The tubular fluid to blood plasma concentration ratio (TF/P ratio) is an index used to measure how well the kidney is working. If substances are able to pass freely from the glomerulus into the Bowman's capsule they will have a TF/P ratio of 1.0, as their concentration in the plasma is the same as in the initial tubular fluid.

(i) Complete **Table 3.1** to show which of the following substances will have a TF/P ratio of 1.0 in a healthy kidney. The first two have been done for you.

Substance	TF/P ratio of 1.0
glucose	✓
serum albumin (protein)	X
sodium ions (Na⁺)	
urea	
red blood cells	

Table 3.1

(2 marks)

(ii) The TF/P ratio of the protein serum albumin is normally less than 1.0 in a healthy kidney, meaning that the concentration of serum albumin is higher in the plasma than the tubular fluid. Explain why this is the case.

(1 mark)

(iii) Kidney failure can be caused by high blood pressure. Suggest why high blood pressure may result in a TF/P ratio of 1.0 for the protein serum albumin.

(3 marks)

(b) A patient has kidney failure as a result of high blood pressure.

(i) Tests reveal that the patient's glomerular filtration rate (GFR) is 1200 cm³ hr⁻¹. The patient reabsorbs 98.2% of her filtrate. Calculate the amount of urine the patient produces each day. Give your answer in cm³ day⁻¹.

(3 marks)

(ii) The patient's doctor prescribes diuretics to reduce her blood pressure. Diuretics can reduce the amount of Na⁺ that is reabsorbed by the nephron. Suggest how diuretics can be used to decrease blood pressure.

(5 marks)

(c) Over time, waste products such as urea build up in the patient's body. Urea is a result of the breakdown of amino acids by the liver.

(i) Name the blood vessel in which urea leaves the liver.

(1 mark)

(ii) The production of urea involves the ornithine cycle. Outline how the ornithine cycle is involved in urea production.

(2 marks)

(iii) Suggest **one** possible health problem the patient may experience as a result of the accumulation of urea in her blood.

(1 mark)

Learning Objectives:

- Know the organisation of the mammalian nervous system, including:
  - the structural organisation of the nervous system into the central and peripheral systems,
  - the functional organisation into the somatic and autonomic nervous systems.
- Know the gross structure of the human brain and the functions of its parts, including the cerebrum, hypothalamus, medulla oblongata, cerebellum and pituitary gland.
- Know what a reflex action is and understand the survival value of reflex actions, including the blinking reflex and knee-jerk reflex.

Specification Reference 5.1.5

1. The Nervous System

You might remember the nervous system from Section 1 — you need to know more about it here. Firstly here's a recap on animal communication systems...

Responding to the environment

You might remember from page 14 that animals increase their chances of survival by responding to changes in their external environment, e.g. by avoiding harmful environments such as places that are too hot or too cold. They also respond to changes in their internal environment to make sure that the conditions are always optimal for their metabolism (all the chemical reactions that go on inside them). Any change in the internal or external environment is called a **stimulus**. Animals continuously need to respond to stimuli — this is a complex process often involving coordination between the nervous system, hormonal system and muscles.

Receptors and effectors

Receptors detect stimuli and effectors bring about a response to a stimulus. Effectors include muscle cells and cells found in glands, e.g. the pancreas. Receptors communicate with effectors via the nervous system or the hormonal (endocrine) system, or sometimes using both. The nervous and hormonal systems coordinate the response.

Structure of the nervous system

The nervous system is split into two main structural systems — the **central nervous system** (**CNS**) and the **peripheral nervous system**. The CNS is made up of the brain and spinal cord, whereas the peripheral nervous system is made up of the neurones that connect the CNS to the rest of the body.

The peripheral nervous system has two different functional systems — the **somatic** and **autonomic** nervous systems. The somatic nervous system controls conscious activities, e.g. running and playing video games. The autonomic nervous system controls unconscious activities, e.g. digestion and heart rate.

The autonomic nervous system is split into the sympathetic and parasympathetic nervous systems, which have opposite effects on the body. The sympathetic nervous system is the 'fight or flight' system that gets the body ready for action. Sympathetic neurones release the neurotransmitter noradrenaline. The parasympathetic system is the 'rest and digest' system that calms the body down. Parasympathetic neurones release the neurotransmitter acetylcholine.

The structure of the nervous system is summarised in Figure 1.

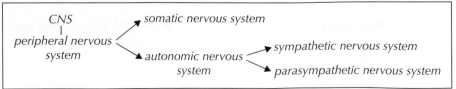

Figure 1: *Organisation of the nervous system.*

The brain

The brain is part of the central nervous system. You need to know the location and function of the five brain structures listed below and shown in Figure 2.

1. Cerebrum

The cerebrum is the largest part of the brain. It's divided into two halves called cerebral hemispheres. The cerebrum has a thin outer layer called the cerebral cortex, which is highly folded. The cerebrum is involved in vision, hearing, learning and thinking.

2. Hypothalamus

The hypothalamus is found just beneath the middle part of the brain. It automatically maintains body temperature at the normal level. It also produces hormones that control the pituitary gland (see below).

3. Medulla oblongata

The medulla oblongata is at the base of the brain, at the top of the spinal cord. It automatically controls breathing rate and heart rate.

4. Cerebellum

The cerebellum is underneath the cerebrum and it also has a folded cortex. It's important for muscle coordination, posture and coordination of balance.

5. Pituitary gland

The pituitary gland is found beneath (and is controlled by) the hypothalamus. It releases hormones and stimulates other glands, e.g. the adrenal glands (see p. 76), to release their hormones.

Exam Tip
Figures 2 and 3 below show cross sections through the brain. You won't always see the brain from this view though — in the exam you might be asked to locate structures when looking at the brain from a different direction, e.g. from below or from the front.

Tip: The hypothalamus is also involved in the control of the water potential of the blood (see pages 62-63).

Figure 3: MRI scan showing a section through the head. The cerebrum is the highly folded structure at the top (orange). The cerebellum (blue) lies below the cerebrum at the back of the head.

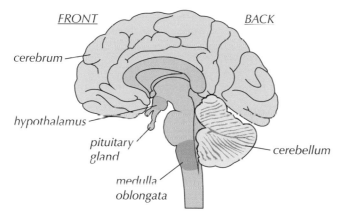

Figure 2: Structures of the brain.

Practice Questions — Application

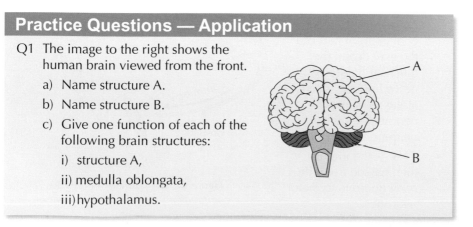

Q1 The image to the right shows the human brain viewed from the front.

a) Name structure A.

b) Name structure B.

c) Give one function of each of the following brain structures:

   i) structure A,

   ii) medulla oblongata,

   iii) hypothalamus.

Tip: See page 15 for more about the structure and function of the different types of neurone.

Tip: Nervous impulses that involve the conscious brain are voluntary responses — you have to think about them. Reflex actions don't involve the conscious brain so they're involuntary responses — your body responds without thinking about it first.

Tip: Not all reflex actions involve a relay neurone — see the knee-jerk example on the next page.

Exam Tip
You need to learn details of the blinking reflex and the knee-jerk reflex for your exams.

Tip: The blinking reflex can also occur because of other stimuli, e.g. hearing a sudden loud noise or a flash of bright light.

Figure 5: *Light micrograph of a cross-section of a human eye showing the cornea (light pink).*

Q2 Dyspraxia is a condition which has been linked to an abnormally developed cerebellum. People with dyspraxia may have difficulty with tasks such as throwing and catching, and may often fall over. Suggest why having an abnormally developed cerebellum could cause these symptoms.

Reflex actions

A reflex action is where the body responds to a stimulus without making a conscious decision to respond. This is because the pathway of communication doesn't involve conscious parts of the brain — instead it goes through unconscious parts of the brain or the spinal cord. Because you don't have to spend time deciding how to respond, information travels really fast from receptors to effectors. Reflex actions are protective — they help organisms to avoid damage to the body because the response happens so quickly.

The pathway of communication linking receptors to effectors in a reflex action typically involves three neurones — a sensory neurone, a relay neurone and a motor neurone (see Figure 4).

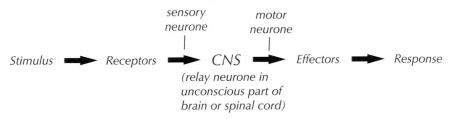

Figure 4: *The pathway of nervous communication in a reflex action.*

Animals have lots of different reflexes to help them survive:

┌─ **Example — Blinking reflex** ──────────────

When your body detects something that could damage your eye, you automatically blink — you quickly close your eyelid to protect your eye, then open your eyelid again.
For example, you blink if your eye is touched:

▪ **Stimulus** — something touches your eye.

▪ **Receptors** — sensory nerve endings in the cornea (front part of the eye) detect the touch stimulus. A nerve impulse is sent along the sensory neurone to a relay neurone in the CNS.

▪ **CNS** — the impulse is then passed from the relay neurone to motor neurones.

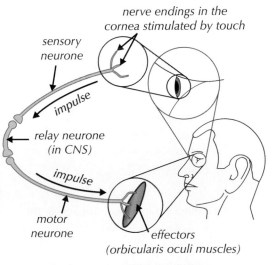

Figure 6: *The pathway of nervous communication in the blinking reflex.*

- **Effectors** — the motor neurones send impulses to the orbicularis oculi muscles that move your eyelids.
- **Response** — these muscles contract causing your eyelids to close quickly and prevent your eye from being damaged.

Tip: If there's a relay neurone involved in the reflex arc then it's possible to override the reflex, e.g. in the blinking reflex your brain could tell your eye to withstand the touch.

Example — Knee-jerk reflex

The knee-jerk reflex works to quickly straighten your leg if the body detects your quadriceps is suddenly stretched. It helps to maintain posture and balance. For example, if your knees buckle after landing from a jump, the reflex causes your quadriceps to contract to keep you upright. This is how it works:

Stimulus — your quadriceps muscle is stretched.

Receptors — stretch receptors in the quadriceps muscle detect that the muscle is being stretched. A nerve impulse is passed along a sensory neurone.

CNS — the sensory neurone communicates directly with a motor neurone in the spinal cord (there is no relay neurone involved).

Effectors — the motor neurone carries the nerve impulse to the quadriceps muscle.

Response — the quadriceps muscle contracts so the lower leg moves forward quickly.

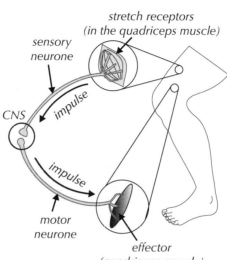

Figure 7: The pathway of nervous communication in the knee-jerk reflex.

Tip: The quadriceps is a group of four muscles at the front of your thigh.

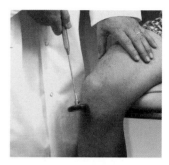

Figure 8: *You can test your knee-jerk reflex by quickly hitting your patellar tendon (just below your knee cap) when your leg is bent.*

Tip: Remember that although the knee-jerk reflex doesn't involve a relay neurone, it still involves the CNS (spinal cord).

Practice Question — Application

Q1 When your hand touches a hot surface, you automatically and quickly withdraw your hand away from the source of heat.

   a) What two pieces of information tell you that the sentence above is describing a reflex action?

   b) The reflex action described involves three neurones. Describe the pathway of nervous communication that occurs in this example.

Practice Questions — Fact Recall

Q1 What two structures is the central nervous system made up of?

Q2 What is the overall role of the autonomic nervous system?

Q3 Name the gland located just below the hypothalamus and describe its function.

Q4 Where is the medulla oblongata located?

Q5 What is a reflex action?

Q6 Describe the pathway of nervous communication in the blinking reflex when it's triggered by something touching the eye.

Exam Tip
The medulla oblongata always refers to the brain structure. (The inner part of some structures, e.g. the adrenal glands, is called the medulla.)

- Understand
  how the 'fight or
  flight' response
  to environmental
  stimuli in mammals
  is coordinated by
  the nervous and
  endocrine systems.

- Know the effects of
  nervous mechanisms
  and hormones on
  heart rate.

- Be able to monitor
  physiological
  functions, for example
  by taking pulse rate
  measurements before,
  during and after
  exercise, or by using
  sensors to record
  electrical activity in
  the heart (PAG11).

- Be able to use
  Student's t-test to
  compare the means of
  data values of two sets
  of data.

  **Specification
  Reference 5.1.5**

Tip: What happens
in the 'fight or flight'
response brings together
topics from different
areas of Biology —
heart rate, breathing,
glycogenolysis, muscle
contraction, etc. This
makes it an ideal topic
for a synoptic exam
question. For more on
synoptic questions, see
the 'Exam Help' section
(pages 290-292).

Tip: Remember, it's
the autonomic nervous
system that's involved in
the control of heart rate
(see page 72).

2. 'Fight or Flight' Response and Heart Rate

For many animal responses it's really important that the nervous and hormonal systems work together. The 'fight or flight' response and the control of heart rate are good examples of how nerves and hormones coordinate a response.

The 'fight or flight' response

When an organism is threatened (e.g. by a predator) it responds by preparing the body for action (e.g. for fighting or running away). This response is called the 'fight or flight' response. Nerve impulses from sensory neurones arrive at the hypothalamus (see page 73), activating both the hormonal (endocrine) system and the sympathetic nervous system.

The pituitary gland is stimulated to release a hormone called ACTH. This causes the cortex of the adrenal gland to release steroidal hormones, which have a range of effects on the body, helping it to respond to stress both in the short and long-term (see page 31).

The sympathetic nervous system is activated, triggering the release of adrenaline from the medulla region of the adrenal gland. The sympathetic nervous system and adrenaline produce a faster response than the hormones secreted by the cortex of the adrenal gland. Their effects include:

- Heart rate is increased and the heart contracts with more force, causing blood to be pumped around the body faster.

- The muscles around the bronchioles relax, causing the airways to widen, so breathing is deeper.

- The intercostal muscles and diaphragm also contract faster and with more strength, increasing the rate and depth of breathing.

- Glycogen is converted into glucose via glycogenolysis (see page 41), so more glucose is available for muscles to respire.

- Muscles in the arterioles supplying the skin and gut constrict, and muscles in the arterioles supplying the heart, lungs and skeletal muscles dilate — so blood is diverted from the skin and gut to the heart, lungs and skeletal muscles. This increases blood flow to skeletal muscles (e.g. in the legs), making them ready for action.

- Erector pili muscles in the skin contract — this makes hairs stand on end so the animal looks bigger.

Control of heart rate — the nervous system

There's a small mass of tissue in the wall of the right atrium of the heart called the sinoatrial node (SAN). The SAN generates electrical impulses that cause the cardiac muscles to contract. The rate at which the SAN fires (i.e. heart rate) is unconsciously controlled by the cardiovascular centre in the medulla oblongata (a structure in the brain — see page 73).

Animals need to alter their heart rate to respond to internal stimuli, e.g. to prevent fainting due to low blood pressure or to make sure the heart rate is high enough to supply the body with enough oxygen.

Internal stimuli are detected by pressure receptors and chemical receptors:

- There are pressure receptors called baroreceptors in the aorta and the carotid arteries. They're stimulated by high and low blood pressure.

- There are chemical receptors called chemoreceptors in the aorta, the carotid arteries and in the medulla oblongata. They monitor the oxygen level in the blood and also carbon dioxide and pH (which are indicators of O_2 level).

Tip: The carotid arteries are major arteries in the neck.

Nerve impulses from receptors are sent to the cardiovascular centre along sensory neurones. The cardiovascular centre processes the information and sends impulses to the SAN along motor neurones.

Control of heart rate in response to different stimuli

1. High blood pressure

Baroreceptors detect high blood pressure and send impulses along sensory neurones to the cardiovascular centre, which sends impulses along parasympathetic neurones. These secrete acetylcholine, which binds to receptors on the SAN. This causes the heart rate to slow down in order to reduce blood pressure back to normal.

2. Low blood pressure

Tip: The effectors in all of these situations are the cardiac muscles of the heart.

Baroreceptors detect low blood pressure and send impulses along sensory neurones to the cardiovascular centre, which sends impulses along sympathetic neurones. These secrete noradrenaline, which binds to receptors on the SAN. This causes the heart rate to speed up in order to increase blood pressure back to normal.

3. High blood O_2, low CO_2 or high blood pH levels

Chemoreceptors detect chemical changes in the blood and send impulses along sensory neurones to the cardiovascular centre, which sends impulses along parasympathetic neurones. These secrete acetylcholine, which binds to receptors on the SAN. This causes the heart rate to decrease in order to return oxygen, carbon dioxide and pH levels back to normal.

Tip: Low blood O_2, high CO_2 or low blood pH levels are a result of increased respiration.

4. Low blood O_2, high CO_2 or low blood pH levels

Chemoreceptors detect chemical changes in the blood and send impulses along sensory neurones to the cardiovascular centre, which sends impulses along sympathetic neurones. These secrete noradrenaline, which binds to receptors on the SAN. This causes the heart rate to increase in order to return oxygen, carbon dioxide and pH levels back to normal.

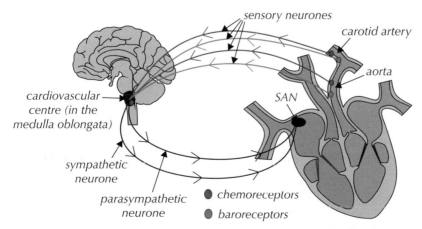

Figure 1: Summary of the control of heart rate by the nervous system.

Control of heart rate — the hormonal system

When an organism is threatened the adrenal glands release adrenaline. Adrenaline binds to specific receptors in the heart. This causes the cardiac muscle to contract more frequently and with more force, so heart rate increases and the heart pumps more blood.

Practice Questions — Application

Q1 Anaemia is a condition in which the oxygen carrying capacity of the blood is reduced. Use your knowledge of the nervous control of heart rate to explain why a person with anaemia is likely to have a more rapid heart rate than someone without anaemia.

Q2 A man is driving when a child runs out onto the road in front of him. He manages to swerve and avoid the child. Immediately afterwards he finds that his heart is beating fast and his breathing rate has increased.

a) What response is the man experiencing and what is the purpose of this response?

b) Name the branch of the autonomic nervous system responsible for the response.

c) The table below shows some other responses that the man's body makes. Copy and complete the table, stating if each response is increased or decreased as a result of the incident.

Response	Increased or decreased?
strength of contraction of heart muscle	
depth of breathing	
blood supply to the gut	
blood supply to the skeletal muscles	
blood glucose level	
blood supply to the skin	

Investigating heart rate

PRACTICAL ACTIVITY GROUP 11

You can investigate how different factors affect your heart rate. For example, you could investigate the effect of exercise on heart rate. When you exercise, your rate of respiration increases. This reduces the pH and the oxygen level in the blood and increases the carbon dioxide level. Chemoreceptors detect these changes and cause heart rate to increase to bring the levels back to normal.

── Example ──

Before you start, make sure you know how to measure your heart rate. Find your pulse in your wrist by placing your index and middle finger where the base of your thumb meets your forearm. Count the number of beats in 15 seconds and then multiply by four to get the number of beats per minute. Then:

1. Measure your heart rate at rest and record it in a table.

2. Do some gentle exercise, such as stepping on and off a step for 5 minutes. Immediately afterwards, measure your heart rate again.

3. Return to a resting position. Measure your heart rate every minute until it returns to the starting rate. Record how long it takes to return to normal.

You would expect your heart rate to increase after this exercise. But if you wanted to find out whether this exercise caused a **significant** increase in heart rate you could collect more results (e.g. by repeating exactly the same experiment using other people) and then carrying out a statistical test.

Heart rate monitors

The investigation in the example above used pulse measurements to monitor heart rate, but you could use an electronic heart rate monitor instead.

There are different types of electronic heart rate monitors, but the ones you're likely to use consist of a chest strap and a wrist monitor. The chest strap contains electrodes (sensors) which detect the electrical activity of the heart (through the skin) as it beats. The data is picked up by the electrodes and then transmitted wirelessly to the wrist monitor, which displays the data as a heart rate in beats per minute (bpm).

There are several advantages of using an electronic heart rate monitor over manually taking your pulse. For example, a monitor can measure your heart rate as you are exercising and keep a continual record of how it changes, whereas manual pulse measurements must be done at intervals.

Using Student's t-test

Student's t-test is a statistical test used to find out whether there is a significant difference in the means of two data sets. The value obtained is compared to a critical value, which helps you decide how likely it is that the results or 'differences in the means' were due to chance.

Student's t-test can be used to determine whether a particular variable, such as exercise, has a significant effect on heart rate or whether any results observed were just due to chance. There are quite a lot of steps involved when performing Student's t-test. The easiest way to understand it is to follow through an example:

┌─ **Example** ─ **Maths Skills** ─────────────────

In an investigation into the effect of regular, intense exercise on resting heart rate, 16 volunteers were divided into two equal groups. One group received six months of endurance training (Set 1) and the other group did not (Set 2). The resting heart rates of both groups were then measured. The results are shown in Figure 3. Use Student's t-test to determine whether endurance training has a significant effect on resting heart rate.

Figure 3:
Table of
results.

	Resting heart rate at end of test period (bpm)							
Data set 1	67	72	65	61	75	78	65	69
Data set 2	89	68	78	70	67	82	94	76

1. Firstly, you need to identify the **null hypothesis**. This is always that the means for the two sets of data are going to be exactly the same, i.e. there is no significant difference between them.
   ▪ So here the null hypothesis is that there is no significant difference between the mean resting heart rate of people who received endurance training and those who did not.

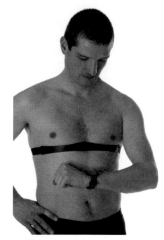

Figure 2: A man using a heart rate monitor with chest strap and wrist monitor.

Tip: Make sure the monitor is clean before each use by wiping the sensors, e.g. with a mild detergent — dirty electrodes can give poor readings.

Tip: You can also get electronic heart rate monitors that are just worn on the wrist and don't use a chest strap — these just measure pulse rate and tend to be less accurate than ones that use a chest strap (although they may be more comfortable).

Tip: The Student's t-test equation used in this example (on the next page) is used to compare the means of two groups of different individuals. There is a different equation that you can use for paired data (data that includes two measurements for each person, e.g. before and after endurance training).

2. Next you need to calculate the **mean** for each data set.
   - Data set 1: $\bar{x} = (67 + 72 + 65 + 61 + 75 + 78 + 65 + 69) \div 8 = \mathbf{69}$
   - Data set 2: $\bar{x} = (89 + 68 + 78 + 70 + 67 + 82 + 94 + 76) \div 8 = \mathbf{78}$

3. Then you need to calculate the **standard deviation** of each data set. For this you'll need to use the following formula:

$$s = \sqrt{\frac{\sum(x - \bar{x})^2}{n - 1}}$$

where, s = standard deviation, $\sum$ = sum of, x = a value in the data set, $\bar{x}$ = mean of the data set, n = number of values in the data set.

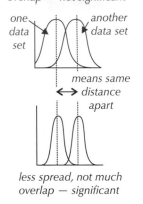
   - So start by working out $(x - \bar{x})^2$ for each value of x (each heart rate in the data set). For each heart rate, you need to take away the mean for that data set and then square the answer:

Data set 1:		Data set 2:	
$(67 - 69)^2 = 4$		$(89 - 78)^2 = 121$	
$(72 - 69)^2 = 9$		$(68 - 78)^2 = 100$	
$(65 - 69)^2 = 16$		$(78 - 78)^2 = 0$	
$(61 - 69)^2 = 64$		$(70 - 78)^2 = 64$	
$(75 - 69)^2 = 36$		$(67 - 78)^2 = 121$	
$(78 - 69)^2 = 81$		$(82 - 78)^2 = 16$	
$(65 - 69)^2 = 16$		$(94 - 78)^2 = 256$	
$(69 - 69)^2 = 0$		$(76 - 78)^2 = 4$	

   - Add up all these numbers to find $\sum(x - \bar{x})^2$: Data set 1: **226**, Data set 2: **682**
   - Divide this number by the number of values in the data set minus 1 then find the square root to get the standard deviation:
     Data set 1: $s = \sqrt{(226 \div 7)} = \mathbf{5.7}$
     Data set 2: $s = \sqrt{(682 \div 7)} = \mathbf{9.9}$

4. Now you've found the mean and standard deviation of each data set, you need to use this **Student's t-test formula** to calculate your t value:

$$t = \frac{\bar{x}_1 - \bar{x}_2}{\sqrt{(s_1^2 / n_1) + (s_2^2 / n_2)}}$$

$\bar{x}$ = mean
s = standard deviation
n = number of values in data set
$_1$ or $_2$ = data set being referred to

   - $t = \dfrac{69 - 78}{\sqrt{(5.7^2 / 8) + (9.9^2 / 8)}} = \mathbf{-2.2}$ (to 1 d.p.)

   You can ignore the minus sign and just use a t value of 2.2.

5. Next, calculate the **degrees of freedom** by doing $(n_1 + n_2) - 2$. Remember, n is the number of values in each data set.
   - So here, degrees of freedom = $(8 + 8) - 2 = \mathbf{14}$

6. Finally, look up the values for t in a **table of critical values** (see Figure 4, next page). If the value obtained for the t-test is greater than the critical value at a probability (or P value) of 5% or less (≤ 0.05), then you can be 95% confident that the difference is significant and not due to chance. You'd reject the null hypothesis.
   - You need to find the critical value at 14 degrees of freedom at $p = 0.05$.

The critical value from the table is **2.145**. The *t* value of **2.2** that you have just calculated is greater than this critical value. This means that the null hypothesis can be rejected and you can say that the mean resting heart rate for the group that received endurance training was significantly lower after six months than for the group that did not receive training.

Abridged from Statistical Tables for Biological Agricultural and Medical Research (6th ed.) © 1963 R.A Fisher and F. Yates. Reprinted with permission of Pearson Education Limited.

degrees of freedom	critical *t* values			
12	1.356	1.782	2.179	2.681
13	1.350	1.771	2.160	2.650
14	1.345	1.761	>2.145	2.624
15	1.341	1.753	2.131	2.602
probability that result is due to chance only	0.2 (20%)	0.1 (10%)	0.05 (5%)	0.02 (2%)

Figure 4: *Table of critical values.*

Exam Tip
You'll be given a table of critical values in the exam.

Practice Question — Application

Q1 An experiment was carried out on the effect of caffeine on heart rate. Fourteen volunteers were given an electronic heart rate monitor. The volunteers were split into two equal groups. One group was given a capsule containing caffeine and the other was given a placebo. After one hour, the heart rate of each volunteer was recorded. The results are shown in the table on the right.

Heart rate after 1 hour (bpm)	
Caffeine	No caffeine
71	58
90	72
82	65
76	67
88	60
85	74
66	78

Tip: Caffeine is a drug that affects the nervous system.

Tip: A placebo is a substance that looks like the real drug being tested, but doesn't contain the drug. It has no physical effects on the person taking it.

a) Explain how an electronic heart rate monitor (that uses a chest strap) can be used to measure heart rate.

b) Using the formulae for standard deviation and Student's t-test and the table of critical values below, determine whether caffeine has a significant effect on heart rate at a 95% confidence level.

$$s = \sqrt{\frac{\sum (x - \bar{x})^2}{n - 1}}$$

$$t = \frac{\bar{x}_1 - \bar{x}_2}{\sqrt{(s_1^2 / n_1) + (s_2^2 / n_2)}}$$

degrees of freedom	critical *t* values			
12	1.356	1.782	2.179	2.681
13	1.350	1.771	2.160	2.650
14	1.345	1.761	2.145	2.624
15	1.341	1.753	2.131	2.602
P value	0.2	0.1	0.05	0.02

Abridged from Statistical Tables for Biological Agricultural and Medical Research (6th ed.) © 1963 R.A Fisher and F. Yates. Reprinted with permission of Pearson Education Limited.

Tip: Remember:
s = standard deviation,
Σ = the sum of,
$\bar{x}$ = mean of a data set,
x = values in data set,
n = number of values in a data set, and
$_1$ or $_2$ = data set being referred to.

Exam Tip
You might not have to carry out all the steps involved in Student's t-test in the exam — still it's good to take the time to practice the full method as you never know what you'll get asked to do in the exam.

Practice Questions — Fact Recall

Q1 Which part of the brain coordinates the 'fight or flight' response?

Q2 a) What type of receptor detects a fall in blood pressure?

b) Where are these receptors located in the body?

Q3 What effect do impulses from parasympathetic neurones have on heart rate?

Q4 Briefly describe how you could investigate the effect of a loud noise on heart rate.

- Know the structure of mammalian muscle.
- Know the mechanism of muscular contraction, including the sliding filament model of muscular contraction and the role of ATP.
- Know how the supply of ATP is maintained in muscles by creatine phosphate.
- Know the structural and functional differences between skeletal, involuntary and cardiac muscle.
- Be able to examine stained sections or photomicrographs of skeletal muscle (PAG1).

Specification Reference 5.1.5

Tip: You also have other types of muscle in your body — the structures of these muscle types are covered on pages 88-89.

Figure 1: *A scanning electron micrograph of a section of muscle fibre with myofibrils (pink and yellow) bundled together.*

3. Muscle Contraction

Muscles are effectors — they contract in response to nervous impulses in order to bring about a response. You need to know their structure and how it enables them to contract.

Movement

The CNS (brain and spinal cord) coordinates muscular movement — it receives sensory information and decides what kind of response is needed. If the response needed is movement, the CNS sends nervous impulses along motor neurones to tell skeletal muscles to contract. Skeletal muscle (also called striated, striped or voluntary muscle) is the type of muscle you use to move, e.g. the biceps and triceps move the lower arm.

Skeletal muscle

Skeletal muscle is made up of large bundles of long cells, called muscle fibres. The cell membrane of muscle fibre cells is called the sarcolemma. Bits of the sarcolemma fold inwards across the muscle fibre and stick into the sarcoplasm (a muscle cell's cytoplasm). These folds are called transverse (T) tubules and they help to spread electrical impulses throughout the sarcoplasm so they reach all parts of the muscle fibre — see Figure 2.

A network of internal membranes called the sarcoplasmic reticulum runs through the sarcoplasm. The sarcoplasmic reticulum stores and releases calcium ions that are needed for muscle contraction. Muscle fibres have lots of mitochondria to provide the ATP that's needed for muscle contraction. They are multinucleate (contain many nuclei) and have lots of long, cylindrical organelles called **myofibrils**. Myofibrils are made up of proteins and are highly specialised for contraction.

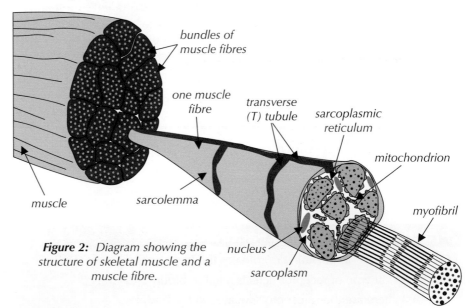

Figure 2: *Diagram showing the structure of skeletal muscle and a muscle fibre.*

Myofibrils

Myofibrils contain bundles of thick and thin myofilaments that move past each other to make muscles contract. The thick myofilaments are made of the protein **myosin** and the thin myofilaments are made of the protein **actin**.

If you look at a myofibril under an electron microscope, you'll see a pattern of alternating dark and light bands (see Figures 3 and 4). Dark bands contain the thick myosin filaments and some overlapping thin actin filaments — these are called A-bands. Light bands contain thin actin filaments only — these are called I-bands.

A myofibril is made up of many short units called **sarcomeres**. The ends of each sarcomere are marked with a Z-line. In the middle of each sarcomere is an M-line. The M-line is the middle of the myosin filaments. Around the M-line is the H-zone. The H-zone only contains myosin filaments.

Tip: There's more detail on the way myosin and actin work in muscle contraction on pages 84-86.

Tip: To remember which band is which, think: d**a**rk = **A**-bands and l**i**ght = **I**-bands.

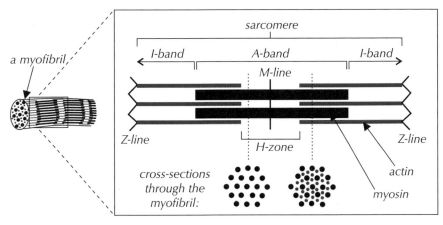

Figure 3: The structure of a sarcomere — a unit of a myofibril.

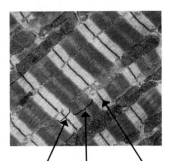

I-band   A-band   Z-line

Figure 4: A transmission electron micrograph of myofibrils showing the banding of myosin (red) and actin (yellow).

The sliding filament model

Muscle contraction is explained by the sliding filament model. This is where myosin and actin filaments slide over one another to make the sarcomeres contract — the myofilaments themselves don't contract. The simultaneous contraction of lots of sarcomeres means the myofibrils and muscle fibres contract. Sarcomeres return to their original length as the muscle relaxes.

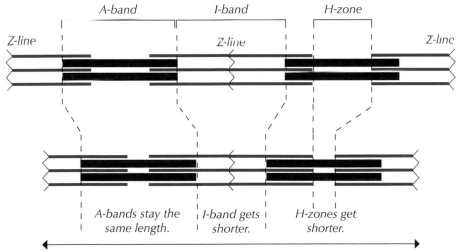

A-bands stay the same length.   I-band gets shorter.   H-zones get shorter.

The Z-lines get closer together — the sarcomeres get shorter.

Figure 5: Sarcomeres during relaxation (top) and contraction (bottom).

Tip: <u>A</u> bands are the only ones that stay the same length.

Q1 Cross-sections from three different sites along a sarcomere are shown below.

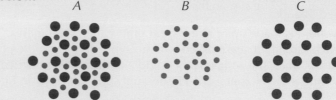

A   B   C

Which cross-section(s) could be from:

a) an I-band?

b) an M-line?

c) an A-band?

d) a Z-line?

Q2 The lengths of three different sections of a sarcomere were measured when a rabbit muscle was relaxed. These values are given in the first column of the table below. Work out which other set of values in the table (options 1-3) shows the lengths of the sections when the muscle was contracted. Explain your answer.

	Relaxed (μm)	Option 1 (μm)	Option 2 (μm)	Option 3 (μm)
A-band	1.5	1.5	1.2	1.5
I-band	0.8	0.5	0.5	1
H-zone	0.7	0.2	0.7	0.2

Myosin and actin filaments

Muscle contraction involves myosin and actin filaments sliding over one another. Here's a bit more detail about the two types of filament:

Myosin filaments

Myosin filaments have globular heads that are hinged, so they can move back and forth. Each myosin head has a binding site for actin and a binding site for ATP — see Figure 6.

Actin filaments

Actin filaments have binding sites for myosin heads, called actin-myosin binding sites. Two other proteins called **tropomyosin** and **troponin** are found between actin filaments. These proteins are attached to each other (troponin holds tropomyosin in place) and they help myofilaments move past each other (see Figure 6).

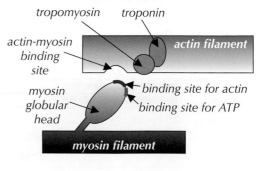

Figure 6: The structure of myosin and actin filaments.

Binding sites in resting muscles

For myosin and actin filaments to slide past each other, the myosin head needs to bind to the actin-myosin binding site on the actin filament. In a resting (unstimulated) muscle the actin-myosin binding site is blocked by tropomyosin — see Figure 7. This means myofilaments can't slide past each other because the myosin heads can't bind to the actin filaments.

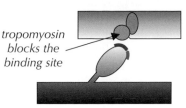

tropomyosin blocks the binding site

Figure 7: *Actin and myosin filaments in resting muscle.*

Muscle contraction

Arrival of an action potential

When an action potential from a motor neurone stimulates a muscle cell, it depolarises the sarcolemma. Depolarisation spreads down the T-tubules to the sarcoplasmic reticulum. This causes the sarcoplasmic reticulum to release stored calcium ions (Ca^{2+}) into the sarcoplasm. This influx of calcium ions into the sarcoplasm triggers muscle contraction.

Tip: Depolarisation makes the sarcolemma less negative than when it's at rest. See page 21 for more on depolarisation.

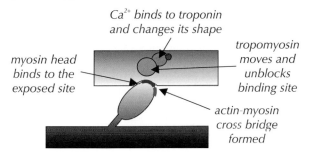

Ca^{2+} binds to troponin and changes its shape

myosin head binds to the exposed site

tropomyosin moves and unblocks binding site

actin-myosin cross bridge formed

Figure 8: *Formation of an actin-myosin cross bridge.*

Tip: If you can't remember your sarcolemma from your sarcoplasmic reticulum then take a look back at page 82.

Calcium ions bind to troponin, causing it to change shape. This pulls the attached tropomyosin out of the actin-myosin binding site on the actin filament. This exposes the binding site, which allows the myosin head to bind. The bond formed when a myosin head binds to an actin filament is called an **actin-myosin cross bridge** — see Figure 8.

Movement of the actin filament

Calcium ions also activate the enzyme ATPase, which breaks down ATP (into ADP + Pi) to provide the energy needed for muscle contraction. The energy released from ATP moves the myosin head to the side, which pulls the actin filament along in a kind of rowing action (see Figure 9).

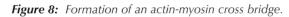

movement of the actin filament

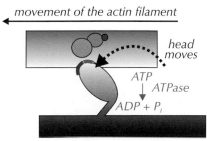

head moves

ATP
ATPase
ADP + P$_i$

Figure 9: *Movement of the myosin head.*

Tip: The movement of the myosin head to the side is called a 'power stroke'.

Breaking of the cross bridge

ATP also provides the energy to break the actin-myosin cross bridge, so the myosin head detaches from the actin filament after it's moved. The myosin head then returns to it's starting position, and reattaches to a different binding site further along the actin filament — see Figure 10. A new actin-myosin cross bridge is formed and the cycle is repeated (attach, move, detach, reattach to new binding site...).

Many actin-myosin cross bridges form and break very rapidly, pulling the actin filament along — which shortens the sarcomere, causing the muscle to contract. The cycle will continue as long as calcium ions are present and bound to troponin.

Tip: As the actin filaments are being moved along, the I-bands are getting shorter and the Z-lines are moving closer together.

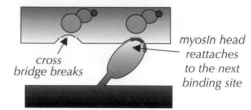

myosin head reattaches to the next binding site

cross bridge breaks

Figure 10: Myosin head forms a new actin-myosin cross bridge.

Return to resting state

When the muscle stops being stimulated, calcium ions leave their binding sites on the troponin molecules and are moved by active transport back into the sarcoplasmic reticulum (this needs ATP too). The troponin molecules return to their original shape, pulling the attached tropomyosin molecules with them. This means the tropomyosin molecules block the actin-myosin binding sites again — see Figure 11.

Muscles aren't contracted because no myosin heads are attached to actin filaments (so there are no actin-myosin cross bridges). The actin filaments slide back to their relaxed position, which lengthens the sarcomere.

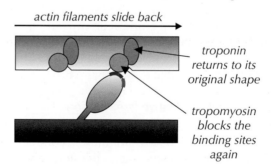

actin filaments slide back

troponin returns to its original shape

tropomyosin blocks the binding sites again

Figure 11: Blocking of the actin-myosin binding sites as the muscle returns to its resting state.

Practice Questions — Application

Q1 Cardiac muscle in the heart has some similarities to skeletal muscle, for example, it has both actin and myosin filaments. Patients who suffer from heart failure may be given positive inotropic agents — these are substances which increase the level of calcium ions in the cytoplasm of muscle cells.

Use your knowledge of muscle contraction to explain why this treatment may be used.

Q2 The graph below shows the calcium ion concentration in the sarcoplasm of a muscle fibre over time.

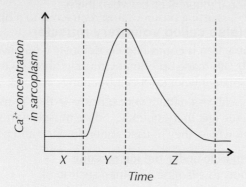

Exam Tip
Remember, it's dead easy to lose marks in the exam by rushing headlong into answering a question without reading it through properly first. Take your time — make sure you understand any information in a table or a graph before attempting the question.

a) During what time period (X, Y or Z):
   i) is the muscle fibre the longest length? Explain your answer.
   ii) would Ca^{2+} ions be bound to troponin? Explain your answer.
   iii) would ATPase be activated? Explain your answer.
b) Describe the movement of calcium ions during time period Z.
c) Describe the event that causes an increase in Ca^{2+} ions in the sarcoplasm at the beginning of time period Y.

Energy for muscle contraction

So much energy is needed when muscles contract that ATP gets used up very quickly. ATP has to be continually generated so exercise can continue — this happens in three main ways:

1. Aerobic respiration

Most ATP is generated via oxidative phosphorylation in the cell's mitochondria. Aerobic respiration only works when there's oxygen so it's good for long periods of low-intensity exercise, e.g. a long walk.

2. Anaerobic respiration

ATP is made rapidly by glycolysis. The end product of glycolysis is pyruvate, which is converted to lactate by lactate fermentation. Lactate can quickly build up in the muscles and cause muscle fatigue (where the muscles can't contract as forcefully as they could do previously). Anaerobic respiration is good for short periods of hard exercise, e.g. a 400 m sprint.

Tip: There's more on aerobic respiration on pages 132-137 and anaerobic respiration on pages 139-140.

3. ATP-creatine phosphate (ATP-CP) system

ATP is made by phosphorylating ADP — adding a phosphate group taken from CP. The equation for this is shown in Figure 12. CP is stored inside cells and the ATP-CP system generates ATP very quickly. CP runs out after a few seconds so it's used during short bursts of vigorous exercise, e.g. a tennis serve. The ATP-CP system is anaerobic (it doesn't need oxygen) and it's alactic (it doesn't form any lactate).

Tip: Many activities use a combination of these systems.

$$ADP + CP \rightarrow ATP + C \text{ (creatine)}$$

Figure 12: *Phosphorylation of ADP by CP.*

Types of muscle

There are three types of muscle in the body — you need to know about the structural and functional differences between them.

Skeletal muscle (also called voluntary muscle)

Skeletal muscle contraction is controlled consciously (you have to voluntarily decide to contract it). It's made up of many muscle fibres — these are multinucleate (have many nuclei) and can be many centimetres long.

Some muscle fibres contract very quickly — they're used for speed and strength but fatigue (get tired) quickly. Some muscle fibres contract slowly and fatigue slowly — they're used for endurance and posture.

Examining skeletal muscle under the microscope

You need to know how to examine a stained section of skeletal muscle under a light microscope or examine a photomicrograph of one.

PRACTICAL ACTIVITY GROUP **1**

Tip: Make sure you do a risk assessment before starting this practical.

Example

This is a photomicrograph of a section through skeletal muscle tissue. The key features that you're likely to see when you look at any stained section of skeletal muscle tissue are pointed out.

Tip: Stained sections or photomicrographs you're given to look at might not look quite like this — it depends on which stain has been used. For example, using a different stain could cause the features to appear different colours.

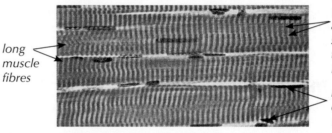

cross-striations (alternating darker and lighter pink stripes — these are the A-bands and I-bands, see page 83)

long muscle fibres

many nuclei in each muscle fibre (stained blue)

Figure 13: *Features of skeletal muscle tissue seen under a light microscope.*

Involuntary muscle (also called smooth muscle)

Involuntary muscle contraction is controlled unconsciously (it'll contract automatically without you deciding to). Involuntary muscle is also called smooth muscle because it doesn't have the striped appearance of voluntary muscle. It's found in the walls of your hollow internal organs, e.g. the gut, the blood vessels. Your gut smooth muscles contract to move food along (peristalsis) and your blood vessel smooth muscles contract to reduce the flow of blood.

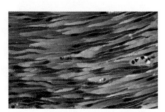

Figure 14: *A light micrograph of a section through involuntary muscle tissue.*

Each muscle fibre is uninucleate (has one nucleus). The muscle fibres are spindle-shaped with pointed ends, and they're only about 0.2 mm long (see Figure 15). The muscle fibres contract slowly and don't fatigue.

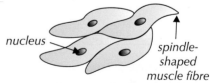

nucleus

spindle-shaped muscle fibre

Figure 15: *The structure of involuntary muscle.*

Cardiac muscle (heart muscle)

Tip: Remember, the rate of contraction of cardiac muscle is controlled involuntarily by the autonomic nervous system (see page 72).

Cardiac muscle contracts on its own — it's myogenic. It's found in the walls of your heart and its function is to pump blood around the body. It's made of muscle fibres connected by intercalated discs, which have low electrical resistance so nerve impulses pass easily between cells. The muscle fibres are branched to allow nerve impulses to spread quickly through the whole muscle (see Figure 16, on the next page).

Each cardiac muscle fibre is uninucleate. The muscle fibres are shaped like cylinders and they're about 0.1 mm long. You can see some cross-striations under a microscope but the striped pattern isn't as strong as it is in skeletal muscle. The muscle fibres contract rhythmically and don't fatigue.

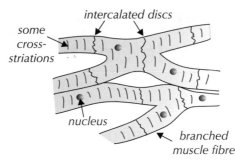

Figure 16: The structure of cardiac muscle.

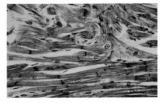

Figure 17: A light micrograph of a section through cardiac muscle tissue.

Practice Questions — Fact Recall

Q1 What are the roles of the following structures within muscle fibres:

a) transverse T-tubules?

b) sarcoplasmic reticulum?

c) mitochondria?

Q2 Describe the structure of an A-band in a myofibril and describe its appearance under an electron microscope.

Q3 What is the sliding filament model of muscle contraction?

Q4 Name the two proteins found between actin filaments that help myofilaments slide past each other.

Q5 Explain how calcium ions in the sarcoplasm allow the formation of actin-myosin cross bridges.

Q6 Describe the role of ATP in muscle contraction.

Q7 a) Give one advantage and one disadvantage of generating ATP via the ATP-creatine phosphate (ATP-CP) system.

b) Give two other ways in which ATP can be generated.

Q8 Copy and complete the table below to show the structural differences between the three types of muscle fibres.

	Skeletal	Involuntary	Cardiac
Number of nuclei			
Length			
Shape of muscle fibres			
Are cross-striations visible under a light microscope?			

Q9 Describe the function of cardiac muscle.

Tip: Remember — skeletal muscle is voluntary muscle, involuntary muscle is smooth muscle and cardiac muscle is heart muscle.

Learning Objectives:

- Understand the action of neuromuscular junctions.

- Know how to monitor muscle contraction and fatigue using sensors to record electrical activity (PAG10 and PAG11).

  Specification Reference 5.1.5

Tip: Synapses are covered in Section 1 — see pages 24-27.

Tip: Acetylcholinesterase (AChE) is an enzyme.

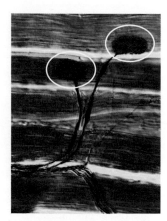

Figure 2: A light micrograph showing neuromuscular junctions (circled) on skeletal muscle.

Tip: The dosage of drugs used to relax muscles during surgery and other medical procedures is very carefully controlled. Also the patient is monitored closely to ensure they are getting enough oxygen.

4. Nerve Impulses and Muscle Contraction

When electrical impulses arrive at muscle cells they trigger the contraction of the muscle by depolarising the cells. This electrical activity can be monitored.

Neuromuscular junctions

A neuromuscular junction is a synapse between a motor neurone and a muscle cell. Neuromuscular junctions work in the same way as synapses between neurones — they release neurotransmitters, which trigger depolarisation in the postsynaptic cell (see pages 24-25). Depolarisation of a muscle cell always causes it to contract (if the threshold level is reached). Neuromuscular junctions use the neurotransmitter acetylcholine (ACh), which binds to receptors called nicotinic cholinergic receptors (see Figure 1). Acetylcholinesterase (AChE) stored in clefts on the postsynaptic membrane is released to break down acetylcholine after use.

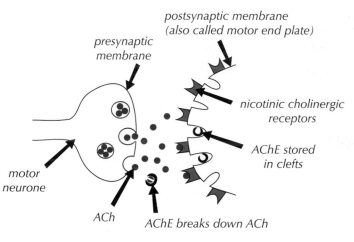

Figure 1: The structure of a neuromuscular junction.

The effect of chemicals

Sometimes a chemical (e.g. a drug) may block the release of the neurotransmitter or affect the way it binds to the receptors on the postsynaptic membrane. This may prevent the action potential from being passed on to the muscle, so the muscle won't contract.

Example

Pancuronium bromide is a non-depolarising, neuromuscular blocking drug. It competes against ACh for the nicotinic cholinergic receptors, binding to them so that the action of ACh is blocked and the muscle cell does not depolarise. It is used during surgery because it relaxes the muscles.

   The action of pancuronium bromide can be reversed by inhibiting the action of AChE so that the concentration of ACh increases. This means it can out-compete the drug for available nicotinic cholinergic receptors.

Chemicals that affect the action of neurotransmitters at neuromuscular junctions can be fatal if they affect the muscles involved in breathing, e.g. the diaphragm and intercostal muscles. If they can't contract, ventilation can't take place and the organism can't respire aerobically.

Detecting electrical activity

PRACTICAL ACTIVITY GROUP **10**

PRACTICAL ACTIVITY GROUP **11**

If you have access to specialist equipment you may be able to investigate muscle contraction and fatigue by monitoring the electrical activity that occurs. Remember, muscles contract in response to nervous impulses — these are electrical signals.

Electrical signals in muscles can be detected by electrodes (sensors) placed on the skin. The electrodes are connected to a computer to allow the electrical signals to be monitored. The procedure is called electromyography and the reading it generates is called an electromyogram (EMG).

To carry out the procedure:

1. First of all you need to attach two electrodes to places on the muscle that you want to record from — in this example we will use the biceps muscle in the arm. A third electrode goes on an inactive point (such as the bony wrist area) to act as a control (see Figure 3).

2. Switch off any other electrical equipment that you don't need as this generates 'noise' that interferes with the electrical signal from the muscle.

3. Connect the electrodes to an amplifier and a computer. (An amplifier increases the strength of the electrical signals from the muscle.)

4. Keep the muscle relaxed. You should see a straight line on the electromyogram.

5. Then contract the muscle by bending your arm. You should see spikes in the graph as motor units are activated to contract the muscle (see Figure 4).

6. If you then lift a weight, the amplitude (height) of the trace on the graph will increase — there are more electrical signals because more motor units are required to lift the weight.

7. If you continue to hold the weight, your muscle will begin to fatigue. This means that the muscle can no longer contract as forcefully as it could previously. On the electromyogram you will see the amplitude of the trace increase further. This is because your brain is trying to activate more motor units to generate the force needed to hold the weight up.

Tip: Make sure you carry out a risk assessment before you begin this practical. You should move any liquids away from the electrical equipment and ensure your hands are dry if you're connecting or disconnecting the electrodes.

Tip: The area of skin where the electrodes are to be attached should be clean — this aids the conductance of the signal.

Tip: A motor unit is made up of a motor neurone and all the muscle fibres that it connects to.

Tip: Muscle fatigue has been linked to muscle cells having an insufficient supply of ATP. This could be due to a lack of oxygen, glucose or creatine phosphate, which limits the rate at which ATP can be regenerated.

Tip: The EMG may look different depending on how the data from the electrodes is processed by the computer software being used.

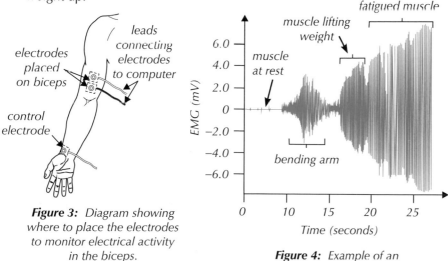

Figure 3: Diagram showing where to place the electrodes to monitor electrical activity in the biceps.

Figure 4: Example of an electromyogram (EMG).

Practice Questions — Application

Tip: An autoimmune disease is where a person's immune system mistakes their own cells for pathogens, so it starts to attack them.

Q1 Myasthenia gravis is an autoimmune disease in which the receptors at neuromuscular junctions are gradually destroyed. Suggest what symptoms a sufferer might have and explain your answer.

Q2 Galantamine is a drug that inhibits the enzyme AChE. Predict the effect of galantamine at a neuromuscular junction and explain your answer.

Q3 The graph below is an electromyogram (EMG) taken from an athlete's forearm. The athlete was asked to pick up a series of weights.

Tip: mV stands for millivolts.

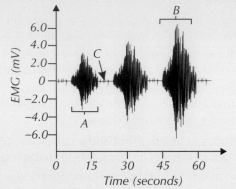

a) Suggest what is happening at point C.

b) Suggest an explanation for the electrical activity shown on the graph during time period A compared with that during time period B.

c) The researcher would like to use electromyography to help athletes train by monitoring the point at which their muscles start to fatigue. He asks the athlete to hold a weight up for as long as he can. Describe and explain what the researcher would expect to see on the EMG trace as the athlete's muscle becomes fatigued.

Practice Questions — Fact Recall

Q1 What is a neuromuscular junction?

Q2 Which neurotransmitter is used at neuromuscular junctions?

Q3 How is neurotransmitter removed from a neuromuscular junction?

Q4 Briefly explain why chemicals that block neurotransmitters at a neuromuscular junction can be fatal.

Q5 Briefly explain how sensors that monitor electrical activity can be used to monitor muscle contraction.

Section Summary

Make sure you know:

- That the mammalian nervous system is split into the central nervous system (brain and spinal cord) and the peripheral nervous system (the neurones that connect the CNS to the rest of the body).

- That the peripheral nervous system is split into the somatic nervous system (which controls conscious activities) and the autonomic nervous system (which controls unconscious activities).

- The functions of the cerebrum (vision, hearing, learning, thinking), the hypothalamus (controlling body temperature and producing hormones that control the pituitary gland), the medulla oblongata (controlling breathing and heart rate), the cerebellum (muscle coordination, posture, balance) and the pituitary gland (releasing hormones and stimulating other glands), and the locations of these structures in the brain.

- That a reflex action is a rapid, involuntary response that doesn't involve conscious parts of the brain and helps to protect the body from damage.

- The pathway of nervous communication in reflexes, including the blinking and knee-jerk reflexes, and how they help to protect the body.

- How the sympathetic nervous system and the hormonal system coordinate the 'fight or flight' to an external stimulus, e.g. a perceived threat.

- How the nervous system is involved in the control of heart rate — baroreceptors and chemoreceptors detect changes in blood pressure or chemistry and send impulses via the autonomic nervous system to the cardiovascular centre in the medulla oblongata. The cardiovascular centre sends signals via sympathetic neurones or parasympathetic neurones to the SAN, which controls heart rate.

- That the hormonal system is also involved in the control of heart rate, and that adrenaline increases heart rate and causes the heart to pump more blood.

- How to investigate physiological functions, such as the effect of exercise on heart rate, by manually recording pulse rate or by using an electrical heart rate monitor.

- How to use Student's t-test to compare the means of two sets of data and to determine whether results are significant.

- That skeletal muscle is made of large bundles of long multinucleate cells called muscle fibres.

- The sliding filament model of muscle contraction — myosin and actin filaments slide over one another to make the sarcomeres contract (the myofilaments themselves don't contract).

- How actin, myosin, calcium ions and ATP work together to make a myofibril contract.

- That energy from ATP is used for muscle contraction and that ATP generation involves aerobic respiration, anaerobic respiration and the ATP-creatine phosphate (ATP-CP) system.

- The structural and functional differences between skeletal (voluntary) muscle, involuntary (smooth) muscle and cardiac (heart) muscle.

- How to examine stained sections or photomicrographs of skeletal muscle.

- That a neuromuscular junction is a synapse between a motor neurone and a muscle cell.

- That neuromuscular junctions use the neurotransmitter acetylcholine (ACh), which binds to nicotinic cholinergic receptors. This triggers depolarisation in the postsynaptic cell. Acetylcholinesterase (AChE) stored in clefts on the postsynaptic membrane is released to break down acetylcholine after use.

- How to use sensors that record electrical activity to monitor muscle contraction and fatigue.

Exam-style Questions

1   Which row correctly describes the pathway of nervous communication in response to low blood pressure?

	Locations of receptors that detect low blood pressure	Source of the impulses sent to the heart along motor neurones	Neurotransmitter secreted by motor neurones	Effect on heart rate
A	carotid arteries, aorta	medulla oblongata	noradrenaline	increase
B	medulla oblongata, aorta	hypothalamus	acetylcholine	decrease
C	carotid arteries, aorta	hypothalamus	noradrenaline	decrease
D	medulla oblongata, aorta	medulla oblongata	acetylcholine	increase

(1 mark)

2   **Fig. 2.1** shows a cross-section through the human brain.

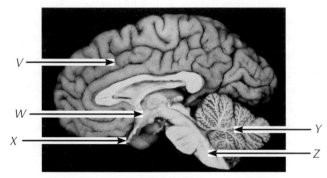

Fig. 2.1

(a)   Name the part of the brain labelled **Z** in **Fig. 2.1** and give its function.

(2 marks)

(b)   Ataxia is condition which can cause difficulty with walking and balance.

    (i)   Suggest the letter of the part of the brain that is often not functioning properly in people with ataxia.

(1 mark)

    (ii)   People with ataxia may also experience difficulty with fine motor skills such as writing. Using this evidence, suggest which part of the peripheral nervous system ataxia affects. Give a reason for your answer.

(1 mark)

    (iii)   People with ataxia may still show normal reflex actions. Suggest why this might be the case.

(1 mark)

    (iv)   A symptom of ataxia can be muscle spasticity, in which a person can experience involuntary and sustained muscle contractions. This symptom can be treated with a drug called trihexyphenidyl, which competes with acetylcholine for receptors on motor end plates. Explain why trihexyphenidyl could relieve muscle spasticity.

(3 marks)

3   Effective control of a person's heart rate is important for their survival.
Heart rate is controlled by the hormonal system and the nervous system.

(a) (i)   During times of danger, more adrenaline will be secreted into a person's
bloodstream. Where is adrenaline released from?

(1 mark)

(ii)   Give **two** ways in which adrenaline affects the heart.

(2 marks)

(iii)   Describe and explain how blood vessels are affected by adrenaline.

(3 marks)

(b)   Heart rate is a measure of how quickly cardiac muscle contracts.
Describe the structure of cardiac muscle.

(2 marks)

4   A bodybuilder lifts weights to increase the size of the muscles in his arms.
Fig. 4.1 shows part of a myofibril in the biceps muscle when it is **contracted**.

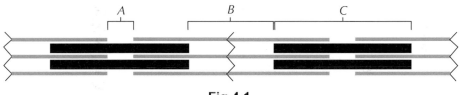

Fig 4.1

(a)   Name the sections of the myofibril labelled **A-C** in **Fig. 4.1**.

(3 marks)

(b)   For each of the sections **A-C**, state how it will appear when the biceps relaxes,
compared to how it appears in **Fig. 4.1**.

(2 marks)

(c)   A myofibril contains myosin filaments.

(i)   Describe the structure of a myosin filament.

(3 marks)

(ii)*   Describe the role of the myosin filament and ATP in muscle contraction.

(6 marks)

The bodybuilder manages to lift an extremely heavy weight with a short
burst of explosive power. He can only sustain the lift for a few seconds.

(d) (i)   Describe how ATP is likely to be generated in the bodybuilder's arm muscles
when he lifts the heavy weight.

(2 marks)

(ii)   Give **one** advantage of ATP being generated in this way.

(1 mark)

(e)   Give **three structural** differences between a muscle fibre in the bodybuilder's
biceps and a muscle fibre in the walls of his blood vessels.

(3 marks)

*The quality of your response will be assessed in this question.

Learning Objectives:

- Be able to explain the different types of plant responses, including:
  - the response to abiotic stress,
  - the response to herbivory, e.g. chemical defences (such as alkaloids, tannins and pheromones) and folding in response to touch (*Mimosa pudica*),
  - the range of tropisms in plants.
- Know about the roles of plant hormones.
- Be able to carry out practical investigations into phototropism and geotropism (PAG11).

  Specification Reference 5.1.5

1. Plant Responses

Plants need to respond to stimuli in order to survive. These next few pages are all about what makes plants grow the way that they do...

Responses to stimuli

Plants, like animals, increase their chances of survival by responding to changes in their environment.

> **Examples**
> - They sense the direction of light and grow towards it to maximise light absorption for photosynthesis.
> - They sense gravity, so their roots and shoots grow in the right direction.
> - Climbing plants have a sense of touch, so they can find things to climb and reach the sunlight.

The examples given above are all tropisms (see next page). Plants are also more likely to survive if they respond to **abiotic stress** and **herbivory**.

Abiotic stress

Abiotic stress is anything that's potentially harmful to a plant that's natural, but nonliving, like a drought (water stress). Plants can respond to abiotic stress, e.g. some respond to extreme cold by producing their own form of antifreeze.

> **Example**
> Carrots produce antifreeze proteins at low temperatures — the proteins bind to ice crystals and lower the temperature that water freezes at, stopping more ice crystals from growing.

Herbivory

Tip: Herbivores are animals that eat plants.

Herbivory is when plants are eaten by animals (including insects). Plants have chemical defences that they can use against herbivory. For example, they can produce toxic chemicals in response to being eaten.

> **Examples**
> - **Alkaloids** — these are chemicals with bitter tastes, noxious smells or poisonous characteristics that deter or kill herbivores, e.g. tobacco plants produce the alkaloid nicotine in response to tissue damage. Nicotine is highly poisonous to many insects.
> - **Tannins** — these taste bitter, and in some herbivores (e.g. cattle, sheep) they can bind to proteins in the gut, making the plant hard to digest. Both of these things deter animals from eating the plant.

Some plants release **pheromones** in response to herbivory. Pheromones are signalling chemicals that produce a response in other organisms.

> **Examples**
> - Some plants release alarm pheromones into the air in response to herbivore grazing. This can cause nearby plants that detect these chemicals to start making chemical defences such as tannins.

- When corn plants are being eaten by caterpillars, they can produce pheromones which attract parasitic wasps. These wasps then lay their eggs in the caterpillars (eww), which eventually kills them.

Other plants are able to fold up in response to being touched.

Figure 1: *A leaf of M. pudica folding up after one of its leaflets has been touched.*

Example —————————————————————————

If a single leaflet (a mini leaf-shaped structure that makes up part of a leaf) of the plant *Mimosa pudica* is touched, a signal spreads through the whole leaf, causing it to quickly fold up. It's thought that this could help protect *Mimosa pudica* against herbivory in a variety of ways, e.g. it may help to knock off any small insects feeding on the plant. It may also scare off animals trying to eat it.

Tropisms

A **tropism** is the response of a plant to a directional stimulus (a stimulus coming from a particular direction). Plants respond to stimuli by regulating their growth. A positive tropism is growth towards the stimulus, whereas a negative tropism is growth away from the stimulus.

Exam Tip
Make sure you remember the name of the touch-sensitive *Mimosa pudica*. It could come up as an example in your exam.

Tip: A positive tropism is growth towards the stimulus and a negative tropism is growth away from it.

Phototropism

Phototropism is the growth of a plant in response to light. Shoots are positively phototropic and grow towards light (see Figure 2). Roots are negatively phototropic and grow away from light (see Figure 3).

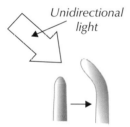

Unidirectional light

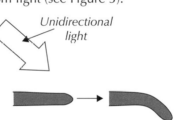

Unidirectional light

Figure 2: *Phototropism in shoots.*   **Figure 3:** *Phototropism in roots.*

Figure 4: *A radish seedling showing positive phototropism.*

Geotropism

Geotropism is the growth of a plant in response to gravity. Shoots are negatively geotropic and grow upwards (see Figure 5). Roots are positively geotropic and grow downwards (see Figure 6).

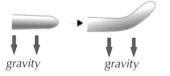

gravity   *gravity*   *gravity*   *gravity*

Figure 5: *Geotropism in shoots.*   **Figure 6:** *Geotropism in roots.*

Figure 7: *A radish seedling showing negative geotropism.*

Other tropisms

There are some other tropisms that you might come across.

Examples ————————————————————————

- Hydrotropism — plant growth in response to water. Roots are positively hydrotropic.
- Thermotropism — plant growth in response to temperature.
- Thigmotropism — plant growth in response to contact with an object.

Growth hormones

Tip: Growth hormones are also called growth substances.

Plants respond to some stimuli using growth hormones — these are chemicals that speed up or slow down plant growth. Growth hormones are produced in the growing regions of the plant (e.g. shoot tips and root tips) and they move to where they're needed in the other parts of the plant.

A growth hormone called **gibberellin** stimulates seed germination, stem elongation, side shoot formation and flowering (there's more about gibberellin on page 103).

Growth hormones called **auxins** stimulate the growth of shoots by cell elongation. Auxins are produced in the tips of shoots in flowering plants and diffuse backwards to stimulate the cell just behind the tips to elongate — this is where cell walls become loose and stretchy, so the cells get longer (see Figure 8). If the tip of a shoot is removed, no auxin will be available and the shoot stops growing. Auxins stimulate growth in shoots but high concentrations inhibit growth in roots.

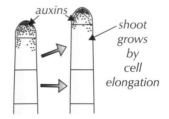

Figure 8: Effect of auxins on shoot growth.

Indoleacetic acid (IAA)

Tip: You should remember the phloem from the first year of your course. It's a tissue which transports sugars around a plant.

Indoleacetic acid (IAA) is an important auxin that's produced in the tips of shoots and roots in flowering plants. It's moved around the plant to control tropisms — it moves by diffusion and active transport over short distances, and via the phloem over long distances. This results in different parts of the plant having different amounts of IAA. The uneven distribution of IAA means there's uneven growth of the plant.

Tip: Remember, root growth is <u>inhibited</u> by high concentrations of IAA. The opposite is true in shoots — high concentrations of IAA <u>promote</u> shoot growth.

Tip: Remember, geotropism is the growth of a plant in response to gravity.

┌─ **Example — phototropism** ─────────────────

IAA moves to the more shaded parts of the shoots and roots, so there's uneven growth.

IAA moves to this side — cells elongate and the shoot bends towards the light. — unidirectional light

IAA moves to this side — growth is inhibited so the root bends away from the light. — unidirectional light

┌─ **Example — geotropism** ─────────────────

IAA moves to the underside of shoots and roots, so there's uneven growth.

IAA moves to this side — cells elongate so the shoot grows upwards.

IAA moves to this side — growth is inhibited so the root grows downwards.

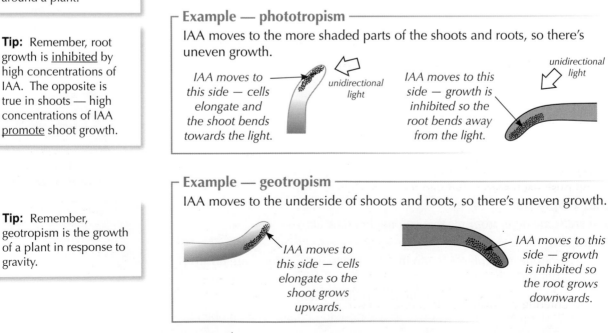

Practical investigations into phototropism

There are lots of experiments that you can do to investigate how plant shoots respond to light. Here's an example:

PRACTICAL ACTIVITY GROUP 11

1. Take nine wheat shoots that are roughly equal in height and plant them in individual pots in the same type of soil.

2. Next, prepare the shoots as follows (see Figure 9):
   - Cover the tips of three shoots with a foil cap (shoot A).
   - Leave three shoots without foil (shoot B).
   - Wrap the bases of the final three shoots with foil, leaving only the tip exposed (shoot C).

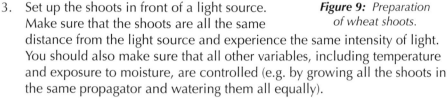

Figure 9: Preparation of wheat shoots.

3. Set up the shoots in front of a light source. Make sure that the shoots are all the same distance from the light source and experience the same intensity of light. You should also make sure that all other variables, including temperature and exposure to moisture, are controlled (e.g. by growing all the shoots in the same propagator and watering them all equally).

4. Leave the shoots to grow for two days.

5. After they've been left for 2 days, record the amount of growth (in mm) and the direction of growth of your shoots. This gives you both quantitative and qualitative data.

You would expect to see some results like the ones shown in Figure 10. The shoots with exposed tips (B and C) should have grown towards the light source (positive phototropism). Covering the tip with a foil cap (shoot A) prevents growth towards the light — it's the tip (where IAA is produced) that's most sensitive to light and because it's covered the shoot should have continued to grow straight up. Covering the base of the shoot with foil (shoot C) should still allow the tip to grow towards the light.

Figure 10: Wheat shoots at the end of the investigation.

Tip: Make sure you do a risk assessment before you carry out any practical work as part of these investigations.

Tip: Using shoots that are roughly the same height and planting them in the same type of soil is to try and control other variables in the experiment that aren't being investigated. Doing this increases the validity of your results.

Tip: Three shoots are used for each preparation to give some repeats. Doing repeats helps to make the results more precise by reducing the effect of random error.

Practical investigations into geotropism

There are lots of ways you could investigate geotropism. Here's one of them:

PRACTICAL ACTIVITY GROUP 11

1. Line three Petri dishes with moist (but not soaking wet) cotton wool. You should use the same volume of water and the same amount of cotton wool in each dish.

2. Space out 10 cress seeds on the surface of the cotton wool in each dish (see Figure 11) and push each seed down into the wool slightly.

3. Tape a lid onto each dish and wrap each one in foil, making sure there are no gaps. The dishes are wrapped in foil to prevent any light reaching the seeds — this would affect your results because shoots from the germinating seeds would grow towards any light entering the dish (due to phototropism).

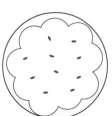

Figure 11: Cress seeds arranged on cotton wool in a Petri dish.

Tip: Using the same volume of water and the same amount of cotton wool in each dish is another example of controlling variables. It helps to ensure that all of the germinating seeds are exposed to the same amount of water and growing medium.

4. Choose somewhere you can leave the dishes where the temperature is likely to be warmish and pretty constant, e.g. a cupboard. Don't put your dishes somewhere that's too cold (i.e. less than room temperature) otherwise your seeds might not germinate.

5. Next, you need to set up your dishes so they're placed at different angles (see Figure 12):

   ▪ Prop one dish upright at a 90° angle (A in Figure 12) — label it and mark which way is 'up' (or 'down'). To keep your dish upright, attach it to a wooden block using tape — you could use a different object as long as it's heavy enough to stop the dish falling over.

   ▪ Place another dish on a slope at a 45° angle (B). As with dish A, use tape to attach the plate to the wooden block to stop it moving.

   ▪ Place the third dish (C) on a flat, horizontal surface.

   Don't forget to label your dishes carefully, so you know which way up each one was when you come to unwrap the dishes at the end of the experiment.

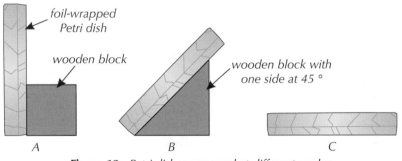

Figure 12: Petri dishes arranged at different angles.

6. Leave the seeds for 4 days.

7. After the 4 days, unwrap each dish and note direction of the shoot and root growth of the cress seedlings.

You should find that whatever angle the dishes were placed at, the shoots have all grown away from gravity (negative geotropism) and the roots have grown towards gravity (positive geotropism).

Practice Questions — Application

Q1   An experiment was carried out to investigate the role of auxin in shoot growth. Eight shoots, equal in height and mass, had their tips removed. Sponges soaked in glucose and either auxin or water were then placed where the tips should be. Four shoots were then placed in the dark (experiment A) and the other four shoots were exposed to a light source, directed at them from the right (experiment B):

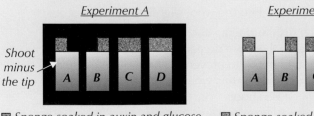
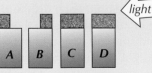

After two days the amount of growth (in mm) and direction of growth was recorded. The results are shown in the table below.

	Growth			
	Shoot A	Shoot B	Shoot C	Shoot D
Experiment A (dark)	6 mm, right	6 mm, left	6 mm, straight	1 mm, straight
Experiment B (light)	8 mm, right	8 mm, right	8 mm, right	3 mm, straight

a) Why did shoot A bend to the right in experiment A?

b) Explain why shoot C grew straight in experiment A.

c) Why did shoots A, B and C grow to the right in experiment B?

d) What was the purpose of Sponge D in both experiments?

e) Suggest why the sponges in experiment A were soaked in glucose.

Q2 Thigmotropism is a plant growth response to touch.

a) In the diagram on the right, does the shoot display positive or negative thigmotropism?

b) Is the concentration of auxins, such as IAA, likely to be highest at the point labelled X or Y? Explain why.

Practice Questions — Fact Recall

Q1 What is meant by the term 'abiotic stress'?

Q2 Give an example of a plant response to herbivory.

Q3 What is a negative tropism?

Q4 What name is given to the growth of a plant in response to light?

Q5 What parts of a plant produce growth hormones?

Q6 Do auxins stimulate or inhibit growth in roots?

Q7 Name one example of an auxin.

Q8 Auxins travel around a plant to control tropisms.

a) How do auxins move over short distances?

b) How do auxins move over long distances?

Q9 Explain how the distribution of auxins affects the growth of:

a) shoots in response to light.

b) roots in response to gravity.

Learning Objectives:

- Be able to carry out practical investigations into the effect of plant hormones on growth (PAG11).

- Understand the experimental evidence for the role of auxins in the control of apical dominance.

- Understand the experimental evidence for the role of gibberellin in the control of seed germination and stem elongation.

- Be able to explain the roles of plant hormones, including their role in seed germination, leaf loss in deciduous plants and stomatal closure.

- Be able to explain the commercial use of plant hormones, including the use of hormones to control ripening, the use of hormonal weed killers and rooting powders.

Specification Reference 5.1.5

2. The Effects of Plant Hormones

As you've seen, plant hormones are involved in tropisms. It's not just tropisms though — hormones are responsible for loads of other effects in plants too...

Auxins and apical dominance

The shoot tip at the top of a flowering plant is called the apical bud. Auxins stimulate the growth of the apical bud and inhibit the growth of side shoots from lateral buds. This is called **apical dominance** — the apical bud is dominant over the lateral buds (see Figure 1).

Apical dominance prevents side shoots from growing — this saves energy and prevents side shoots from the same plant competing with the shoot tip for light. Because energy isn't being used to grow side shoots, apical dominance allows a plant in an area where there are loads of other plants to grow tall very fast, past the smaller plants, to reach the sunlight.

If you remove the apical bud then the plant won't produce auxins, so the side shoots will start growing by cell division and cell elongation (see Figure 2). However, if you replace the tip with a source of auxin, side shoot development is inhibited. This demonstrates that apical dominance is controlled by auxin (see Figure 3).

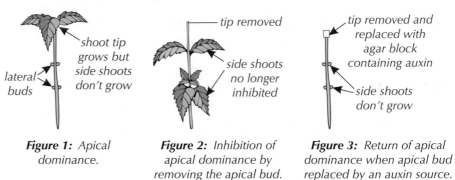

Figure 1: Apical dominance.

Figure 2: Inhibition of apical dominance by removing the apical bud.

Figure 3: Return of apical dominance when apical bud replaced by an auxin source.

Auxins become less concentrated as they move away from the apical bud to the rest of the plant. If a plant grows very tall, the bottom of the plant will have a low auxin concentration so side shoots will start to grow near the bottom.

Investigating the role of auxins in apical dominance

PRACTICAL ACTIVITY GROUP **11**

Scientists have demonstrated the role of auxins in apical dominance in experiments like the one below. You could also do this experiment yourself:

1. Plant 30 plants of the same type (e.g. pea plants) that are a similar age, height and weight in pots containing the same type of soil.

2. Count and record the number of side shoots growing from the main stem of each plant. These might be tricky to spot — they may be located where the stalks of leaves join to the main stem.

3. For 10 plants, remove the tip of the shoot and apply a paste containing auxins to the top of the stem.

4. For another 10 plants, remove the tip of the shoot and apply a paste without auxins to the top of the stem.

Figure 4: The redwood tree displays apical dominance and grows tall enough to reach the sunlight in a thick forest.

5. Leave the final 10 plants as they are — these are your untreated controls. Remember, you always need to have controls (e.g. without the hormone, untouched) for comparison — so you know the effect you see is likely to be due to the hormone and not any other factor.

6. Leave your plants to grow for six days. You need to keep all the plants in the same conditions — the same light intensity, water, etc. This makes sure any variables that may affect your results are controlled, which makes your experiment valid.

7. After six days, count the number of side shoots growing from the main stem of each of your plants.

You might get results like these:

	average number of side shoots per plant	
	start of experiment	end of experiment
untreated plants (control group)	4	5
tips removed, auxin paste applied	4	5
tips removed, paste without auxins applied	4	9

The results in the table show that removing the tips of shoots caused extra side shoots to grow, but removing tips and applying auxins prevented extra side shoots from growing. The results suggest auxins inhibit the growth of side shoots — providing evidence that auxins are involved in apical dominance.

Gibberellins

Gibberellins are growth hormones that are produced in young leaves and in seeds. They stimulate seed germination, stem elongation, side shoot formation and flowering.

Gibberellins stimulate the stems of plants to grow by stem elongation — this helps plants to grow very tall. If a dwarf variety of a plant is treated with gibberellin, it will grow to the same height as the tall variety. Unlike auxins, gibberellins don't inhibit plant growth in any way.

Gibberellins stimulate seed germination by triggering the breakdown of starch into glucose in the seed. The plant embryo in the seed can then use the glucose to begin respiring and release the energy it needs to grow. Gibberellins are inhibited (and so seed germination is prevented) by the hormone abscisic acid.

Auxins and gibberellins

Auxins and gibberellins sometimes work together to affect plant growth. They're often **synergistic** — this means that they work together to have a really big effect.

⌐ Example ────────────
Auxins and gibberellins work together to help plants grow very tall.

Auxins and gibberellins are sometimes **antagonistic** — this means they oppose each other's actions.

⌐ Example ────────────
Gibberellins stimulate the growth of side shoots but auxins inhibit the growth of side shoots.

Tip: Remember to do a risk assessment before starting practical work.

Tip: It's really important that you keep the conditions the same for each plant — if you don't, you can't be sure what's actually causing your results.

Tip: Experiments can provide evidence to support an idea. For example, the results of this experiment support the idea that auxins are involved in apical dominance. One piece of evidence can't confirm a theory is true though. See pages 1-3 for more on this.

Figure 5: *Gibberellins play an important role in the germination and stem elongation of corn seeds.*

Investigating the role of gibberellins in stem elongation

PRACTICAL ACTIVITY GROUP **11**

Scientists have done lots of experiments to provide evidence for the role of gibberellins in plant growth.

> ┌ **Example** ─────────────────────────
> Scientists have produced genetically altered seeds that are unable to produce gibberellins. These seeds are unable to germinate unless they are given gibberellins.

Tip: It's a good idea to wear gloves when handling soils. This will help prevent you coming into contact with any microorganisms present in the soil.

There are many different ways of investigating the role of gibberellins in **stem elongation**. Here's an example of how you could do it:

1. Plant 40 plants (e.g. dwarf pea plants) that are a similar age, height and mass in pots containing the same type of soil.

2. Leave 20 plants to grow, watering them all in the same way and keeping all other conditions the same. These plants are your negative controls.

3. Leave the other 20 plants to grow in the same conditions, except water them with a dilute solution of gibberellin (e.g. 100 mg dm^{-3} gibberellin).

4. Let all the plants grow for 28 days.

5. Every 7 days measure the length of the stem of each plant. Calculate the mean stem length for the plants watered normally and the plants watered with gibberellin.

Tip: Remember, negative controls are used to check that only the independent variable (i.e. watering with gibberellin) is affecting the dependent variable (i.e. growth of plant stems).

You might get results a bit like these:

time / days	mean stem length / cm	
	plants watered normally	plants watered with gibberellin
0	14	14
7	15	17
14	18	27
21	19	38
28	23	46

You can use your results to calculate the growth rate of plants:

Tip: mg dm^{-3} means milligram per decimetre cubed (or 0.001 g per cubic decimetre). One cubic decimetre is equivalent to one litre.

- Plants watered normally:
  Mean growth in 28 days = 23 cm − 14 cm = 9 cm
  Mean rate of growth over 28 days = 9 cm ÷ 28 days
  $$= \textbf{0.32 cm/day} \text{ or } \textbf{0.32 cm day}^{-1}$$

- Plants watered with gibberellin:
  Mean growth in 28 days = 46 cm − 14 cm = 32 cm
  Mean rate of growth over 28 days = 32 cm ÷ 28 days
  $$= \textbf{1.14 cm day}^{-1}$$

The results in the table and the growth rates calculated show that stems grow more when watered with a dilute solution of gibberellin. This provides evidence that gibberellin stimulates stem elongation.

Leaf loss in deciduous plants

Tip: The technical term for leaf loss is <u>abscission</u>.

Deciduous plants are plants that lose their leaves in winter. Losing their leaves helps plants to conserve water (lost from leaves) during the cold part of the year, when it might be difficult to absorb water from the soil (the soil water may be frozen), and when there's less light for photosynthesis.

Leaf loss is triggered by the shortening day length in the autumn and is controlled by hormones:

- **Auxins inhibit leaf loss** — auxins are produced by young leaves. As the leaf gets older, less auxin is produced, leading to leaf loss.

- **Ethene stimulates leaf loss** — ethene is produced by ageing leaves. As the leaves get older, more ethene is produced. A layer of cells (called the abscission layer — see Figure 6) develops at the bottom of the leaf stalk (where the leaf joins the stem). The abscission layer separates the leaf from the rest of the plant. Ethene stimulates the cells in the abscission layer to expand, breaking the cell walls and causing the leaf to fall off.

Auxins are antagonistic (work in opposition) to ethene.

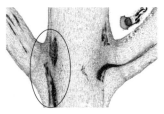

Figure 6: Light micrograph of a developing abscission layer (dark purple, circled) between a plant's leaf stalk and stem.

Stomatal closure

Plants need to be able to close their stomata in order to reduce water loss through **transpiration**. They do this using guard cells. Guard cells are found either side of a stomatal pore. When the guard cells are full of water, they are plump and turgid and the pore is open. When the guard cells lose water, they become flaccid, making the pore close (see Figure 7).

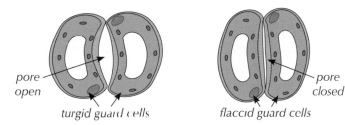

pore open

turgid guard cells

pore closed

flaccid guard cells

Figure 7: Guard cell turgidity causes the opening and closing of stomata.

The plant hormone **abscisic acid** (**ABA**) is able to trigger stomatal closure:

1. ABA binds to receptors on the guard cell membranes. This causes specific ion channels to open, which allows calcium ions to enter the cytosol from the vacuole.

2. The increased concentration of calcium ions in the cytosol causes other ion channels to open. These ion channels allow ions (such as potassium ions) to leave the guard cells, raising the water potential of the cells.

3. Water then leaves the guard cells by osmosis.

4. The guard cells become flaccid and the stomata close.

Tip: You covered transpiration in the first year of your course. As a reminder, it's the evaporation of water from a plant's surface, especially the leaves.

Tip: You met water potential in Year 1 too. It's the likelihood of water molecules to diffuse into or out of solution. If you raise the water potential of a solution, then water is more likely to move out of it, via osmosis.

Commercial uses of plant hormones

Plant hormones have several different commercial applications. E.g. the fruit industry uses plant hormones to control how different fruits develop.

Ethene

Ethene stimulates enzymes that break down cell walls, break down chlorophyll and convert starch into sugars. This makes the fruit soft, ripe and ready to eat.

┌─ **Example** ─────────────────────────
│ Bananas are harvested and transported before they're ripe because
│ they're less likely to be damaged this way. They're then exposed to
│ ethene on arrival so they all ripen at the same time on the shelves and
│ in people's homes.
└────────────────────────

Figure 8: Unripe bananas (top) can be exposed to ethene so that they ripen (bottom).

Auxins

Auxins are also used commercially by farmers and gardeners.

┌─ Examples ──

■ Auxins are used in selective weedkillers (herbicides) — they make weeds produce long stems instead of lots of leaves. This makes the weeds grow too fast, so they can't get enough water or nutrients, so they die.

■ Auxins are used as rooting hormones (e.g. in rooting powder) — they make a cutting (part of the plant, e.g. a stem cutting) grow roots. The cutting can then be planted and grown into a new plant. Many cuttings can be taken from just one original plant and treated with rooting hormones, so lots of the same plant can be grown quickly and cheaply from just one plant.

Figure 9: *Auxins enable cuttings to grow roots and grow into new plants.*

Practice Questions — Application

A student is investigating the effect of watering plants with different concentrations of gibberellin on plant height. She plants 60 plants and over the following 6 weeks she waters 20 of the plants with water, 20 of the plants with a 50 mg dm⁻³ gibberellin solution and the remaining 20 plants with a 100 mg dm⁻³ gibberellin solution. She grows all the plants under the same conditions.

Q1 The student chooses plants of the same type with similar characteristics. Explain why she does this.

Q2 Which set of plants would you expect to have the longest average stem length at the end of the 6 weeks? Explain your answer.

Q3 One of the plants has an initial stem length of 8 cm. By the end of the experiment it has grown to 26 cm.

a) Calculate the average growth rate of this plant. Give your answer in cm day⁻¹ and to 2 d.p.

b) Calculate the percentage increase in growth.

Tip: Make sure you know how to calculate percentage increases. A percentage change (i.e. a percentage increase or decrease) can be calculated using the formula shown below:

$$\frac{\text{final value} - \text{original value}}{\text{original value}} \times 100$$

Practice Questions — Fact Recall

Q1 Apical dominance prevents side shoots from growing. Explain the advantage of this in plants.

Q2 Describe how gibberellins stimulate seed germination.

Q3 a) Why do deciduous plants lose their leaves in winter?

b) What role do auxins play in leaf loss?

c) What effect does ethene have on the abscission layer?

Q4 Stomata can close to help reduce water loss from a plant.

a) Which type of cells are found either side of a stomatal pore and control its opening and closure?

b) Name a hormone which can trigger stomatal closure.

Q5 Describe how ethene can be used to ripen fruit.

Section Summary

Make sure you know:

- That to increase their chances of survival, plants need to respond to stimuli in their environment, and that these stimuli include abiotic (natural, but nonliving) stresses and herbivory (being eaten by animals, including insects).

- That plant responses to herbivory include the production of chemical defences (such as alkaloids, tannins and pheromones) and folding in response to touch (as seen in *Mimosa pudica*).

- That plants exhibit a range of different tropisms, including phototropism (growth in response to light) and geotropism (growth in response to gravity).

- That growth hormones (e.g. auxins and gibberellin) coordinate how a plant responds to changes in its environment, e.g. indoleacetic acid (IAA) moves to shaded parts of shoots and roots to control growth in response to the direction of light and gravity.

- How to carry out practical investigations looking at phototropism and geotropism (PAG11).

- That apical dominance is when the apical bud (the shoot tip at the top of a flowering plant) inhibits the growth of side shoots from lateral buds and that this occurs because auxins produced by the shoot tip inhibit the development of these lateral buds.

- How to carry out practical investigations into the effect of plant hormones on growth (PAG11).

- About experimental evidence that supports the role of auxins in the control of apical dominance.

- That gibberellins stimulate the stems of plants to elongate and that they stimulate seeds to germinate by triggering the breakdown of starch into glucose in the seed.

- About experimental evidence that supports the role of gibberellin in the control of seed germination and stem elongation.

- That auxins inhibit leaf loss and ethene stimulates leaf loss in deciduous plants.

- That abscisic acid (ABA) can trigger the closure of stomata by causing guard cells to become flaccid.

- How plant hormones are used commercially, e.g. ethene is used to control when fruit ripens, auxins are used as selective weedkillers and as rooting hormones.

Exam-style Questions

1   The following statements describe steps in the closure of stomata triggered by the hormone abscisic acid (ABA). They are **not** in the correct order.

    1   Calcium ions enter the cytosol of the guard cell.

    2   The water potential of the cell increases.

    3   Potassium ions leave the guard cell.

    4   Water leaves the guard cells by osmosis.

    5   The guard cells become flaccid.

    6   ABA binds to receptors on guard cell membranes.

    Which option states the correct order of events in the closure of stomata?

    A   1, 3, 6, 5, 4, 2   **C**   5, 2, 1, 3, 4, 6

    B   6, 1, 3, 2, 4, 5   **D**   6, 1, 2, 3, 5, 4

(1 mark)

2   Scientists took three Goosegrass seedlings and planted them in individual pots with soil taken from the same source. They let each seedling grow for 15 days in the conditions shown in **Fig. 2.1**.

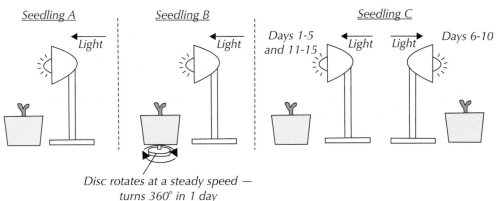

Fig. 2.1

    (a)   Suggest what response the scientists were testing with this experiment.

(1 mark)

    (b)   The scientists didn't include a control in their experiment. Describe the conditions that should have been used for a seedling acting as a control.

(2 marks)

    (c)   Suggest why the scientists used soil taken from the same source for all the seedlings.

(1 mark)

(d) Describe and explain the pattern of growth in the three plants that you would expect to see by the end of the experiment.

(3 marks)

(e) Explain the role of growth hormones in controlling the direction of growth in this experiment.

(3 marks)

3 Part of a gardener's job is to maintain the size and shape of plants being grown in a commercial greenhouse. **Fig. 3.1** shows a plant that is growing in the greenhouse.

Buds are labelled with the numbers **1-5** and the dashed line labelled **X** is a location where the stem could be cut.

(a) State the name that can be used to describe buds **2-5**.

(1 mark)

(b) (i) The gardener removes bud **1** from the plant. Explain the effect this would have on the growth of the plant.

(2 marks)

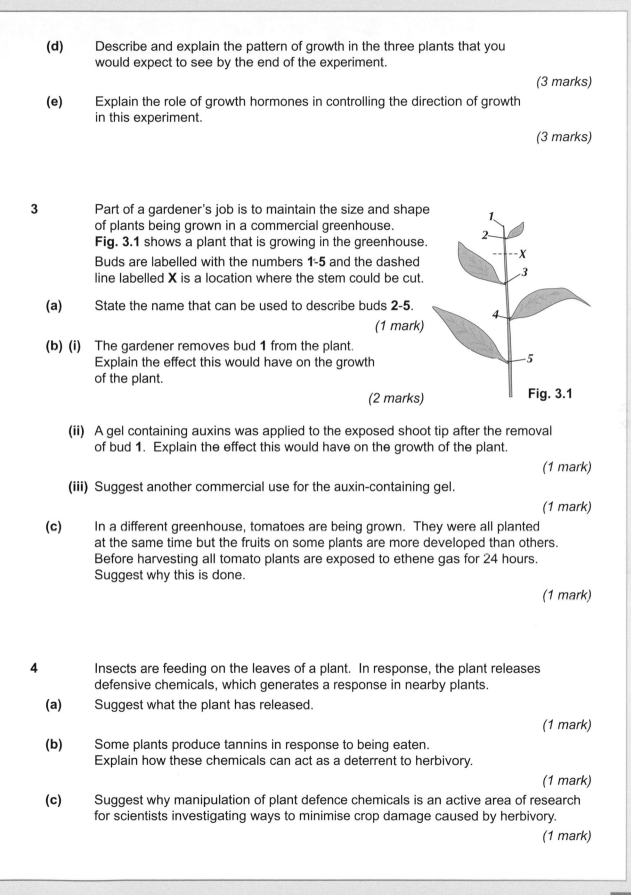

Fig. 3.1

(ii) A gel containing auxins was applied to the exposed shoot tip after the removal of bud **1**. Explain the effect this would have on the growth of the plant.

(1 mark)

(iii) Suggest another commercial use for the auxin-containing gel.

(1 mark)

(c) In a different greenhouse, tomatoes are being grown. They were all planted at the same time but the fruits on some plants are more developed than others. Before harvesting all tomato plants are exposed to ethene gas for 24 hours. Suggest why this is done.

(1 mark)

4 Insects are feeding on the leaves of a plant. In response, the plant releases defensive chemicals, which generates a response in nearby plants.

(a) Suggest what the plant has released.

(1 mark)

(b) Some plants produce tannins in response to being eaten. Explain how these chemicals can act as a deterrent to herbivory.

(1 mark)

(c) Suggest why manipulation of plant defence chemicals is an active area of research for scientists investigating ways to minimise crop damage caused by herbivory.

(1 mark)

Learning Objectives:

- Understand the need for cellular respiration, including examples of why plants, animals and microorganisms need to respire.

- Understand the interrelationship between the processes of photosynthesis and respiration, including the relationship between the raw materials and products of the two processes.

Specification References 5.2.1, 5.2.2

1. Storing and Releasing Energy

Energy is required for all life processes. This means that being able to store and release energy is really important for plants and animals.

Why is energy important?

Living things need energy for biological processes to occur.

┌─ **Examples** ─────────────────────────────────────
- Plants need energy for things like photosynthesis, active transport (e.g. to take in minerals via their roots), DNA replication and cell division.
- Animals need energy for things like muscle contraction, maintenance of body temperature, active transport, DNA replication and cell division.
- Microorganisms need energy for things like DNA replication, cell division, protein synthesis and sometimes motility (movement).

Without energy, these biological processes would stop and the plant, animal or microorganism would die.

Photosynthesis and energy

Plants can make their own food (glucose). They do this using photosynthesis. Photosynthesis is the process where energy from light is used to make glucose from water (H_2O) and carbon dioxide (CO_2). (The light energy is converted to chemical energy in the form of glucose — $C_6H_{12}O_6$.) The overall equation is:

$$6CO_2 + 6H_2O + \text{Energy} \longrightarrow C_6H_{12}O_6 + 6O_2$$

Tip: The glucose made in photosynthesis by plants is needed for use in respiration in both plants and animals.

Energy is stored in the glucose until the plants release it by respiration. Animals can't make their own food. So, they obtain glucose by eating plants (or other animals), then respire the glucose to release energy.

Respiration and energy

Living cells release energy from glucose — this process is called respiration. This energy is used to power all the biological processes in a cell. There are two types of respiration:

- **Aerobic respiration** — respiration using oxygen.
- **Anaerobic respiration** — respiration without oxygen.

Aerobic respiration produces carbon dioxide and water, and releases energy. The overall equation is:

$$C_6H_{12}O_6 + 6O_2 \longrightarrow 6CO_2 + 6H_2O + \text{Energy}$$

ATP

As you learned in Module 2, ATP (adenosine triphosphate) is the immediate source of energy in a cell.

A cell can't get its energy directly from glucose. So, in respiration, the energy released from glucose is used to make ATP. ATP is made from the nucleotide base adenine, combined with a ribose sugar and three phosphate groups (see Figure 1). It carries energy around the cell to where it's needed.

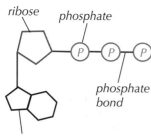

ribose   phosphate

phosphate bond

adenine

Figure 1: *The structure of adenosine triphosphate (ATP). It consists of adenine, ribose and three phosphate groups.*

ATP is synthesised from ADP (adenosine diphosphate) and inorganic phosphate (P_i) using energy from an energy-releasing reaction, e.g. the breakdown of glucose in respiration. The energy is stored as chemical energy in the phosphate bond (see Figure 2). The enzyme **ATP synthase** catalyses this reaction.

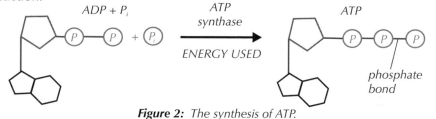

Figure 2: The synthesis of ATP.

This process is known as **phosphorylation** — adding phosphate to a molecule. ADP is phosphorylated to ATP.

ATP then diffuses to the part of the cell that needs energy. Here, it's broken down back into ADP and inorganic phosphate (P_i). Chemical energy is released from the phosphate bond and used by the cell. **ATPase** catalyses this reaction.

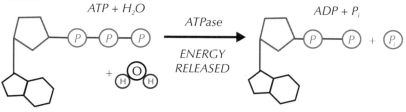

Figure 3: The breakdown of ATP.

This process is known as **hydrolysis**. It's the splitting (lysis) of a molecule using water (hydro).

ATP's properties

ATP has specific properties that make it a good energy source.

- ATP stores or releases only a small, manageable amount of energy at a time, so no energy is wasted.
- It's a small, soluble molecule so it can be easily transported around the cell.
- It's easily broken down, so energy can be easily released.
- It can transfer energy to another molecule by transferring one of its phosphate groups.
- ATP can't pass out of the cell, so the cell always has an immediate supply of energy.

The compensation point

Plants carry out both photosynthesis and respiration. Both processes can occur at the same time and at different rates. The rate at which photosynthesis takes place is partly dependent on the light intensity of the environment that the plant is in (see page 121).

There's a particular level of light intensity at which the rate of photosynthesis exactly matches the rate of respiration. This is called the **compensation point** for light intensity.

Tip: Inorganic phosphate (P_i) is just the fancy name for a single phosphate.

Tip: Adenosine diphosphate has <u>two</u> phosphates. Adenosine triphosphate has <u>three</u> phosphates.

Tip: In a cell there's a constant cycle between ADP and P_i, and ATP. This allows energy to be stored and released as it's needed.

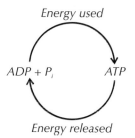

Tip: It's important to remember that ATP doesn't make energy — it's a store of energy. Energy is used to make ATP, then it's released when ATP is hydrolysed to ADP and P_i.

Tip: The products of photosynthesis (e.g. O_2) can be used as reactants in respiration and vice versa. Reactants can also come from elsewhere (e.g. O_2 can come from air).

Tip: The compensation point is different for different species of plants.

Exam Tip
Graphs showing the compensation point won't always show oxygen generation. If you haven't seen the factors used on the scales of the graph before, don't panic. Just remember that the compensation point is the point at which photosynthesis and respiration are occurring at the same rate and apply your knowledge to work it out from the graph you've been given.

One way to work out the compensation point for a plant is to measure the rate at which oxygen is produced and used by a plant at different light intensities. Because photosynthesis produces oxygen and respiration uses it, in this case, the compensation point is the light intensity at which oxygen is being used as quickly as it is produced (see the example below). The rate of CO_2 production and use could also be measured — photosynthesis uses CO_2 and respiration produces it.

Example — Maths Skills

The graph below shows the net oxygen generation by a plant grown in a controlled environment under different light intensities. When the rate of oxygen production equals the rate of oxygen usage, oxygen generation is zero. This is the compensation point.

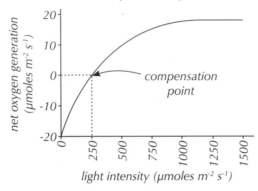

In this example, the compensation point occurs at a light intensity of 250 µmoles m^{-2} s^{-1}.

Practice Question — Application

Q1 The graph on the right shows the CO_2 uptake of a plant over the course of a day in early spring.

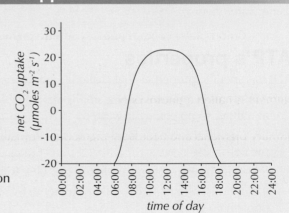

a) Give the times when compensation points occur.

b) Suggest and explain why the compensation points occur at these particular times.

Practice Questions — Fact Recall

Q1 Name three biological processes in plants that need energy.

Q2 Outline the relationship between the raw materials and products of photosynthesis and respiration.

Q3 What is the function of ATP?

Q4 Describe the structure of a molecule of ATP.

Q5 a) What is ATP broken down into by ATPase?

b) By what process is ATP broken down?

2. Photosynthesis and the Light-dependent Reaction

In photosynthesis, light energy is used to make glucose. It involves a series of reactions, but before we get stuck into it you need to know a bit of background information...

Chloroplasts

Photosynthesis takes place in the chloroplasts of plant cells. Chloroplasts are small, flattened organelles found in plant cells (see Figure 1). They have a double membrane called the chloroplast envelope. Thylakoids (fluid-filled sacs) are stacked up in the chloroplast into structures called grana (singular = granum). The grana are linked together by bits of thylakoid membrane called lamellae (singular = lamella).

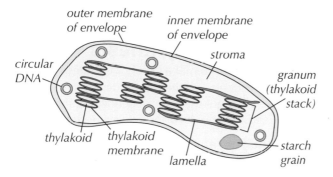

circular DNA — outer membrane of envelope — inner membrane of envelope — stroma — granum (thylakoid stack) — thylakoid — thylakoid membrane — lamella — starch grain

Figure 1: *The structure of a chloroplast.*

Chloroplasts contain **photosynthetic pigments** (e.g. chlorophyll a, chlorophyll b and carotene). These are coloured substances that absorb the light energy needed for photosynthesis. The pigments are found in the thylakoid membranes — they're attached to proteins. The protein and pigment is called a **photosystem**.

A photosystem contains two types of photosynthetic pigments — primary pigments and accessory pigments. Primary pigments are **reaction centres** where electrons are excited during the light-dependent reaction (see pages 115-116) — in most chloroplasts the primary pigment is chlorophyll a. Accessory pigments make up **light-harvesting systems**. These surround reaction centres and transfer light energy to them to boost the energy available for electron excitement to take place. There are two photosystems used by plants to capture light energy. Photosystem I (or PSI) absorbs light best at a wavelength of 700 nm and photosystem II (PSII) absorbs light best at 680 nm.

Contained within the inner membrane of the chloroplast and surrounding the thylakoids is a gel-like substance called the stroma — see Figure 1. It contains enzymes, sugars and organic acids. Chloroplasts have their own DNA. It's found in the stroma and is often circular. There can be multiple copies in each chloroplast. Carbohydrates produced by photosynthesis and not used straight away are stored as starch grains in the stroma.

Learning Objectives:

- Know the structure of a chloroplast and the sites of the two main stages of photosynthesis.
- Know the components of a chloroplast including outer membrane, lamellae, grana, thylakoid, stroma and DNA.
- Understand the importance of photosynthetic pigments in photosynthesis, including reference to light harvesting systems and photosystems.
- Understand the light-dependent stage of photosynthesis, including how energy from light is harvested and used to drive the production of chemicals which can be used as a source of energy for other metabolic processes (ATP and reduced NADP), with reference to electron carriers and cyclic and non-cyclic photophosphorylation. Also understand the role of water in this stage.
- Understand the chemiosmotic theory, including the electron transport chain, proton gradients and ATP synthase in photophosphorylation.

Specification References 5.2.1, 5.2.2

Redox reactions

Redox reactions are reactions that involve **oxidation** and **reduction**. They occur in photosynthesis (and in respiration) so it's really important that you get your head round them:

- If something is reduced it has gained electrons (e⁻), and may have gained hydrogen or lost oxygen.
- If something is oxidised it has lost electrons, and may have lost hydrogen or gained oxygen.
- Oxidation of one molecule always involves reduction of another molecule.

Tip: One way to remember electron and hydrogen movement is OILRIG. **O**xidation **I**s **L**oss, **R**eduction **I**s **G**ain.

Tip: When hydrogen is transferred between molecules, electrons are transferred too.

Coenzymes

A coenzyme is a molecule that aids the function of an enzyme. They usually work by transferring a chemical group from one molecule to another. A coenzyme used in photosynthesis is **NADP**. NADP transfers hydrogen from one molecule to another — this means it can reduce (give hydrogen to) or oxidise (take hydrogen from) a molecule.

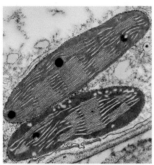

Figure 2: A cross-sectional image of two chloroplasts.

Tip: Reduced NADP is also written as NADPH — it's NADP that's gained a hydrogen. Remember OILRIG — reduction is gain.

The stages of photosynthesis

There are actually two stages that make up photosynthesis — the light-dependent reaction and the light-independent reaction. The next few pages are all about the light-dependent reaction, but before we get into all that you need to know how the two stages link together.

1. The light-dependent reaction

As the name suggests, this reaction needs light energy — see Figure 3. It takes place in the thylakoid membranes of the chloroplasts. Here, light energy is absorbed by photosynthetic pigments in the photosystems and converted to chemical energy. The light energy is used to add a phosphate group to ADP to form ATP, and to reduce NADP to form reduced NADP. (Reduced NADP is an energy-rich molecule because it can transfer hydrogen, and so electrons, to other molecules.) ATP transfers energy and reduced NADP transfers hydrogen to the light-independent reaction. During the process water (H_2O) is oxidised to oxygen (O_2).

Tip: See pages 118-119 for loads more information on the Calvin cycle.

2. The light-independent reaction (the Calvin cycle)

As the name suggests, this reaction doesn't use light energy directly. (But it does rely on the products of the light-dependent reaction.) It takes place in the stroma of the chloroplast — see Figure 3. Here, the ATP and reduced NADP from the light-dependent reaction supply the energy and hydrogen to make glucose from CO_2.

Tip: The light-independent reaction can take place in the dark. However, it needs the products of the light-dependent reaction (ATP and reduced NADP) so in reality it only continues for a little while after it gets dark.

Figure 3: How the light-dependent and light-independent reactions link together in a chloroplast.

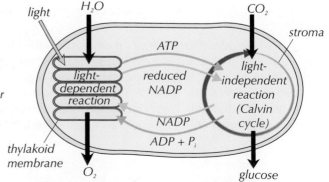

The light-dependent reaction

In the light-dependent reaction, the light energy absorbed by the photosystems is used for three things:

1. Making ATP from ADP and inorganic phosphate. This is called **photophosphorylation** — it's the process of adding phosphate to a molecule using light.

2. Making reduced NADP from NADP.

3. Splitting water into protons (H^+ ions), electrons and oxygen. This is called **photolysis** — it's the splitting (lysis) of a molecule using light (photo) energy.

The light-dependent reaction actually includes two types of photophosphorylation — non-cyclic and cyclic. Each of these processes has different products and is explained on the next couple of pages.

Non-cyclic photophosphorylation

Non-cyclic photophosphorylation produces ATP, reduced NADP and oxygen (O_2). To understand the process you need to know that the photosystems in the thylakoid membranes (see page 113) are linked by **electron carriers**. Electron carriers are proteins that transfer electrons. The photosystems and electron carriers form an **electron transport chain** — a chain of proteins through which excited electrons flow. There are several processes going on all at once in non-cyclic photophosphorylation — they're shown in the diagrams below and on the next page.

1. Light energy excites electrons in chlorophyll

Light energy is absorbed by PSII. The light energy excites electrons in chlorophyll. The electrons move to a higher energy level (i.e. they have more energy — see Figure 4). These high-energy electrons move along the electron transport chain to PSI.

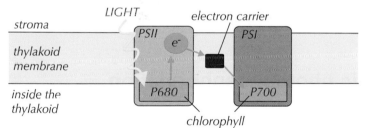

2. Photolysis of water produces protons, electrons and oxygen

As the excited electrons from chlorophyll leave PSII to move along the electron transport chain, they must be replaced. Light energy splits water into protons (H^+ ions), electrons and oxygen. (So the oxygen in photosynthesis comes from water.) The reaction is: $H_2O \longrightarrow 2H^+ + \frac{1}{2}O_2$

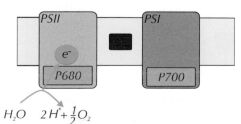

Tip: Not all of the electron carriers are shown in these diagrams.

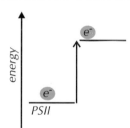

Figure 4: *Light energy excites electrons in PSII, moving them to a higher energy level.*

Tip: If too much light energy has been absorbed, plants release some of the excess energy by emitting fluorescent light. This is called chlorophyll fluorescence.

Tip: The O_2 produced from the photolysis of water is really important. It diffuses out of the chloroplast and eventually into the atmosphere for us to breathe. Good old plants.

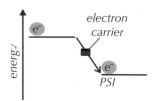

Figure 5: *The excited electrons lose energy as they pass down the electron transport chain.*

Tip: The process of electrons flowing down the electron transport chain and creating a proton gradient across the membrane to drive ATP synthesis is called chemiosmosis. It's described by the chemiosmotic theory.

Tip: Remember a 'proton' is just another word for a hydrogen ion (H^+).

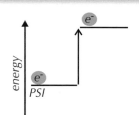

Figure 6: *Light energy excites electrons in PSI to an even higher energy level.*

Tip: The ATP and reduced NADP made here in the light-dependent reaction are really important for use later on in the light-independent reaction (see pages 118-119).

Tip: ATP is formed in the same way in cyclic photophosphorylation as in non-cyclic photophosphorylation — by the movement of protons across the thylakoid membrane.

3. Energy from the excited electrons makes ATP

The excited electrons lose energy as they move along the electron transport chain (see Figure 5). This energy is used to transport protons (H^+ ions) into the thylakoid, via membrane proteins called proton pumps, so that the thylakoid has a higher concentration of protons than the stroma. This forms a proton gradient across the membrane. Protons move down their concentration gradient, into the stroma, via an enzyme called ATP synthase. The energy from this movement combines ADP and inorganic phosphate (P_i) to form ATP.

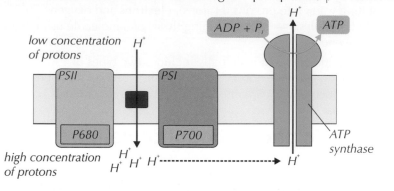

4. Energy from the excited electrons generates reduced NADP

Light energy is absorbed by PSI, which excites the electrons again to an even higher energy level (see Figure 6). Finally, the electrons are transferred to NADP, along with a proton from the stroma, to form reduced NADP.

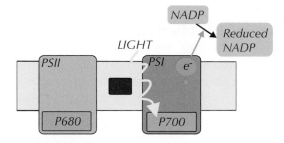

Cyclic photophosphorylation

Cyclic photophosphorylation only produces ATP and only uses PSI. It's called 'cyclic' because the electrons from the chlorophyll molecule aren't passed onto NADP, but are passed back to PSI via electron carriers. This means the electrons are recycled and can repeatedly flow through PSI. This process doesn't produce any reduced NADP or oxygen — it only produces small amounts of ATP.

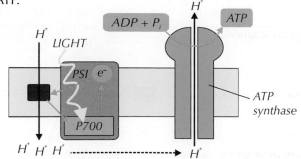

Practice Questions — Application

This diagram on the right shows a process in the light-dependent reaction.

Tip: Tempting as it is, you need to be able to answer this question without looking back at the last couple of pages.

Q1 The object labelled A in the diagram is transported across the thylakoid membrane, so that its concentration is higher in the thylakoid than in the stroma.

   a) What is the name of object A?

   b) Explain why it is important that the concentration of object A is higher inside the thylakoid than in the stroma.

Q2 What is the name of structure C?

Q3 Which structure, C or D, is involved in cyclic photophosphorylation?

Q4 What does cyclic photophosphorylation produce?

Practice Questions — Fact Recall

Q1 The diagram on the right shows a chloroplast. Label the parts A-I.

Q2 a) What are photosynthetic pigments?

   b) Name the primary photosynthetic pigment in most chloroplasts.

Q3 What are light-harvesting systems and what is their purpose?

Q4 What are the two photosystems used by plants called?

Q5 NADP is a coenzyme used in photosynthesis. What chemical group does it transfer between molecules?

Q6 Where in the chloroplast does the light-dependent reaction occur?

Q7 Which products of the light-dependent reaction are needed in the light-independent reaction?

Q8 What is photophosphorylation?

Q9 What is the electron transport chain?

Q10 a) Name the products of the photolysis of water.

   b) What is the purpose of photolysis in the light-dependent reaction?

Q11 Name the photosystem(s) involved in and the product(s) of:

   a) non-cyclic photophosphorylation,

   b) cyclic photophosphorylation.

Tip: Make sure you get your head round what happens in cyclic and non-cyclic phosphorylation (see previous two pages) — don't get them mixed up.

Learning Objectives:

- Understand the fixation of carbon dioxide and the light-independent stage of photosynthesis, including how the products of the light-dependent stage are used in the light-independent stage (Calvin cycle) to produce triose phosphate (TP) with reference to ribulose bisphosphate (RuBP), ribulose bisphosphate carboxylase (RuBisCO) and glycerate 3-phosphate (GP).

- Know the uses of triose phosphate (TP), including as a starting material for the synthesis of carbohydrates, lipids and amino acids, and the recycling of TP to regenerate the supply of RuBP.

Specification Reference 5.2.1

Tip: The Calvin cycle is also called carbon dioxide fixation, because carbon from CO_2 is 'fixed' into an organic molecule.

Photosynthesis Map

The light-dependent reaction   You are here

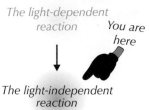

The light-independent reaction

3. Light-independent Reaction

The light-independent reaction is the second (and final, phew) stage of photosynthesis. It uses the products of the light-dependent reaction (ATP and reduced NADP) to make organic substances for the plant.

The Calvin cycle

The light-independent reaction is also called the Calvin cycle. It takes place in the stroma of the chloroplasts. It makes a molecule called **triose phosphate** from carbon dioxide (CO_2) and **ribulose bisphosphate** (a 5-carbon compound). Triose phosphate can be used to make glucose and other useful organic substances. There are a few steps in the cycle, and it needs ATP and H^+ ions to keep it going. The reactions are linked in a cycle (see Figure 1), which means the starting compound, ribulose bisphosphate, is regenerated.

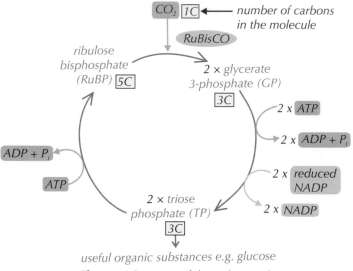

Figure 1: *One turn of the Calvin cycle.*

Here's what happens at each stage in the cycle:

1. Formation of glycerate 3-phosphate

Carbon dioxide enters the leaf through the stomata and diffuses into the stroma of the chloroplast. Here, it's combined with ribulose bisphosphate (RuBP), a 5-carbon compound. This gives an unstable 6-carbon compound, which quickly breaks down into two molecules of a 3-carbon compound called **glycerate 3-phosphate** (GP). **Ribulose bisphosphate carboxylase** (RuBisCO) catalyses the reaction between carbon dioxide and RuBP.

$$RuBP\ (5C) + CO_2 \xrightarrow[\quad RuBisCO \quad]{} unstable\ 6C\ compound \longrightarrow 2 \times GP\ (3C)$$

2. Formation of triose phosphate

The 3-carbon compound GP is reduced to a different 3-carbon compound called triose phosphate (TP). ATP (from the light-dependent reaction) provides the energy to do this. This reaction also requires H^+ ions, which come from reduced NADP (also from the light-dependent reaction). Reduced NADP is recycled to NADP (for use in the light-dependent reaction again). Triose phosphate is then converted into many useful organic compounds, e.g. glucose (see pages 119-120).

$$2 \times GP\ (3C) \xrightarrow[\quad 2 \times ATP \quad 2 \times ADP + P_i \quad]{\quad 2 \times reduced\ NADP \quad 2 \times NADP \quad} 2 \times TP\ (3C)$$

3. Regeneration of ribulose bisphosphate

Five out of every six molecules of TP produced in the cycle aren't used to make useful organic compounds, but to regenerate RuBP. Regenerating RuBP uses the rest of the ATP produced by the light-dependent reaction.

$$2 \times TP\ (3C) \xrightarrow{\quad ATP \quad ADP + Pi \quad} RuBP\ (5C)$$

Useful organic compounds (1C)

Hexose sugars

A hexose sugar is a monosaccharide that has six carbon atoms, e.g. glucose (see Figure 2). One hexose sugar is made by joining two molecules of triose phosphate (TP) together. Hexose sugars can be used to make larger carbohydrates (see next page).

The Calvin cycle needs to turn six times to make one hexose sugar. The reason for this is that three turns of the cycle produces six molecules of triose phosphate (because two molecules of TP are made for every one CO_2 molecule used). Five out of six of these TP molecules are used to regenerate ribulose bisphosphate (RuBP). This means that for three turns of the cycle only one TP is produced that's used to make a hexose sugar.

As a hexose sugar has six carbons, two TP molecules are needed to form one hexose sugar. This means the cycle must turn six times to produce two molecules of TP that can be used to make one hexose sugar — see Figure 3. Six turns of the cycle need 18 ATP and 12 reduced NADP from the light-dependent reaction.

This might seem a bit inefficient, but it keeps the cycle going and makes sure there's always enough RuBP ready to combine with carbon dioxide taken in from the atmosphere.

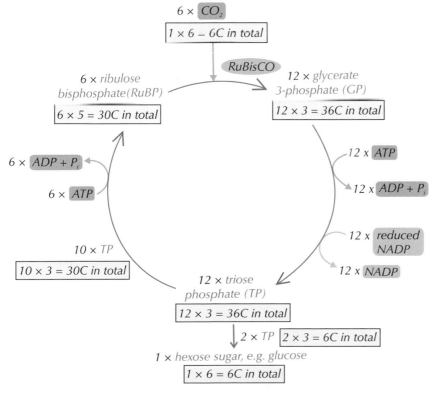

Figure 3: Six turns of the Calvin cycle.

Tip: Useful organic compounds have more than one carbon atom, e.g. glucose has six carbon atoms. This means the cycle has to turn more than once to make them — see below.

Tip: It's really important that RuBP is regenerated. If it wasn't then glycerate 3-phosphate wouldn't be formed, the Calvin cycle would stop and photosynthesis would be unable to continue.

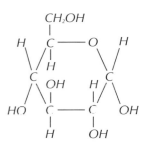

Figure 2: The structure of glucose, a hexose sugar.

Exam Tip
If you're asked in the exam to work out how many turns of the Calvin cycle are needed to produce a certain number of hexose sugars you need to remember that five out of every six TP molecules are used to regenerate RuBP.

Tip: Six turns of the Calvin cycle produce 12 GP molecules because one turn produces 2 GP, so $6 \times 2 = 12$ GP.

Carbohydrates, lipids and amino acids

The Calvin cycle is the starting point for making all the organic substances a plant needs. Triose phosphate (TP) and glycerate 3-phosphate (GP) molecules are used to make carbohydrates, lipids and amino acids:

- **Carbohydrates** — hexose sugars are made from two triose phosphate molecules (see the previous page) and larger carbohydrates (e.g. sucrose, starch, cellulose — see Figure 4) are made by joining hexose sugars together in different ways.

- **Lipids** — these are made using glycerol, which is synthesised from triose phosphate, and fatty acids, which are synthesised from glycerate 3-phosphate.

- **Amino acids** — some amino acids are made from glycerate 3-phosphate.

Figure 4: *Cellulose strands in a plant cell wall made from hexose sugars.*

Tip: The Calvin cycle can be summarised as follows:

Inputs
CO_2
ATP
Reduced NADP

↓

Outputs
Organic substances
RuBP

Exam Tip
Don't panic if you get a diagram of the Calvin cycle in the exam that doesn't look exactly the same as the one on the previous page (e.g. it might have extra or fewer stages) — as long as you remember the key points then you'll be fine.

Exam Tip
If you're asked to 'discuss the fate' of a molecule in the Calvin cycle, you just need to write about what happens to it.

Practice Questions — Application

The diagram on the right shows a simplified version of the Calvin cycle.

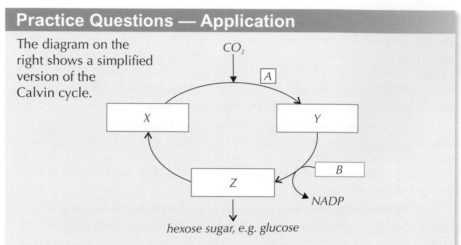

Q1 Name the molecules X, Y and Z.

Q2 Name enzyme A and coenzyme B.

Q3 Copy the diagram and draw on where ATP is used in the Calvin cycle (including how many molecules of ATP are used).

Practice Questions — Fact Recall

Q1 What is the role of carbon dioxide in the Calvin cycle?

Q2 a) Write out an equation that shows how two molecules of triose phosphate are formed.

   b) Is this reaction an oxidation or reduction reaction?

Q3 Describe the role of ATP in the Calvin cycle.

Q4 If six molecules of triose phosphate (TP) are produced by the Calvin cycle, how many of these will be used to regenerate ribulose bisphosphate?

Q5 To make one hexose sugar:

   a) How many turns of the Calvin cycle are needed?

   b) How many molecules of ATP are needed?

   c) How many molecules of reduced NADP are needed?

Q6 Describe how the products of the Calvin cycle are used to make the following organic substances:
   a) large carbohydrates,   b) lipids,   c) some amino acids.

4. Limiting Factors in Photosynthesis

There are optimum conditions for photosynthesis. If you're a budding gardener then these pages are for you...

Optimum conditions for photosynthesis

The ideal conditions for photosynthesis vary from one plant species to another. Most plants in temperate climates, like in the UK, would be happy with the conditions below and on the next page.

1. High light intensity of a certain wavelength

Light is needed to provide the energy for the light-dependent reaction — the higher the intensity of the light, the more energy it provides. Only certain wavelengths of light are used for photosynthesis. The photosynthetic pigments chlorophyll a, chlorophyll b and carotene only absorb the red and blue light in sunlight (see Figure 1).

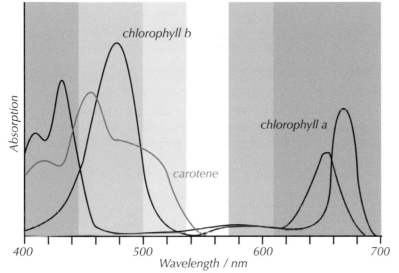

Figure 1. *The wavelengths of light absorbed by chlorophylls a and b, and carotene.*

2. Temperature around 25 °C

Photosynthesis involves enzymes (e.g. ATP synthase, RuBisCO). If the temperature falls below 10 °C the enzymes become inactive, but if the temperature is more than 45 °C they may start to **denature** (lose structure and function). Also, at high temperatures:

- Stomata close to avoid losing too much water. This causes photosynthesis to slow down because less carbon dioxide enters the leaf when the stomata are closed.
- The thylakoid membranes may be damaged. This could reduce the rate of the light-dependent stage reactions by reducing the number of sites available for electron transfer.
- The membrane around the chloroplast could be damaged, which could cause enzymes important in the Calvin cycle to be released into the cell. This would reduce the rate of the light-independent stage reactions.
- Chlorophyll could be damaged. This would reduce the amount of pigment that can absorb light energy, which would reduce rate of the light-dependent stage reactions.

Tip: If you exposed a plant to only green light, there would be little or no photosynthesis because most of the green light is reflected rather than being absorbed. This is why plants look green.

Tip: The width of the opening of stomata is called the stomatal aperture.

Tip: Remember: stomata are pores in the epidermis of a plant which allow gas exchange.

3. Carbon dioxide at 0.4%

Carbon dioxide makes up 0.04% of the gases in the atmosphere. Increasing this to 0.4% gives a higher rate of photosynthesis, but any higher and the stomata start to close.

Limiting factors of photosynthesis

Light, temperature and carbon dioxide can all limit photosynthesis. All three of these things need to be at the right level to allow a plant to photosynthesise as quickly as possible. If any one of these factors is too low or too high, it will limit photosynthesis (slow it down). Even if the other two factors are at the perfect level, it won't make any difference to the speed of photosynthesis as long as that factor is at the wrong level.

Examples

- On a warm, sunny, windless day, it's usually carbon dioxide that's the limiting factor.
- At night it's usually the light intensity that's the limiting factor.

Figure 2: As night falls, light intensity begins to limit the rate of photosynthesis.

However, any of these factors could become the limiting factor, depending on the environmental conditions. The graphs below and on the next page show the effect of each limiting factor on the rate of photosynthesis:

Examples

Light intensity

Between points A and B, the rate of photosynthesis is limited by the light intensity. So as the light intensity increases, so can the rate of photosynthesis. Point B is the **saturation point** — increasing light intensity after this point makes no difference, because something else has become the limiting factor. The graph now levels off.

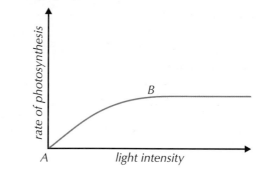

Temperature

Both these graphs level off when light intensity is no longer the limiting factor. The graph at 25 °C levels off at a higher point than the one at 15 °C, showing that temperature must have been a limiting factor at 15 °C.

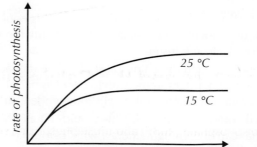

Carbon dioxide concentration

Both these graphs level off when light intensity is no longer the limiting factor. The graph at 0.4% carbon dioxide (CO_2) levels off at a higher point than the one at 0.04%, so carbon dioxide concentration must have been a limiting factor at 0.04% carbon dioxide. The limiting factor here isn't temperature because it's the same for both graphs (25 °C).

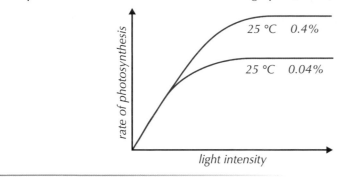

Water stress

Water stress can also affect photosynthesis. When plants don't have enough water, their stomata will close to preserve what little water they do have, leading to less CO_2 entering the leaf for the Calvin cycle and slowing photosynthesis down.

Figure 3: Lamps in greenhouses provide light at night.

Increasing plant growth

Commercial growers (e.g. farmers) know the factors that limit photosynthesis and therefore limit plant growth. This means they can create an environment where plants get the right amount of everything that they need, which increases growth and so increases yield. Growers create optimum conditions in **glasshouses**, as shown in Figure 4.

Limiting Factor	Management in Glasshouse
Carbon dioxide concentration	Carbon dioxide is added to the air, e.g. by burning a small amount of propane in a carbon dioxide generator.
Light	Light can get in through the glass. Lamps provide light at night time.
Temperature	Glasshouses trap heat energy from sunlight, which warms the air. Heaters and cooling systems can also be used to keep a constant optimum temperature.

Figure 4: Techniques used by growers to create optimum conditions in a glasshouse.

Limiting factors and the Calvin cycle

Light intensity, temperature and CO_2 concentration all affect the rate of photosynthesis, which means they affect the levels of glycerate 3-phosphate (GP), ribulose bisphosphate (RuBP) and triose phosphate (TP) in the Calvin cycle.

Tip: See pages 118-119 for how GP, TP and RuBP are made in the Calvin cycle.

Tip: Light intensity doesn't affect the Calvin cycle directly because light isn't needed for the reactions of the Calvin cycle. However, the Calvin cycle does depend on the products from the light-dependent reaction, so it is indirectly affected by light intensity.

Light intensity

In low light intensities, the products of the light-dependent stage (reduced NADP and ATP) will be in short supply (see Figure 5). This means that conversion of GP to TP and RuBP is slow. So the level of GP will rise as it's still being made, but it isn't being used up as quickly. The levels of TP and RuBP will fall as they're used up to make GP, but aren't being remade as quickly — see Figure 6.

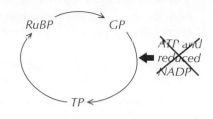

Figure 5: The effect of low light intensity on the Calvin cycle.

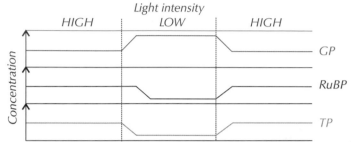

Figure 6: The effect of light intensity on the levels of GP, RuBP and TP.

Tip: Unlike light intensity, temperature does affect the Calvin cycle directly because it affects enzyme activity.

Temperature

All the reactions in the Calvin cycle are catalysed by enzymes (e.g. RuBisCO). At low temperatures, all of the reactions will be slower as the enzymes work more slowly. This means the levels of RuBP, GP and TP will fall. GP, TP and RuBP are affected in the same way at very high temperatures, because the enzymes will start to denature (see Figure 7).

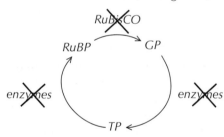

Figure 7: The effect of temperature on the Calvin cycle.

Carbon dioxide concentration

At low CO_2 concentrations, conversion of RuBP to GP is also slow as there's less CO_2 to combine with RuBP to make GP — see Figure 8. So the level of RuBP will rise as it's still being made, but isn't being used up. The levels of GP and TP will fall as they're used up to make RuBP, but aren't being remade.

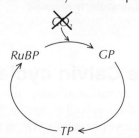

Figure 8: The effect of low CO_2 concentration on the Calvin cycle.

Practice Questions — Application

Q1 A farmer grows two tomato crops — one in a greenhouse and the other outside. He records the average plant height each week for seven weeks. The results are shown in the graph below.

a) For each tomato crop, calculate the percentage difference in the average plant height between week two and week five.

b) Describe three ways in which the farmer may have created ideal conditions in the greenhouse in order to increase photosynthesis.

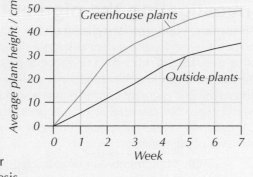

Q2 Technicians at a plant-growing company were trying to reduce the running costs of their greenhouses. In one greenhouse, they reduced the amount of water used to water the plants by 40%. In a second greenhouse, they replaced the paraffin heaters that they used to heat the greenhouse with electric heaters, which maintained the same temperature, but were cheaper to run. The changes resulted in slower growth of the plants in the greenhouses, due to a reduced rate of photosynthesis.

a) Suggest why reducing the amount of water given to the plants could result in a reduced rate of photosynthesis.

b) Suggest why replacing the paraffin heaters with electric heaters could result in a reduced rate of photosynthesis.

Q3 a) Jen has two house plants. She puts plant A under a light with a wavelength of 520 nm and plant B under a light with a wavelength of 480 nm. All other conditions the two plants are kept in are the same. After 4 weeks she measures the height of both plants. Which plant do you think was tallest? Explain your answer.

b) Jen keeps another house plant in her conservatory, which gets sun throughout the day and can reach temperatures of 40 °C. She regularly waters the plant but it's beginning to die. Suggest why this might be and explain your answer.

Tip: Look back at page 121 for a recap on the wavelengths of light used for photosynthesis.

Practice Questions — Fact Recall

Q1 Explain why a low light intensity decreases the rate of the Calvin cycle, even though it's a light-independent reaction.

Q2 Describe how the following would affect the concentration of RuBP in the Calvin cycle:

a) low light intensity,

b) low temperature,

c) low concentration of CO_2.

- Be able to use thin layer chromatography (TLC) to separate photosynthetic pigments (PAG6).
- Be able to carry out practical investigations into factors affecting the rate of photosynthesis (PAG11).

Specification Reference 5.2.1

5. Photosynthesis Experiments

You need to know how to carry out two types of experiment related to different aspects of photosynthesis for your exams.

Investigating the pigments in leaves

All plants contain several different photosynthetic pigments in their leaves. Each pigment absorbs a different wavelength of light, so having more than one type of pigment increases the range of wavelengths of light that a plant can absorb. In addition to photosynthetic pigments, some plants also have other pigments in their leaves, which play other essential roles, e.g. protecting the leaves from excessive UV radiation. Different species of plants contain different proportions and mixtures of pigments.

A sample of pigments can be extracted from the leaves of a plant and separated using thin-layer chromatography (TLC). You can then identify the pigments present in the sample by calculating their **R_f values**. An R_f value is the distance a substance has moved through the stationary phase in relation to the solvent. Each pigment has a specific R_f value, under specific conditions, which can be looked up in a database.

Tip: Make sure you carry out a risk assessment before you do this experiment. Be especially aware of the hazards involved with using propanone, petroleum ether and the chromatography solvent, which are toxic and highly flammable.

Tip: It's best to do steps 2 and 5 in a fume cupboard as the chemicals used are volatile (evaporate easily) and the vapours are hazardous.

--- Example ---

Like all types of chromatography, TLC involves a mobile phase (in this case a liquid solvent) and a stationary phase (in TLC, this is a chromatography plate — a solid plate of glass or plastic with a thin layer of gel, which the pigments can travel through, on top). Here's how you do it:

1. Grind up several leaves (spinach works nicely) with some anhydrous sodium sulfate, then add a few drops of propanone.

2. Transfer the liquid to a test tube, add some petroleum ether and gently shake the tube. Two distinct layers will form in the liquid — the top layer is the pigments mixed in with the petroleum ether.

3. Transfer some of the liquid from the top layer into a second test tube with some anhydrous sodium sulfate.

4. Draw a horizontal pencil line near the bottom of a chromatography plate. Build up a concentrated spot of the liquid from step 3 on the line by applying several drops, ensuring each one is dry before the next is added. This is the point of origin.

5. Once the point of origin is completely dry, put the plate into a glass beaker with some prepared solvent (e.g. a mixture of propanone, cyclohexane and petroleum ether) — just enough so that the point of origin is a little bit above the solvent. Put a lid on the beaker and leave the plate to develop. As the solvent spreads up the plate, the different pigments (solutes) move with it, but at different rates — so they separate.

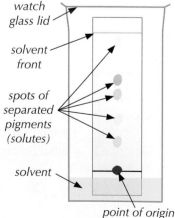

watch glass lid

solvent front

spots of separated pigments (solutes)

solvent

point of origin

Figure 2: *Diagram showing plant pigments separated by thin layer chromatography.*

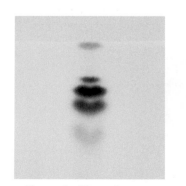

Figure 1: *Plant pigments that have been separated by thin-layer chromatography.*

6. When the solvent has nearly reached the top, take the plate out and mark the solvent front (the furthest point the solvent has reached) with a pencil and leave the plate to dry in a well-ventilated place.

Tip: The pattern of spots you end up with is called a chromatogram.

7. There should be several new coloured spots on the chromatography plate between the point of origin and the solvent front. These are the separated pigments. You can calculate their R_f values and look them up in a database to identify what the pigments are.
You can calculate the R_f value using this formula:

$$R_f \text{ value} = \frac{\text{distance moved by the solute}}{\text{distance moved by the solvent}}$$

Tip: R_f values are always between 0 and 1.

Tip: The stationary phase and solvent that you use will affect the R_f value. If you're looking up R_f values, you need to check that they were recorded under the same conditions as your experiment.

Practice Question — Application

Q1 A scientist uses thin-layer chromatography to separate out the photosynthetic pigments from a mixture obtained from plant leaves. The chromatogram that he produces is shown on the right.

a) Calculate the R_f value of spot Y.   7.90 cm

solvent front
Y
9.00 cm
X
3.47 cm

b) The scientist carried out the same experiment using paper chromatography. Suggest why the R_f values he obtained were different to those calculated from his first experiment.

Investigating the rate of photosynthesis

Canadian pondweed (*Elodea*) can be used to measure the effect of light intensity, temperature and CO_2 concentration on the rate of photosynthesis. The rate at which oxygen is produced by the pondweed can be easily measured and this corresponds to the rate of photosynthesis.

PRACTICAL ACTIVITY GROUP **11**

Example

The apparatus below is used to measure the effect of light intensity on photosynthesis.

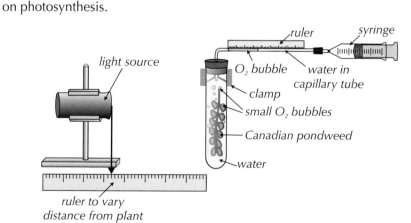

ruler   syringe
light source O_2 bubble   water in capillary tube
clamp
small O_2 bubbles
Canadian pondweed
water
ruler to vary distance from plant

Tip: Make sure you think about and address the risks involved in this experiment before you begin. Pond water can be an infection risk, so make sure you cover any cuts and grazes, and wash your hands well after you've finished the experiment.

Here's how the experiment works:

1. A source of white light is placed at a specific distance from the pondweed.

2. The pondweed is left to photosynthesise for a set amount of time. As it photosynthesises, the oxygen released will collect in the capillary tube.

3. At the end of the experiment, the syringe is used to draw the gas bubble in the tube up alongside a ruler and the length of the gas bubble is measured. This is proportional to the volume of O_2 produced.

4. Any variables that could affect the results should be controlled, e.g. temperature, the time the weed is left to photosynthesise.

5. The experiment is repeated and the average length of gas bubble is calculated, to make the results more precise.

6. The whole experiment is then repeated with the light source placed at different distances from the pondweed.

Tip: The volume of O_2 can also be measured by counting the number of small O_2 bubbles released by the pondweed, but this is less accurate.

The apparatus used in this experiment can be adapted to measure the effect of temperature and CO_2 on photosynthesis, e.g. the test tube of pondweed is put into a beaker of water at a set temperature and CO_2 is bubbled into the test tube (then the experiment's repeated with different temperatures of water / concentrations of CO_2).

Practice Question — Fact Recall

Q1 Describe an experiment involving pondweed that could be used to determine the effect of light intensity on the rate of photosynthesis. (Make sure you include a brief description of the apparatus.)

Section Summary

Make sure you know...

- That plants, animals and microorganisms need energy to power biological processes (e.g. photosynthesis, active transport, DNA replication, cell division, muscle contraction, maintenance of body temperature and protein synthesis).

- That plants are able to produce their own food, but animals can't make their own food and so rely on eating plants or other animals.

- That in photosynthesis, light energy is used to produce complex organic molecules such as glucose.

- That plants and animals release energy from the products of photosynthesis by respiration.

- That ATP is the immediate source of energy in a cell. It is used to carry out biological processes.

- That ATP consists of the base adenine, a ribose sugar and three phosphate groups.

- What a plant's compensation point is and how to work it out using a suitable graph.

- That photosynthesis takes place in the chloroplasts of plants.

- That a photosynthetic pigment is a coloured substance that absorbs light energy in photosynthesis.

- That a photosystem contains primary pigments, which are reaction centres for the light-dependent stage of photosynthesis, and accessory pigments, which surround reaction centres and transfer light energy to them to boost the energy available for electron excitation to take place.

- That photosynthesis has two stages — the light-dependent reaction (which takes place in the thylakoid membranes) and the light-independent reaction (which takes place in the stroma).

- That the light-dependent reaction includes non-cyclic photophosphorylation and cyclic photophosphorylation. In both processes, light energy is absorbed by the chlorophyll in photosystems and used to excite electrons. As the electrons move down the electron transport chain they lose energy, which is used to generate a proton gradient across the thylakoid membrane. The subsequent movement of protons down their concentration gradient is used to produce ATP. This method of ATP production is called chemiosmosis, which is described by the chemiosmotic theory. In non-cyclic photophosphorylation, reduced NADP is also produced.

- That the protons and electrons needed for the light-dependent reaction come from the photolysis of water — the splitting of water using light, which also produces oxygen. It happens in non-cyclic photophosphorylation.

- That in the light-independent reaction, carbon dioxide (CO_2) enters the Calvin cycle, where it is combined with ribulose bisphosphate (RuBP) to form two molecules of glycerate 3-phosphate (GP). These two molecules of GP are then reduced to two molecules of triose phosphate (TP) using ATP and reduced NADP from the light-dependent reaction. Five out of every six molecules of TP are used to regenerate RuBP (allowing the Calvin cycle to continue), while the remaining TP is used to produce organic substrates such as carbohydrates, lipids and amino acids.

- That a limiting factor is a variable that can slow down the rate of a reaction. The limiting factors of photosynthesis are light intensity, temperature and carbon dioxide concentration. Water stress can also play a role.

- How the limiting factors of photosynthesis affect the concentrations of GP, RuBP and TP in the Calvin cycle.

- How photosynthetic pigments can be separated using thin layer chromatography.

- That photosynthetic pigments separated by thin layer chromatography can be identified by calculating their R_f values and comparing them to a database.

- That the rate of photosynthesis can be investigated by measuring the effect of changing light intensity, temperature and CO_2 concentration on the rate of oxygen production in pondweed.

Exam-style Questions

1 Plants use photosynthesis to produce glucose.

(a) Photosynthesis occurs in the chloroplasts.
Fig. 1.1 shows the structure of a chloroplast.

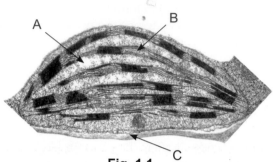

Fig. 1.1

(i) Identify the structures labelled **A – C**.

(3 marks)

(ii) Which of the structures **A – C** is the site of the light-independent reaction of photosynthesis?

(1 mark)

(b) Chloroplasts contain photosynthetic pigments, which are organised into photosystems. Photosystems contain primary and accessory pigments.

What is the purpose of each these types of photosynthetic pigment in a photosystem?

(2 marks)

(c) Glucose is synthesised from a 3-carbon compound produced in the light-independent reaction of photosynthesis.

(i)* Describe how this 3-carbon compound is produced.

(6 marks)

(ii) Only one out of six of the 3-carbon compounds produced in the light-independent reaction is converted into glucose. Describe what happens to the other five.

(2 marks)

(d) The glucose generated in photosynthesis is used to make ATP.
Name the process in which glucose is used to make ATP.

(1 mark)

*The quality of your response will be assessed in this question.

2   DNIP is an artificial hydrogen acceptor that can be used to measure the rate of photosynthesis. When DNIP is reduced it turns from blue to colourless. In the presence of NADP, DNIP is reduced first. A scientist used DNIP to investigate the rate of photosynthesis in plant chloroplasts under three different conditions. The results are shown below.

Tube	Condition	Colour after 24 hours
A	Unboiled chloroplasts kept in the dark	blue
B	Unboiled chloroplasts kept in the light	colourless
C	Boiled chloroplasts kept in the light	blue

(a)   Explain the result for tube B.

(3 marks)

(b)   Explain the results for tubes A and C.

(2 marks)

(c)   Describe the role of reduced NADP in the light-independent reaction of photosynthesis.

(2 marks)

3   A student carried out a study into the effect of different factors on the rate of photosynthesis in a certain species of plant. He calculated the rate of photosynthesis by measuring how much oxygen was released by the plants over a period of time.

(a)   Is this an accurate way of calculating the rate of photosynthesis? Explain your answer.

(1 mark)

(b)   The student carried out three experiments in his study — the results of which are shown in **Fig. 3.1**. In each experiment the plants had an adequate supply of water.

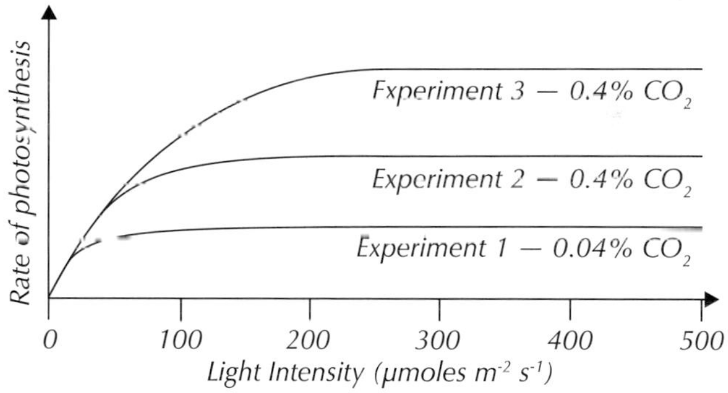

Fig. 3.1

(i)   Describe and explain the results of experiment 1.

(3 marks)

(ii)   What is the limiting factor of photosynthesis in experiment 2? Explain your answer.

(2 marks)

(c)   The student extended experiment 2 by measuring the amount of RuBP and TP produced by the plant over time. After 5 minutes, the student lowered the CO_2 concentration of the plants to 0.04%. Describe and explain what effect the lowering of CO_2 concentration had on the levels of RuBP and TP in the plants.

(2 marks)

1. Aerobic Respiration

Respiration is the process that allows cells to produce ATP from glucose. The next few pages are about aerobic respiration — respiration using oxygen.

Mitochondria

Most of the reactions in respiration take place in the mitochondria. You covered the mitochondrial structure in Year 1, but you might want to refresh your memory of it before you start this page — see Figure 1.

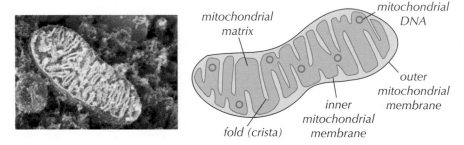

Figure 1: *A mitochondrion in a nerve cell (left) and mitochondrial structure (right).*

Coenzymes

As you saw in photosynthesis, a coenzyme is a molecule that aids the function of an enzyme by transferring a chemical group from one molecule to another. Coenzymes used in respiration include **NAD**, **coenzyme A** and **FAD**. NAD and FAD transfer hydrogen from one molecule to another. This means they can reduce (give hydrogen to) or oxidise (take hydrogen from) a molecule. Coenzyme A transfers acetate between molecules (see page 134).

Aerobic respiration

There are four stages in aerobic respiration:

1. Glycolysis.

2. The link reaction.

3. The Krebs cycle.

4. Oxidative phosphorylation.

The first three stages are a series of reactions. The products from these reactions are used in the final stage to produce loads of ATP. The first stage happens in the cytoplasm of cells and the other three stages take place in the mitochondria.

All cells use glucose to respire, but organisms can also break down other complex organic molecules (e.g. fatty acids, amino acids), which can then be respired.

Stage 1 — Glycolysis

Glycolysis makes **pyruvate** from glucose. Glycolysis involves splitting one molecule of glucose (with 6 carbons — 6C) into two smaller molecules of pyruvate (3C). The process happens in the cytoplasm of cells.
Glycolysis is the first stage of both aerobic and anaerobic respiration and doesn't need oxygen to take place — so it's an anaerobic process.

There are two stages in glycolysis — phosphorylation and oxidation. First, ATP is used to phosphorylate glucose to triose phosphate. Phosphorylation is the process of adding phosphate to a molecule. Then triose phosphate is oxidised, releasing ATP. Overall there's a net gain of 2 ATP.

Aerobic Respiration Map

Glycolysis

Link Reaction

You are here

Krebs Cycle

Oxidative Phosphorylation

1. Phosphorylation

Glucose is phosphorylated by adding a phosphate from a molecule of ATP. This creates one molecule of hexose phosphate and a molecule of ADP. Hexose phosphate is phosphorylated by ATP to form hexose bisphosphate and another molecule of ADP. Then, hexose bisphosphate is split up into 2 molecules of triose phosphate.

2. Oxidation

Triose phosphate is oxidised (loses hydrogen), forming 2 molecules of pyruvate. NAD collects the hydrogen ions, forming 2 reduced NAD. 4 ATP are produced, but 2 were used up in stage one, so there's a net gain of 2 ATP.

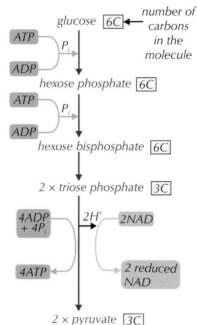

Tip: Remember the first part of OILRIG, (page 114) — oxidation is loss, so when triose phosphate is oxidised it loses hydrogen.

Tip: Reduced NAD is also called NADH.

Tip: Glycolysis takes place in the cytoplasm of cells because glucose can't cross the outer mitochondrial membrane. Pyruvate can cross this membrane, so the rest of the reactions in respiration occur within the mitochondria.

The products of glycolysis

Here's what happens to all the products of glycolysis...

Products from glycolysis	Where it goes
2 reduced NAD	To oxidative phosphorylation
2 pyruvate	To the link reaction
2 ATP (net gain)	Used for energy

Practice Questions — Application

The diagram below is a simplified representation of glycolysis:

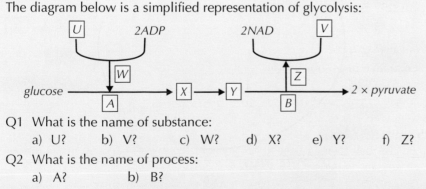

Q1 What is the name of substance:
   a) U?   b) V?   c) W?   d) X?   e) Y?   f) Z?

Q2 What is the name of process:
   a) A?   b) B?

Q3 What parts of the process are missing off the diagram above?

Tip: Decarboxylation is the removal of carbon dioxide from a molecule.

Aerobic Respiration Map

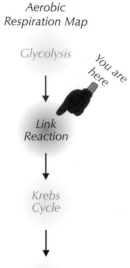

Stage 2 — The link reaction

Pyruvate is actively transported into the matrix of the mitochondria. Here, the link reaction converts pyruvate to acetyl coenzyme A. Pyruvate is **decarboxylated**, so one carbon atom is removed from pyruvate in the form of carbon dioxide. NAD is reduced to NADH — it collects hydrogen from pyruvate, changing pyruvate into acetate. Acetate is combined with coenzyme A (CoA) to form acetyl coenzyme A (acetyl CoA). No ATP is produced in this reaction.

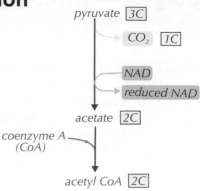

The products of the link reaction

Two pyruvate molecules are made for every glucose molecule that enters glycolysis. This means the link reaction and the third stage (the Krebs cycle) happen twice for every glucose molecule.

Here's what happens to the products of two link reactions (i.e. for one glucose molecule):

Products from two link reactions	Where it goes
2 acetyl coenzyme A	To the Krebs cycle
2 carbon dioxide	Released as a waste product
2 reduced NAD	To oxidative phosphorylation

Aerobic Respiration Map

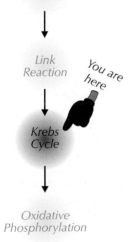

Tip: In respiration carbon dioxide is produced in the link reaction and the Krebs cycle.

Stage 3 — The Krebs cycle

The Krebs cycle produces reduced coenzymes and ATP. It involves a series of oxidation-reduction reactions, which take place in the matrix of the mitochondria. The cycle happens once for every pyruvate molecule, so it goes round twice for every glucose molecule.

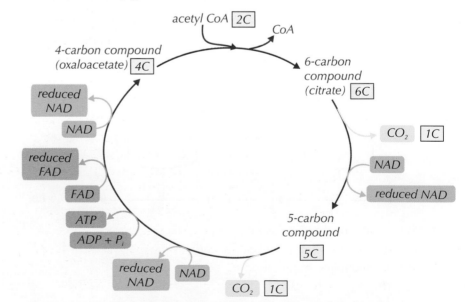

Figure 2: *One turn of the Krebs cycle.*

Here's what happens at each stage in the Krebs cycle:

1. Formation of citrate

The acetyl group from acetyl CoA (produced in the link reaction) combines with oxaloacetate to form citrate (citric acid). This is catalysed by citrate synthase. Coenzyme A goes back to the link reaction to be used again.

Tip: Coenzyme A transfers acetate between molecules (see page 132 for a reminder on coenzymes).

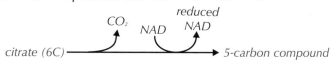

$$oxaloacetate~(4C) + acetyl~CoA~(2C) \xrightarrow{\hspace{1cm}CoA} citrate~(6C)$$

2. Formation of a 5-carbon compound

The 6C citrate molecule is converted to a 5C molecule. Decarboxylation occurs, where carbon dioxide is removed. **Dehydrogenation** also occurs. The hydrogen is used to produce reduced NAD from NAD.

Tip: Dehydrogenation is the removal of hydrogen from a molecule.

$$citrate~(6C) \xrightarrow[\hspace{2cm}]{CO_2~~~NAD~~~\substack{reduced\\NAD}} 5\text{-}carbon~compound$$

3. Regeneration of oxaloacetate

The 5C molecule is then converted to a 4C molecule. (There are some intermediate compounds formed during this conversion, but you don't need to know about them.) Decarboxylation and dehydrogenation occur, producing one molecule of reduced FAD and two of reduced NAD. ATP is produced by the direct transfer of a phosphate group from an intermediate compound to ADP. When a phosphate group is directly transferred from one molecule to another it's called **substrate-level phosphorylation**. Citrate has now been converted into oxaloacetate.

Tip: See previous page if you can't remember what decarboxylation is.

Tip: Remember, reduced NAD may be written as NADH. Reduced FAD may also be written as FADH$_2$. Don't worry, they still mean the same things.

$$\substack{5\text{-}carbon\\compound} \xrightarrow[\hspace{4cm}]{CO_2~~NAD~~\substack{reduced\\NAD}~~\substack{ADP\\+P_i}~~ATP~~FAD~~\substack{reduced\\FAD}~~NAD~~\substack{reduced\\NAD}} \substack{oxaloacetate\\(4C)}$$

The products of the Krebs cycle

Some products of the Krebs cycle are reused, some are released and others are used for the next stage of respiration — oxidative phosphorylation.

Product from one Krebs cycle	Where it goes
1 coenzyme A	Reused in the next link reaction
Oxaloacetate	Regenerated for use in the next Krebs cycle
2 carbon dioxide	Released as a waste product
1 ATP	Used for energy
3 reduced NAD	To oxidative phosphorylation
1 reduced FAD	To oxidative phosphorylation

Tip: The table only shows the products of <u>one</u> turn of the Krebs cycle. The cycle turns <u>twice</u> for one glucose molecule, so one glucose molecule produces twice as much as what's shown in the table.

Practice Questions — Application

Q1 The diagram below shows part of the Krebs cycle:

$$oxaloacetate \longrightarrow citrate \longrightarrow 5C\text{-}intermediate$$

a) How many carbon atoms do oxaloacetate and citrate each have?

b) What happens to turn the 5C-intermediate back into oxaloacetate?

Q2 If six molecules of glucose were respired, how many molecules of CO_2 would be produced from the Krebs cycle?

Q3 Fats can be broken down and converted into acetyl coenzyme A. Explain how this allows fats to be respired.

Tip: Remember that the Krebs cycle is just that... a cycle — some of its products need to be recycled for the process to continue.

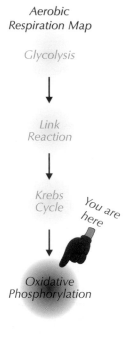

Aerobic Respiration Map

Glycolysis

Link Reaction

Krebs Cycle

You are here

Oxidative Phosphorylation

Tip: Oxidative phosphorylation takes place in the inner mitochondrial membrane.

Tip: The regenerated coenzymes from the electron transport chain are reused in the Krebs cycle.

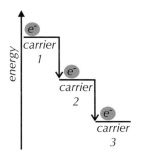

Figure 3: As electrons move along the electron transport chain, they lose energy.

Tip: The job of a carrier is to transfer electrons. When a carrier receives electrons it's reduced and when it passes on electrons it becomes oxidised again.

Stage 4 — Oxidative phosphorylation

Oxidative phosphorylation is the process where the energy carried by electrons, from reduced coenzymes (reduced NAD and reduced FAD), is used to make ATP. (The whole point of the previous stages is to make reduced NAD and reduced FAD for the final stage.)

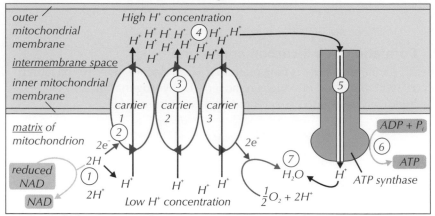

The numbers in the diagram above correspond to these steps:

1. Hydrogen atoms are released from reduced NAD and reduced FAD as they're oxidised to NAD and FAD. The hydrogen atoms split into protons (H^+) and electrons (e^-).

2. The electrons move along the **electron transport chain** (made up of three electron carriers), losing energy at each carrier (see Figure 3). The electron transport chain is located in the inner mitochondrial membrane. This membrane is folded into cristae, which increases the membrane's surface area to maximise respiration.

3. This energy is used by the electron carriers to pump protons from the mitochondrial matrix into the intermembrane space (the space between the inner and outer mitochondrial membranes).

4. The concentration of protons is now higher in the intermembrane space than in the mitochondrial matrix — this forms an electrochemical gradient (a concentration gradient of ions).

5. Protons move down the electrochemical gradient, back into the mitochondrial matrix, via ATP synthase.

6. This movement drives the synthesis of ATP from ADP and inorganic phosphate (P_i). This process of ATP production driven by the movement of H^+ ions across a membrane (due to electrons moving down an electron transport chain) is called chemiosmosis (which is described by the **chemiosmotic theory**).

7. In the mitochondrial matrix, at the end of the transport chain, the protons, electrons and oxygen (from the blood) combine to form water. Oxygen is said to be the **final electron acceptor**.

Practice Questions — Application

Antimycin A inhibits carrier 2 in the electron transport chain of oxidative phosphorylation.

Q1 If antimycin A was added to isolated mitochondria, what state (oxidised or reduced) would carriers 1 and 3 be in after its addition? Explain your answers.

Q2 Suggest why antimycin A can be used as a fish poison.

Stages of aerobic respiration

Glycolysis, the link reaction and the Krebs cycle are basically a series of reactions which produce ATP, reduced NAD, reduced FAD and CO_2. The reduced coenzymes (NAD and FAD) are then used in oxidative phosphorylation, to produce loads more ATP. The overall process is shown below:

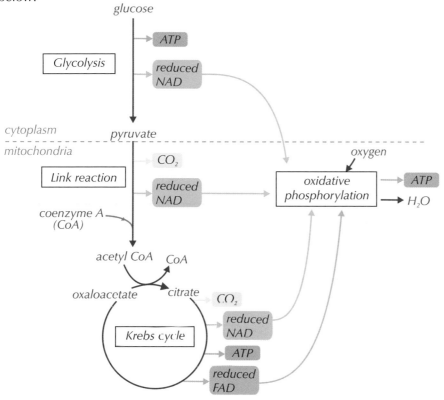

Tip: Don't forget oxygen's role in respiration. It's the final electron acceptor in the electron transport chain in oxidative phosphorylation (see previous page).

Tip: Remember that the whole purpose of respiration is to produce ATP to fuel biological processes. That's why it's happening continuously in plant and animal cells, and microorganisms.

Aerobic respiration and ATP

As you know, oxidative phosphorylation makes ATP using energy from the reduced coenzymes — 2.5 ATP are made from each reduced NAD and 1.5 ATP are made from each reduced FAD.

The table below shows that a cell can make 32 ATP from one molecule of glucose in aerobic respiration. (Remember, one molecule of glucose produces 2 pyruvate, so the link reaction and Krebs cycle happen twice.)

Stage of respiration	Molecules produced	Number of ATP molecules
Glycolysis	2 ATP	**2**
Glycolysis	2 reduced NAD	2 × 2.5 = **5**
Link Reaction (×2)	2 reduced NAD	2 × 2.5 = **5**
Krebs cycle (×2)	2 ATP	**2**
Krebs cycle (×2)	6 reduced NAD	6 × 2.5 = **15**
Krebs cycle (×2)	2 reduced FAD	2 × 1.5 = **3**
		Total ATP = **32**

Tip: For each molecule of glucose, 28 molecules of ATP are produced by oxidative phosphorylation (i.e. that's the ATP made from reduced NAD and reduced FAD).

Exam Tip
You really need to
know this stuff for your
exam. If you find you're
struggling to answer
a question go back to
the relevant page and
make sure you really
understand what's
going on.

Q1 Where in the cell does glycolysis take place?

Q2 What is ATP used for in glycolysis?

Q3 How is pyruvate transported into the mitochondria?

Q4 Where in the mitochondria does the link reaction take place?

Q5 a) In the link reaction, pyruvate is converted into acetate.
Describe how this happens.

b) The second stage of the link reaction relies on coenzyme A.
What is the role of coenzyme A in the link reaction?

c) State what happens to the products of the link reaction.

Q6 During the Krebs cycle ATP is produced by the direct transfer of a
phosphate group from an intermediate compound to ADP.
What name is given to this process?

Q7 After each turn of the Krebs cycle, what happens to:

a) coenzyme A?   b) oxaloacetate?

Q8 During oxidative phosphorylation, what happens to electrons as they
move down the electron transport chain?

Q9 What is chemiosmosis?

Q10 What is said to be the final electron acceptor in oxidative
phosphorylation?

Q11 Give one example of a decarboxylation reaction in respiration.

Q12 Draw out the table below and fill it in with crosses to show where
the following substances are made in respiration.

Substance	Glycolysis	Link reaction	Krebs cycle	Oxidative phosphorylation
ATP				
reduced NAD				
reduced FAD				
CO_2				

2. Anaerobic Respiration

How cells respire aerobically is covered on pages 132-137. This page is all about how cells respire anaerobically.

What is anaerobic respiration?

Anaerobic respiration is a type of respiration that doesn't use oxygen. Like aerobic respiration, it starts with glycolysis. However, unlike aerobic respiration it doesn't involve the link reaction, the Krebs cycle or oxidative phosphorylation.

There are two types of anaerobic respiration — alcoholic fermentation and lactate fermentation. These two processes are similar, because they both take place in the cytoplasm, they both produce two ATP per molecule of glucose and they both start with glycolysis (which produces pyruvate). They differ in which organisms they occur in and what happens to the pyruvate (see below).

Lactate fermentation

Lactate fermentation occurs in mammals and produces lactate. Reduced NAD (from glycolysis) transfers hydrogen to pyruvate to form lactate and NAD — see Figure 1. NAD can then be reused in glycolysis. The production of lactate regenerates NAD. Glycolysis needs NAD in order to take place. This means glycolysis can continue even when there isn't much oxygen around, so a small amount of ATP can still be produced to keep some biological processes going.

Figure 1: The reactions of lactate fermentation.

Our cells can tolerate a high level of lactate (and the coinciding low pH conditions) for short periods of time. For example, during short periods of hard exercise, when they can't get enough ATP from aerobic respiration. However, too much lactate is toxic and is removed from the cells into the bloodstream. The liver takes up lactate from the bloodstream and converts it back into glucose in a process called gluconeogenesis (see p. 41).

Alcoholic fermentation

Alcoholic fermentation occurs in yeast cells and produces ethanol. CO_2 is removed from pyruvate to form ethanal. Reduced NAD (from glycolysis) transfers hydrogen to ethanal to form ethanol and NAD — see Figure 3. NAD can then be reused in glycolysis. The production of ethanol also regenerates NAD so glycolysis can continue when there isn't much oxygen around.

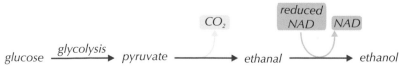

Figure 3: The reactions of alcoholic fermentation.

Learning Objectives:

- Understand the process of anaerobic respiration in eukaryotes, including anaerobic respiration in mammals and yeast and the benefits of being able to respire anaerobically.
- Know why anaerobic respiration produces a much lower yield of ATP than aerobic respiration.

Specification Reference 5.2.2

Tip: Some bacteria carry out lactate fermentation too.

Tip: Remember, NAD is needed to oxidise triose phosphate to pyruvate in glycolysis — see page 133.

Figure 2: Yeast cells can respire anaerobically using alcoholic fermentation.

Tip: Alcoholic fermentation also occurs in plants.

Anaerobic respiration and ATP

The ATP yield from anaerobic respiration is always lower than from aerobic respiration. This is because anaerobic respiration only includes one energy-releasing stage (glycolysis), which only produces 2 ATP per glucose molecule. The energy-releasing reactions of the Krebs cycle and oxidative phosphorylation need oxygen, so they can't occur during anaerobic respiration.

Tip: Aerobic respiration produces 32 ATP per molecule of glucose — see page 137.

Practice Questions — Application

Q1 Kate is competing in a 100 m sprint. Towards the end of the race her body cannot supply oxygen to the muscle cells in her legs quickly enough.

a) Will Kate's muscle cells begin respiring aerobically or anaerobically towards the end of the race?

b) How many molecules of ATP are produced per molecule of glucose by this type of respiration?

c) Write out the word equation for this reaction.

Q2 The diagram below shows the two fates of glucose in anaerobic conditions.

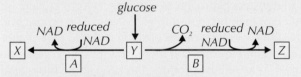

a) What is the name of substance:

i) X? ii) Y? iii) Z?

b) Which process, A or B:

i) is lactate fermentation?

ii) happens in plant cells?

iii) can happen in bacterial cells?

c) How many molecules of ATP are made by each of these processes?

Practice Questions — Fact Recall

Q1 Where in the cell does anaerobic respiration take place?

Q2 Give one similarity between aerobic respiration and anaerobic respiration.

Q3 In which organisms do the following occur:

a) lactate fermentation?   b) alcoholic fermentation?

Q4 Describe what happens to pyruvate in lactate fermentation.

Q5 Describe what happens to ethanal in alcoholic fermentation.

Q6 a) If aerobic respiration produces 32 ATP per molecule of glucose, how many fewer ATP molecules does anaerobic respiration produce?

b) Explain why anaerobic respiration gives a lower yield of ATP than aerobic respiration.

3. Respiratory Substrates

Glucose isn't the only molecule that can be respired...

What is a respiratory substrate?

Any biological molecule that can be broken down in respiration to release energy is called a respiratory substrate. Cells respire glucose, but they also respire other carbohydrates, lipids and proteins — these are all respiratory substrates. Different respiratory substrates enter respiration at different points. Glucose enters right at the beginning — at the start of glycolysis. Proteins and lipids enter respiration at the Krebs cycle.

Energy values of respiratory substrates

Different respiratory substrates release different amounts of energy when they're respired — as shown by their different energy values in Figure 1. Lipids have the highest energy value, followed by proteins, then carbohydrates. This is because most ATP is made in oxidative phosphorylation, which requires hydrogen atoms from reduced NAD and reduced FAD. This means that respiratory substrates that contain more hydrogen atoms per unit of mass cause more ATP to be produced when respired. Lipids contain the most hydrogen atoms per unit of mass, followed by proteins and then carbohydrates.

Respiratory Substrate	Average Energy Value (kJ g^{-1})
Carbohydrates	15.8
Lipids	39.4
Proteins	17.0

Figure 1: *The average energy values of different respiratory substrates.*

Respiratory quotients

When an organism respires a specific respiratory substrate, the respiratory quotient (RQ) can be worked out. The respiratory quotient is the volume of carbon dioxide produced when that substrate is respired, divided by the volume of oxygen consumed, in a set period of time. You calculate it using these equations:

$$RQ = \frac{\text{Volume of } CO_2 \text{ released}}{\text{Volume of } O_2 \text{ consumed}}$$ or $$RQ = \frac{\text{Molecules of } CO_2 \text{ released}}{\text{Molecules of } O_2 \text{ consumed}}$$

Example

You can work out the RQ for cells that only respire glucose.

First you need the basic equation for aerobic respiration:

$$C_6H_{12}O_6 + 6O_2 \rightarrow 6CO_2 + 6H_2O + energy$$

From the equation you can see that for every six molecules of oxygen consumed, six molecules of carbon dioxide are released.

So, you just need to plug these numbers into the RQ equation:

$$RQ \text{ for glucose} = \frac{\text{Molecules of } CO_2 \text{ released}}{\text{Molecules of } O_2 \text{ released}} = \frac{6}{6} = 1$$

Respiratory quotients have been worked out for the respiration of other respiratory substrates — see Figure 2. Lipids and proteins have an RQ value lower than one because more oxygen is needed to oxidise fats and lipids than to oxidise carbohydrates.

Respiratory substrate	RQ
Lipids (triglycerides)	0.7
Proteins or amino acids	0.9
Carbohydrates	1

Figure 2: *The respiratory quotients of different respiratory substrates.*

Learning Objectives:
- Know the difference in relative energy values of carbohydrates, lipids and proteins as respiratory substrates.
- Understand the use and interpretation of the respiratory quotient (RQ), including calculating the respiratory quotient using the formula:

$$RQ = \frac{CO_2 \; produced}{O_2 \; consumed}$$

Specification Reference 5.2.2

Exam Tip:
The two equations on the left mean the same thing. The volume of gas is equal to the number of molecules of that gas. In the exam you'll get the equation written in terms of volumes, but the other equation may be easier to use, as shown below.

Exam Tip
Make sure you know how to calculate a respiratory quotient — it could come up in the exam.

Tip: Oleic acid is a fatty acid. Fatty acids make up triglycerides (lipids), so you would expect oleic acid to have an RQ of about 0.7 looking at Figure 2. Like other lipids, oleic acid enters respiration at the Krebs cycle.

Figure 3: *This equipment measures O_2 intake and CO_2 output, which could be used to calculate the RQ of the man during exercise.*

Tip: Don't forget, carbohydrates have an RQ of 1, lipids have an RQ of about 0.7 and proteins have an RQ of around 0.9.

Example

Oleic acid ($C_{18}H_{34}O_2$) is a fatty acid that can be respired. The equation for aerobic respiration using oleic acid is:

$$2C_{18}H_{34}O_2 + 51O_2 \rightarrow 36CO_2 + 34H_2O + energy$$

So, the RQ for oleic acid = $\dfrac{\text{Molecules of } CO_2 \text{ released}}{\text{Molecules of } O_2 \text{ released}}$ = $\dfrac{36}{51}$ = 0.71

Uses of the respiratory quotient

You can work out the respiratory quotient for a whole organism as well as a particular substrate. The respiratory quotient for a whole organism is an average of all the respiratory quotients for all the different molecules the organism is respiring. You can work it out by directly measuring the volume of oxygen consumed and the volume of carbon dioxide released, and then putting these figures into the equation on the previous page.

The respiratory quotient for an organism is useful because it tells you what kind of respiratory substrate an organism is respiring and what type of respiration it's using (aerobic or anaerobic).

Examples

- Under normal conditions the usual RQ for humans is between 0.7 and 1.0. An RQ in this range shows that some fats (lipids) are being used for respiration, as well as carbohydrates like glucose. Protein isn't normally used by the body for respiration unless there's nothing else.

- High RQs (greater than 1) mean that an organism is short of oxygen, and is having to respire anaerobically as well as aerobically.

- Plants sometimes have a low RQ. This is because the CO_2 released in respiration is used for photosynthesis (so it's not measured).

Tip: The equation for calculating RQ is:

$\dfrac{\text{Volume of } CO_2 \text{ released}}{\text{Volume of } O_2 \text{ consumed}}$

Tip: Don't forget — you can use either the volumes of CO_2 and O_2, or the number of molecules of these gases, to work out the RQ.

Practice Questions — Application

Q1 The equation for the respiration of a mystery molecule is:
$$C_{57}H_{104}O_6 + 80O_2 \rightarrow 57CO_2 + 52H_2O$$
a) Calculate the respiratory quotient of the mystery molecule.
b) Suggest whether this molecule is a carbohydrate, a protein or a lipid. Explain your answer.

Q2 Robert consumes about 250 ml of O_2 per minute and releases around 180 ml of CO_2.
a) Calculate Robert's respiratory quotient.
b) Robert eats a bowl of pasta for lunch. After lunch, Robert's respiratory quotient increases to nearly 1. Suggest why.

Practice Questions — Fact Recall

Q1 What is a respiratory substrate?
Q2 Explain why lipids have a higher energy value than carbohydrates or proteins?
Q3 Which have the highest RQ — lipids, proteins or carbohydrates?
Q4 Why are the respiratory quotients of organisms useful?

4. Respiration Experiments

These pages give you some experiments that you could use to carry out investigations into the respiration rates of organisms.

Investigating the respiration rates of yeast

Yeast are single-celled organisms that can be grown in culture. They can respire aerobically when plenty of oxygen is available and anaerobically when oxygen isn't available. Both aerobic and anaerobic respiration (see page 139) in yeast produce CO_2. So the rate of CO_2 production gives an indication of the yeast's respiration rate. One way to measure CO_2 production is by using a gas syringe to collect the CO_2 as shown in the methods below:

> PRACTICAL ACTIVITY GROUP **4**
>
> PRACTICAL ACTIVITY GROUP **11**

Example — Aerobic Respiration

1. Put a known volume and concentration of substrate solution (e.g. glucose) in a test tube.

2. Add a known volume of buffer solution to keep the pH constant. (Choose the optimum pH for the yeast you're testing — usually 4-6.)

3. Place the test tube in a water bath set to 25 °C. This ensures that the temperature stays constant throughout the experiment. Leave it there for 10 minutes to allow the temperature of the substrate to stabilise.

4. Add a known mass of dried yeast (e.g. *Saccharomyces cerevisiae*) to the test tube and stir for two minutes.

5. After the yeast has dissolved into the solution, put a bung with a tube attached to a gas syringe in the top of the test tube. The gas syringe should be set to zero.

6. Start a stop watch as soon as the bung has been put in the test tube.

7. As the yeast respire, the CO_2 formed will travel up the tube and into the gas syringe, which is used to measure the volume of CO_2 released.

8. At regular time intervals (e.g. every minute), record the volume of CO_2 that is present in the gas syringe. Do this for a set amount of time (e.g. 10 minutes).

9. A control experiment should also be set up, where no yeast is present. No CO_2 should be formed without the yeast.

10. Repeat the experiment three times. Use your data to calculate the mean rate of CO_2 production.

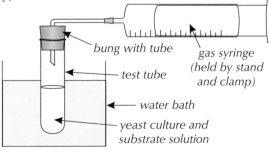

bung with tube
gas syringe (held by stand and clamp)
test tube
water bath
yeast culture and substrate solution

Figure 1: *Diagram showing how apparatus can be set up to measure aerobic respiration in yeast.*

Learning Objectives:

- Be able to carry out practical investigations into respiration rates in yeast, under aerobic and anaerobic conditions (PAG4, PAG11).

- Be able to carry out practical investigations into the effect of factors such as temperature, substrate concentration and different respiratory substrates on the rate of respiration (PAG4, PAG10, PAG11).

Specification Reference 5.2.2

Tip: Make sure you think about and address all the risks involved in the experiments on pages 143-146 before you carry them out.

Tip: A buffer solution is able to resist changes in pH when small amounts of acid or alkali are added.

Tip: The yeast will only respire aerobically until the oxygen trapped in the tube is all used up. If you wanted to run the experiment for more time or with more yeast or glucose, you could use a conical flask that can trap more oxygen.

Tip: To calculate the rate of CO_2 production, divide the total volume of CO_2 produced at a particular temperature by the number of minutes the apparatus was left for.

Tip: To test that the gas produced is definitely CO_2, connect the yeast and substrate solution to a test tube of limewater rather than a gas syringe. The limewater will turn cloudy in the presence of CO_2.

Tip: You could look up published results about the rate of respiration in yeast and see how they compare to yours. If there are any differences, you could try and work out what caused them and how you could improve the way you carried out your own experiment.

Example — Anaerobic Respiration

1. Set up the apparatus according to steps 1-4 of the experiment on the previous page.

2. After the yeast has dissolved into the substrate solution, trickle some liquid paraffin down the inside of the test tube so that it settles on and completely covers the surface of the solution. This will stop oxygen getting in, which will force the yeast to respire anaerobically.

3. Put a bung, with a tube attached to a gas syringe, in the top of the test tube. The gas syringe should be set to zero.

4. Perform steps 6-10 from the method on the previous page.

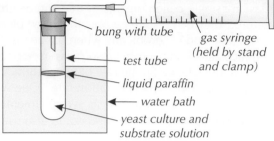

bung with tube
gas syringe (held by stand and clamp)
test tube
liquid paraffin
water bath
yeast culture and substrate solution

Figure 2: *Diagram showing how apparatus can be set up to measure anaerobic respiration in yeast.*

The only difference between these experiments is the presence or absence of oxygen, so you can directly compare your results for both experiments with each other to find out how the respiration rate of yeast under aerobic and anaerobic conditions differs.

You can also easily adapt these methods to investigate the effects of variables, such as temperature, substrate concentration and the use of different respiratory substrates (e.g. sucrose), on the respiration rate. For example, to investigate the effect of different temperatures on the respiration rate, you could perform the experiment with the test tubes in water baths set at different temperatures.

Practice Question — Application

Q1 A scientist is investigating the effect of pH on aerobic respiration in two different species of yeast. The mean rate of CO_2 production is indicative of the respiration rate. Her results are shown in the graph below.

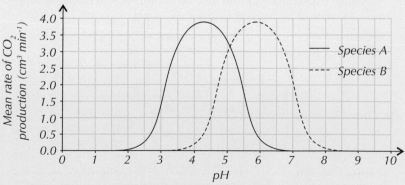

a) Describe an experiment the scientist could have done to obtain the results shown in the graph.

b) The results show that each species has a different optimum pH. Suggest an explanation for this.

c) At pH 5.5, how much faster is the mean rate of CO_2 production by species B than species A? Give your answer as a percentage.

d) The scientist also carried out the same experiment using boiled yeast of each species. Explain why.

Using a respirometer to measure oxygen consumption

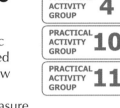

Respirometers can be used to indicate the rate of aerobic respiration by measuring the amount of oxygen consumed by an organism over a period of time. The example below shows how a respirometer can be used to measure the respiration rate of woodlice. You could also use it to measure the respiration rate of other small organisms or of plant seeds.

┌─ **Example** ──────────────────────────────

The apparatus is set up as shown below:

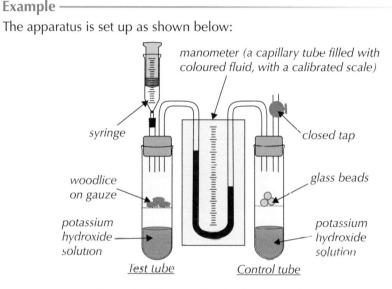

manometer (a capillary tube filled with coloured fluid, with a calibrated scale)

syringe

closed tap

woodlice on gauze

glass beads

potassium hydroxide solution

potassium hydroxide solution

Test tube   *Control tube*

Figure 3: *Diagram showing how a respirometer can be set up to measure oxygen consumption.*

Each tube contains potassium hydroxide solution, which absorbs carbon dioxide. The control tube is set up in exactly the same way as the test tube, but without the woodlice, to make sure the results are only due to the woodlice respiring (e.g. it contains beads that have the same mass as the woodlice). Coloured fluid is added to the manometer by dipping the end of the capillary tube into a beaker full of fluid. Capillary action will make the fluid move into the tube.

Here's how the experiment works:

1. The syringe is then used to set the fluid to a known level.

2. The apparatus is then left for a set period of time (e.g. 20 minutes). During that time, there'll be a decrease in the volume of air in the test tube, due to oxygen consumption by the woodlice (all the CO_2 produced is absorbed by the potassium hydroxide). The decrease in the volume of air will reduce the pressure in the tube and cause the coloured liquid in the manometer to move towards the test tube.

Figure 4: *A respirometer set up to measure the rate of respiration by germinating peas (left). Glass beads are being used as a control (right).*

Tip: This experiment has some limitations. For example, it can be difficult to accurately read the meniscus of the fluid in the manometer.

Tip: You can use a respirometer to investigate the effect of different factors on the rate of respiration by changing the independent variable.

3. The distance moved by the liquid in a given time is measured. This value can then be used to calculate the volume of oxygen taken in by the woodlice per minute. (You also need to know the diameter of the capillary tube in the manometer to do this.)

4. Any variables that could affect the results are controlled and kept the same (e.g. volume of potassium hydroxide and mass of woodlice).

5. To produce more precise results, the experiment is repeated and a mean volume of O_2 is calculated.

Using sensors and data loggers

Respirometers can be set up with an electronic oxygen sensor to measure the oxygen concentration inside the respirometer chamber at set intervals and also with data loggers to automatically record the data measured by the sensor. Using technology like this reduces the chance of human error when it comes to recording data. The data collected by the data logger can be put into data analysis software, which can help you to analyse your data and draw conclusions from your experiment.

(HOW SCIENCE WORKS)

Practice Questions — Fact Recall

Q1 If you were measuring anaerobic respiration in yeast, why would you add a layer of liquid paraffin to the yeast solution in the test tube before sealing the tube with a rubber bung?

Q2 Suggest a negative control experiment that could be included when measuring the rate of respiration of yeast in a test tube.

Q3 In a respirometer, what is the function of the potassium hydroxide solution?

Q4 If you were using a respirometer to measure the oxygen consumed by germinating peas with a mass of 10 g, what mass of glass beads would you have in the control tube?

Section Summary

Make sure you know...

- The structure and components of a mitochondrion, including the inner and outer mitochondrial membranes, cristae, mitochondrial matrix and mitochondrial DNA.

- That NAD and FAD are coenzymes that transfer hydrogen between molecules during respiration and that coenzyme A is a coenzyme that transfers acetate between molecules during respiration.

- That there are four stages of aerobic respiration — glycolysis, the link reaction, the Krebs cycle and oxidative phosphorylation.

- That glycolysis happens in the cytoplasm of a cell, and that the link reaction and the Krebs cycle occur in the mitochondrial matrix.

- That in glycolysis, ATP is used to phosphorylate glucose to hexose bisphosphate. Hexose bisphosphate then splits into two molecules of triose phosphate, which are then oxidised to pyruvate. There is a net gain of two ATP and two reduced NAD, per molecule of glucose. That in the link reaction, pyruvate is converted to acetate (via decarboxylation and the reduction of NAD). Then acetate is combined with coenzyme A to form acetyl coenzyme A.

- That in the Krebs cycle, acetyl coenzyme A (a 2C molecule) combines with oxaloacetate (4C) to produced citrate (6C). Citrate is decarboxylated and dehydrogenated to produce a 5-carbon compound, which is then used to regenerate oxaloacetate. During these reactions reduced NAD, reduced FAD, ATP and CO_2 are produced.

- That ATP is produced in the Krebs cycle by substrate-level phosphorylation — a phosphate group is directly transferred from an intermediate molecule to ADP.

- That oxidative phosphorylation occurs in the inner mitochondrial membrane.

- That oxidative phosphorylation uses electrons from reduced NAD and reduced FAD to make ATP. Electrons travel down the electron transport chain (which is made up of three electron carriers), losing energy at each carrier. This energy is used to form a proton gradient across the inner mitochondrial membrane. The protons then move down the concentration gradient through ATP synthase, making ATP by chemiosmosis (as described by the chemiosmotic theory).

- That oxygen is the final electron acceptor in aerobic respiration.

- That there are two types of anaerobic respiration (lactate fermentation and alcoholic fermentation) and the similarities between them — they both happen in the cytoplasm, they both produce 2 ATP per glucose molecule and they both start with glycolysis.

- The differences between lactate fermentation and alcoholic fermentation — lactate fermentation occurs in mammals and produces lactate, and alcoholic fermentation occurs in yeast cells and produces ethanol.

- That anaerobic respiration allows glycolysis to continue even when there's not much oxygen around, meaning that some ATP is still produced and some biological processes can continue.

- That anaerobic respiration produces a much lower yield of ATP than aerobic respiration because it only includes one energy releasing stage (glycolysis), which only produces 2 ATP per glucose molecule.

- That a respiratory substrate is any molecule that can be broken down in respiration to release energy.

- That lipids, carbohydrates and proteins have different relative energy values as respiratory substrates.

- How to calculate respiratory quotients.

- How to use the respiratory quotient of a whole organism to determine what respiratory substrates the organism is respiring or what type of respiration it is using.

- How to carry out investigations into respiration rates in yeast under aerobic and anaerobic conditions.

- How to carry out investigations into the effects of different factors on the rate of respiration.

- How to investigate an organism's respiration rate using a respirometer.

1   Petite mutants are yeast cells that have mutations in genes that are important for mitochondrial function. They are called petite mutants because they grow and divide to form unusually small colonies when grown in medium with a low glucose concentration. **Fig. 1.1** below shows the structure of a mitochondrion from a normal yeast cell and **Fig. 1.2** shows a mitochondrion from a petite mutant.

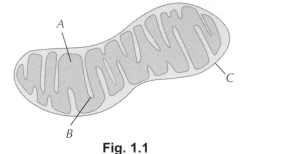

Fig. 1.1

Fig. 1.2

(a) (i) Name structures **A**, **B** and **C** in Fig. 1.1.

(3 marks)

    (ii) State how the structure of the mitochondrion in **Fig. 1.2** differs from that in **Fig. 1.1**.

(1 mark)

(b) (i) Petite mutants lack functioning mitochondria but they can still produce ATP by glycolysis. Explain why.

(1 mark)

    (ii) Hexose bisphosphate is an intermediate compound in glycolysis. Describe how hexose bisphosphate is formed from a molecule of glucose.

(3 marks)

    (iii) Describe the role of coenzyme NAD in glycolysis.

(2 marks)

(c)   Normal yeast cells can respire a range of different respiratory substrates, including glycerol ($C_3H_8O_3$). The equation for the respiration of glycerol is:

$$2C_3H_8O_3 + 7O_2 \rightarrow 6CO_2 + 8H_2O$$

The respiratory quotient (RQ) is defined as:

$$RQ = \frac{\text{Volume of } CO_2 \text{ released}}{\text{Volume of } O_2 \text{ consumed}}$$

Calculate the respiratory quotient of glycerol.

(2 marks)

2   The link reaction is a stage of aerobic respiration.
Which row correctly describes the link reaction?

	Site of reaction	Fate of NAD	Decarboxylation occurs?	Product of reaction
A	mitochondrial matrix	NAD is oxidised	yes	pyruvate
B	inner mitochondrial membrane	NAD is reduced	no	pyruvate
C	inner mitochondrial membrane	NAD is oxidised	no	acetyl CoA
D	mitochondrial matrix	NAD is reduced	yes	acetyl CoA

(1 mark)

3   **Fig. 3.1** shows a simplified version of the Krebs cycle.

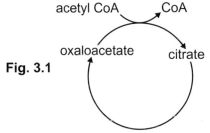

Fig. 3.1

Which row correctly shows the number of molecules of by-products produced as citrate is reconverted into oxaloacetate?

	CO_2	reduced NAD	reduced FAD	ATP
A	3	1	0	2
B	2	3	1	1
C	2	1	1	2
D	0	2	2	1

(1 mark)

4   In oxidative phosphorylation hydrogen atoms are released from reduced NAD and reduced FAD.

(a) (i)   Describe the reactions in respiration in which these reduced coenzymes are produced.

(5 marks)

(ii)   The hydrogen atoms split up into hydrogen ions and electrons.
Describe the movement of electrons in oxidative phosphorylation.

(3 marks)

(b)   DNP is an uncoupler. This means it carries H^+ ions from the intermembrane space back into the matrix of mitochondria during oxidative phosphorylation. Describe **and** explain the effect that DNP would have on the production of ATP in animal cells.

(4 marks)

Learning Objectives:

- Be able to explain the regulatory mechanisms that control gene expression at:
  - the transcriptional level (including transcription factors in eukaryotes and the *lac* operon),
  - post-transcriptional level (including the editing of primary mRNA and the removal of introns to produce mature mRNA),
  - post-translational level (including the activation of proteins by cyclic AMP).

  Specification Reference 6.1.1

Tip: You'll have covered transcription and translation in Module 2 in Year 1 of your course.

Tip: It's easy to remember what activators and repressors do — it's all in the name. Activators <u>activate</u> transcription and repressors <u>repress</u> transcription.

1. Regulating Gene Expression

In cells, genes are transcribed and then translated into proteins. This process is tightly controlled. When you think about it, it needs to be — the proteins that the genes code for determine all sorts, from the structure of the cell to the regulation of metabolic reactions.

Controlling gene expression

All the cells in an organism carry the same genes (DNA), but the structure and function of different cells varies. This is because not all the genes in a cell are expressed (transcribed and used to make a functional protein) — they are selectively switched on or off. Because cells show different gene expression, different proteins are made and these proteins modify the cell — they determine the cell structure and control cell processes (including the expression of more genes, which produce more proteins).

Gene expression (and therefore protein synthesis) can be controlled at the **transcriptional**, **post-transcriptional** and **post-translational** level. This happens via a number of different mechanisms.

Transcriptional level control

Gene expression can be controlled at the transcriptional level by altering the rate of transcription of genes. E.g. increased transcription produces more mRNA, which can be used to make more protein. This is controlled by **transcription factors** — proteins that bind to DNA and switch genes on or off by increasing or decreasing the rate of transcription. Factors that start transcription are called **activators** and those that stop transcription are called **repressors**.

The shape of a transcription factor determines whether it can bind to DNA or not, and can sometimes be altered by the binding of some molecules, e.g. certain hormones and sugars. This means the amount of some molecules in an environment or a cell can control the synthesis of some proteins by affecting transcription factor binding.

- In eukaryotes, transcription factors bind to specific DNA sites near the start of their target genes (see Figure 1) — these are the genes they control the expression of.

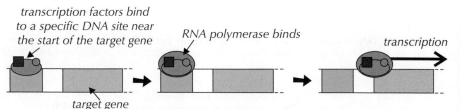

transcription factors bind to a specific DNA site near the start of the target gene

RNA polymerase binds

transcription

target gene

Figure 1: *Diagram to show a transcription factor activating transcription.*

- In prokaryotes control of gene expression often involves transcription factors binding to **operons** (see next page).

Operons

An operon is a section of DNA that contains a cluster of **structural genes** that are all transcribed together, as well as **control elements** and sometimes a **regulatory gene** — see Figure 2.

The structural genes code for useful proteins, such as enzymes. The control elements include a **promoter** (a DNA sequence located before the structural genes that RNA polymerase binds to) and an **operator** (a DNA sequence that transcription factors bind to). The regulatory gene codes for an activator or a repressor.

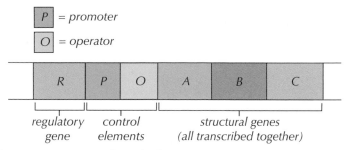

Figure 2: Diagram to show the basic structure of a prokaryotic operon.

Example — the *lac* operon in *E. coli*

E. coli is a bacterium that respires glucose, but it can use lactose if glucose isn't available. The genes that produce the enzymes needed to respire lactose are found on an operon called the *lac* operon. The *lac* operon has three structural genes — lacZ, lacY and lacA, which produce proteins that help the bacteria digest lactose (including β-**galactosidase** and **lactose permease**). Here's how it works:

Lactose NOT present

The regulatory gene (lacI) produces the lac repressor, which is a transcription factor that binds to the operator site when there's no lactose present. This blocks transcription because RNA polymerase can't bind to the promoter.

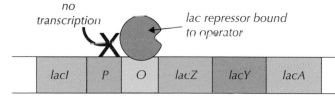

lacZ, lacY and lacA aren't transcribed

Lactose present

When lactose is present, it binds to the repressor, changing the repressor's shape so that it can no longer bind to the operator site. RNA polymerase can now begin transcription of the structural genes.

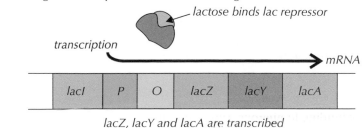

lacZ, lacY and lacA are transcribed

Exam Tip
You need to learn this example for your exam.

Tip: By binding to the operator, the lac repressor blocks RNA polymerase from binding to the promoter and beginning transcription.

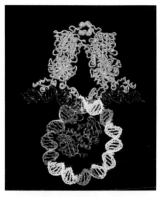

Figure 3: Molecular model of the lac repressor (pink) binding to DNA.

Post-transcriptional level control

Control of gene expression can also take place after genes have been transcribed. After transcription, mRNA in eukaryotic cells is edited — that's because genes in eukaryotic DNA contain sections that don't code for amino acids. These sections of DNA are called **introns**. All the bits that do code for amino acids are called **exons**.

During transcription the introns and exons are both copied into mRNA. mRNA strands containing introns and exons are called **primary mRNA transcripts** (or pre-mRNA). Introns are removed from primary mRNA strands by a process called splicing — introns are removed and the exons are joined together to form **mature mRNA** strands (see Figure 4). This takes place in the nucleus. The mature mRNA then leaves the nucleus for the next stage of protein synthesis (translation).

Tip: In prokaryotes, mRNA is produced directly from DNA without splicing taking place. There's no need for splicing because there are no introns in prokaryotic DNA.

Tip: The primary mRNA strand shown here is complementary to the bottom strand of the DNA sequence (the DNA template strand):

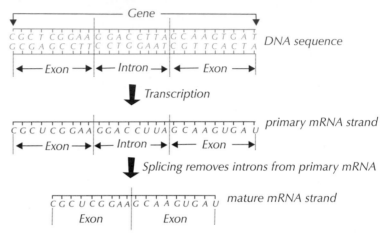

Figure 4: Primary mRNA is spliced to produce mature mRNA.

Post-translational level control

Some proteins aren't functional straight after they have been synthesised (i.e. after translation) — they need to be activated to work (become a functional protein). Like protein synthesis, protein activation is also controlled by molecules, e.g. hormones and sugars.

cAMP

Some molecules that control protein activation work by binding to cell membranes and triggering the production of **cyclic AMP** (cAMP) inside the cell. cAMP then activates proteins inside the cell by altering their three-dimensional (3D) structure. For example, altering the 3D structure can change the active site of an enzyme, making it become more or less active.

Tip: The control molecules (e.g. hormones) bind to specific protein receptors in the cell membrane.

Tip: cAMP is a second messenger — it relays the message from the control molecule to the inside of the cell (see pages 30-31).

--- Example — activation of protein kinase A (PKA) by cAMP ---

PKA is an enzyme made of four subunits. When cAMP isn't bound, the four units are bound together and are inactive. When cAMP binds, it causes a change in the enzyme's 3D structure, releasing the active subunits — PKA is now active.

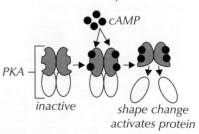

Practice Questions — Application

In the presence of lactose, normal *E. coli* produce the enzyme
β-galactosidase, which is coded for by a structural gene on the *lac* operon.
In the absence of lactose, β-galactosidase is not produced.

An experiment was carried out in which different *E. coli* mutants were
isolated and grown in media containing either lactose or glucose.
The mutants had mutations (changes in their DNA base sequence),
which meant they behaved differently to normal *E. coli*.

Tip: There's more on mutations on pages 157-159.

To detect whether the bacteria produced working β-galactosidase, a
chemical that turns yellow in the presence of active β-galactosidase was
added to the medium. The bacteria were left for some time, after which
the colour was recorded and the production of mRNA (that codes for
β-galactosidase) was measured. The results are shown in the table below.

Medium	Mutant	mRNA	Colour
Glucose	Normal	No	No yellow
Lactose	Normal	Yes	Yellow
Glucose	Mutant 1	Yes	Yellow
Lactose	Mutant 1	Yes	Yellow
Glucose	Mutant 2	No	No yellow
Lactose	Mutant 2	Yes	No yellow

Q1 Suggest three variables that should have been controlled in this
experiment.

Q2 Explain why normal *E. coli* bacteria were included in this test.

Q3 Describe and suggest an explanation for:

    a) the Mutant 1 results,

    b) the Mutant 2 results.

Q4 A different group of scientists also carried out the experiment using
the same method and *E. coli* mutants. They achieved very similar
results. What does this suggest about the results of this experiment?

Tip: Remember, variables are quantities that have the potential to change. There's more about variables on p. 3.

Practice Questions — Fact Recall

Q1 a) What is a transcription factor?

    b) Explain what the two types of transcription factor do.

    c) Describe where transcription factors bind
in eukaryotic gene expression.

Q2 Describe the function of the following parts of an operon:

    a) structural genes,

    b) control elements,

    c) a regulatory gene.

Q3 Describe how the *lac* operon controls protein
production in *E. coli* when lactose is not present.

Q4 In eukaryotes, mRNA is edited before translation.
What is the result of this?

Q5 Describe how molecules like hormones control protein activation.

Tip: *Drosophila* are 'model organisms' — scientists use them to study how genes control development, then apply their findings to other, more complex animals (like humans).

Figure 2: *A mutation in a Hox gene has caused this* Drosophila *to grow legs in place of antennae. This shows that Hox genes are important in development.*

2. Body Plans

The development of an organism follows a careful plan, controlled by proteins. Some of these proteins activate (start) or repress (stop) transcription of developmental genes. Other proteins cause unneeded cells to break down and die.

Body plans and Hox genes

A body plan is the general structure of an organism.

> **Example**
>
> The *Drosophila* fruit fly has various body parts (head, abdomen, etc.) that are arranged in a particular way — this is its body plan.

Proteins control the development of a body plan — they help set up the basic body plan so that everything is in the right place, e.g. legs grow where legs should grow. The proteins that control body plan development are coded for by genes called **Hox genes**.

> **Example**
>
> Two Hox gene clusters control the development of the *Drosophila* body plan — one controls the development of the head and anterior thorax (yellow in Figure 1) and the other controls the development of the posterior thorax and abdomen (red in Figure 1).

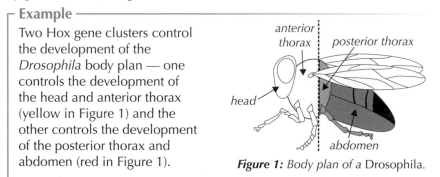

Figure 1: *Body plan of a* Drosophila.

Similar Hox genes are found in animals, plants and fungi, which means that body plan development is controlled in a similar way in flies, mice, humans, etc. Hox genes have regions called **homeobox sequences**, which are highly conserved — this means that these sequences have changed very little during the evolution of different organisms that possess these homeobox sequences.

How do Hox genes control development?

Homeobox sequences code for a part of the protein called the **homeodomain**. The homeodomain binds to specific sites on DNA, enabling the protein to work as a transcription factor (see page 150). The proteins bind to DNA at the start of developmental genes, activating or repressing transcription and so altering the production of proteins involved in the development of the body plan (see Figure 3).

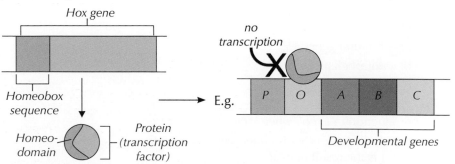

Figure 3: *Diagram to show how a protein coded for by a Hox gene may act as a transcription factor to repress the transcription of developmental genes.*

Mitosis and apoptosis

Both mitosis (part of the cell cycle where one cell divides to form two daughter cells) and apoptosis are involved in the development of body plans.

What is apoptosis?

Some cells die and break down as a normal part of development. This is a highly controlled process called **apoptosis**, or programmed cell death. Once apoptosis has been triggered the cell is broken down in a series of steps. These steps are shown in Figure 4.

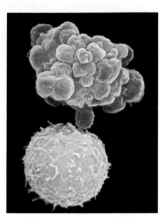

Figure 5: A normal white blood cell (bottom) and one undergoing apoptosis (top). The cell membrane of the apoptotic cell has formed blebs (round blobs).

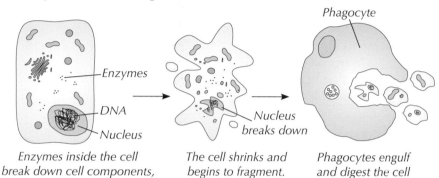

Phagocyte

Enzymes

DNA

Nucleus

Nucleus breaks down

Enzymes inside the cell break down cell components, e.g. proteins, DNA.

The cell shrinks and begins to fragment.

Phagocytes engulf and digest the cell fragments.

Figure 4: The main steps in apoptosis.

The roles of mitosis and apoptosis in development

Mitosis and differentiation create the bulk of the body parts and then apoptosis refines the parts by removing unwanted structures.

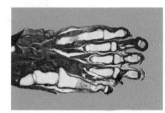

Figure 6: Light micrograph of a developing human hand. You can still see the connecting tissue between the fingers that would eventually undergo apoptosis.

> ### Examples
>
> - When hands and feet first develop in humans, the digits (fingers and toes) are connected. They're only separated when cells in the connecting tissue undergo apoptosis.
> - As tadpoles develop into frogs, their tail cells are removed by apoptosis.
> - An excess of nerve cells are produced during the development of the nervous system. Nerve cells that aren't needed undergo apoptosis.

During development, genes that control mitosis and genes that control apoptosis are switched on and off in appropriate cells. This means that some new cells are produced whilst some cells die, and the correct body plan develops.

Responses of genes that regulate the cell cycle and apoptosis

The genes that regulate progression through the cell cycle (e.g. cells undergoing mitosis) and apoptosis can respond to both internal and external stimuli.

Figure 7: A developing tadpole. The tail will be lost as the cells undergo apoptosis.

> ### Examples
>
> - An internal stimulus could be DNA damage. If DNA damage is detected during the cell cycle, this can result in the expression of genes which cause the cycle to be paused and can even trigger apoptosis.
> - An external stimulus, such as stress caused by a lack of nutrient availability, could result in gene expression that prevents cells from undergoing mitosis. Gene expression which leads to apoptosis being triggered can also be caused by an external stimulus such as attack by a pathogen.

Figure 8: Arabidopsis thaliana.

Practice Questions — Application

Q1 It is thought that the process of apoptosis may play a role in plant development.

   a) What is the end result of apoptosis?

   b) Suggest how apoptosis may affect plant development.

Q2 Several studies have been carried out into the development of the plant *Arabidopsis thaliana*.

It has been found that a change to the base sequence of the ag-1 gene affects flower development in *Arabidopsis thaliana* — the change causes petals to grow in place of stamens (the long, thin structures that produce pollen).

   a) Using the information given above, explain why ag-1 is classed as a Hox gene.

   b) Ag-1 contains a homeobox sequence. Explain how a homeobox sequence helps to control an organism's development.

   c) Explain why studying *Arabidopsis thaliana* could help scientists to understand development in a wide range of organisms, not just plants.

Practice Questions — Fact Recall

Q1 What is a body plan?

Q2 Name the genes that control the development of a body plan.

Q3 Explain why development of body plans is similar in animals, plants and fungi.

Q4 Outline the process of apoptosis.

Q5 Explain how mitosis is involved in the development of body plans.

Q6 State the two types of stimuli that genes regulating the cell cycle and apoptosis can respond to and give an example of each.

3. Gene Mutations

Learning Objectives:
- Recall types of gene mutations and their possible effects on protein function and production, including substitution, insertion or deletion of one or more nucleotides.
- Be able to explain the possible effects of these gene mutations (i.e. beneficial, neutral or harmful).

Specification Reference 6.1.1

Genes are pretty awesome. However, their base sequences can sometimes be mutated, changing the protein that gets produced.

What are mutations?

Any change to the base (nucleotide) sequence of DNA is called a **mutation**. The types of mutations that can occur include:

- **Substitution** — one or more bases are swapped for another base, e.g. ATGCCT becomes ATTCCT (G is swapped for T).

- **Deletion** — one or more bases are removed, e.g. ATGCCT becomes ATCT (GC is removed).

- **Insertion** — one or more bases are added, e.g. ATGCCT becomes ATGACCT (A is added).

The order of DNA bases in a gene determines the order of amino acids in a particular protein. If a mutation occurs in a gene, the primary structure (amino acid chain) of the protein it codes for could be altered.

Tip: Mutations can occur spontaneously (e.g. through errors in DNA replication), but exposure to mutagenic agents (e.g. UV light, ionising radiation and certain chemicals) may increase the rate at which mutations occur.

Example

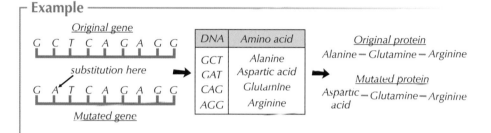

DNA	Amino acid
GCT	Alanine
GAT	Aspartic acid
CAG	Glutamine
AGG	Arginine

A change in the primary structure may change the final 3D shape of the protein so it doesn't work properly, e.g. active sites in enzymes may not form properly, meaning that substrates can't bind to them. Mutations might also result in a protein not being produced at all (see page 159).

Tip: For a protein with a single polypeptide chain, the final 3D shape is called the tertiary structure.

Frameshift mutations

Some mutations can have a huge effect on the base sequence of a gene. For example, adding or deleting a base changes the number of bases present, causing a shift in all the base triplets that follow. This is called a frameshift mutation — when an insertion or deletion changes the way the rest of the base sequence is read. The earlier a frameshift mutation appears in the base sequence, the more amino acids are affected and the greater the mutation's effect on the protein.

Tip: If the number of bases added or removed is a multiple of three, it won't cause a frameshift mutation because the triplets that follow the mutation will still be read correctly. So a deletion of three bases might actually affect a protein less seriously than the deletion of one base.

Examples

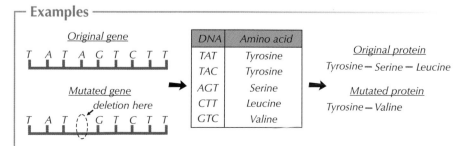

DNA	Amino acid
TAT	Tyrosine
TAC	Tyrosine
AGT	Serine
CTT	Leucine
GTC	Valine

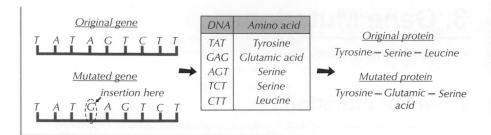

DNA	Amino acid
TAT	Tyrosine
GAG	Glutamic acid
AGT	Serine
TCT	Serine
CTT	Leucine

Original gene: T A T A G T C T T

Mutated gene (insertion here): T A T G A G T C T

Original protein: Tyrosine — Serine — Leucine

Mutated protein: Tyrosine — Glutamic acid — Serine

Exam Tip
You could be asked to predict how much a mutation will affect a protein's structure. Just remember that a frameshift mutation affects more amino acids than a substitution mutation, so it will have a bigger overall effect on the protein's structure.

Tip: A substitution mutation is more likely to have a neutral effect on a protein than a frameshift mutation because it only affects one amino acid.

Mutations that don't affect an organism

Different mutations affect proteins in different ways. Some mutations can have a **neutral** effect on a protein's function. They may have a neutral effect because:

- The mutation changes a base in a triplet, but the amino acid that the triplet codes for doesn't change. This happens because some amino acids are coded for by more than one triplet.

Example
Both TAT and TAC code for tyrosine, so if TAT is changed to TAC the amino acid won't change.

- The mutation produces a triplet that codes for a different amino acid, but the amino acid is chemically similar to the original so it functions like the original amino acid.

Example
Arginine (AGG) and lysine (AAG) are coded for by similar triplets — a substitution mutation can swap the amino acids. But this mutation could have a neutral effect on a protein as the amino acids are chemically similar.

- The mutated triplet codes for an amino acid not involved with the protein's function.

Example
If the affected amino acid is located far away from an enzyme's active site, the protein will work as it normally does.

A neutral effect on protein function won't affect an organism overall.

Mutations that do affect an organism

Some mutations do affect a protein's function — they can make a protein more or less active, e.g. by changing the shape of an enzyme's active site. If protein function is affected it can have a **beneficial** or **harmful** effect on the whole organism.

Mutations with beneficial effects

These have an advantageous effect on an organism, i.e. they increase its chance of survival.

Tip: Just to confuse things, some mutations alter a protein's function, but the effect is neither harmful nor beneficial to the whole organism. This means that the mutation doesn't affect the organism's chances of survival.

Example
Some bacterial enzymes break down certain antibiotics. Mutations in the genes that code for these enzymes could make them work on a wider range of antibiotics. This is beneficial to the bacteria because antibiotic resistance can help them to survive.

Mutations that are beneficial to the organism are passed on to future generations by the process of natural selection.

Mutations with harmful effects

These have a disadvantageous effect on an organism, i.e. they decrease its chance of survival.

┌─ Examples ───

- Cystic fibrosis (CF) can be caused by a deletion of three bases in the gene that codes for the CFTR (cystic fibrosis transmembrane conductance regulator) protein. The mutated CFTR protein folds incorrectly, so it's broken down. This leads to excess mucus production, which affects the lungs of CF sufferers.

- Certain mutations in the BRCA1 gene can increase the risk of developing breast cancer. BRCA1 produces a protein that helps to repair breaks in DNA. But mutations in the BRCA1 gene itself can result in a very short protein that can't do its job. This may lead to uncontrolled cell division and the development of cancer.

Mutations can also affect whether or not a protein is produced. E.g. if a mutation occurs at the start of a gene, so that RNA polymerase can't bind to it and begin transcription, the protein coded for by the gene won't be made. The loss of production of a protein can have harmful effects — some genetic disorders are caused by this.

┌─ Example ───

The HBB gene codes for the beta-globin protein, which is a component of haemoglobin. The genetic disorder beta thalassaemia can be caused by a mutation in the region of the HBB gene where transcription is initiated. A mutation in this region leads to little or no production of beta-globin, which leads to low levels of haemoglobin. As a result, red blood cell development is disrupted and less oxygen can be transported to the body's cells.

Practice Questions — Application

The table below shows some amino acids and the base triplets that code for them. The following letters represent part of the DNA base sequence of a gene:

CTTCATGATACA

Look at the four mutated base sequences below.

Mutation A: CTCCATGATACA

Mutation B: CTTCATCATACA

Mutation C: CTTATGATACA

Mutation D: CTTTATCATGATACA

Base Triplet(s)	Amino Acid
GAT	Asp
CAT	His
ATA	Ile
CTT/CTC	Leu
ATG	Met
ACA	Thr
TAT	Tyr

Q1 For each of the base sequences:

a) State the type of mutation that has taken place.

b) Give the amino acid sequence coded for by the mutated gene.

Q2 Explain which mutation is likely to have:

a) the least serious effect on the structure of the protein produced,

b) the most serious effect on the structure of the protein produced.

Tip: Natural selection is the process by which heritable characteristics in a population change over time due to selection pressures. If an individual has an allele which increases their chance of survival (which could have arisen by mutation), it's more likely to reproduce and pass on this advantageous allele to its offspring. So the frequency of this allele is likely to increase from generation to generation — see page 190.

Tip: Beta thalassaemia can have some severe symptoms. These include weakness, shortness of breath, abnormal bone development and growth problems (i.e. children failing to grow at a normal rate).

Exam Tip
If you're asked how a mutation affects protein structure in the exam, don't fall into the trap of only writing about how the mutation will change the base sequence. Make sure you make it clear how the altered base sequence will affect both the amino acid sequence and the protein's structure.

Practice Questions — Fact Recall

Q1   What is a mutation?

Q2   Give three ways in which a mutation may have a neutral effect on the protein produced by a gene.

Q3   Explain how a mutation may be beneficial to an organism.

Q4   Give one example of how a mutation can lead to a protein not being produced.

Section Summary

Make sure you know...

- That there are regulatory mechanisms that control gene expression (and therefore protein synthesis) at three different levels: the transcriptional level, the post-transcriptional level and the post-translational level.

- That at the transcriptional level, the control of gene expression in eukaryotes involves transcription factors, and in prokaryotes (e.g. bacteria) it often involves operons (sections of DNA that contain structural genes, control elements and sometimes a regulatory gene).

- How the *lac* operon in *E. coli* controls the production of the enzymes needed to respire lactose — the genes that code for the enzymes are only switched on (transcribed) in the presence of lactose.

- That at the post-transcriptional level, gene expression is controlled by the editing of primary mRNA. Introns are removed from primary mRNA (by a process called splicing) to produce mature mRNA.

- That the post-translational control of gene expression includes some proteins being activated before they can work. An example of this is the activation of proteins by cyclic AMP (cAMP) — cAMP activates proteins by altering their 3D structure.

- That a body plan is the general structure of an organism.

- That the development of the body plan in animals, plants and fungi is controlled in a similar way, by a similar group of genes called Hox genes.

- That the homeobox sequences within Hox genes are very similar in animals, plants and fungi, and these sequences have changed very little during evolution.

- How Hox genes and the homeobox sequences they contain control the development of body plans by regulating transcription.

- That apoptosis (programmed cell death) is a highly controlled process that leads to cells being broken down in stages.

- How mitosis and apoptosis are important mechanisms involved in the development of different parts of the body — mitosis (and cell differentiation) creates the bulk of body parts and then apoptosis can refine these parts by removing unwanted structures.

- That the genes that regulate the cell cycle (including mitosis) and apoptosis are able to respond to internal cell stimuli (e.g. DNA damage) and external stimuli (e.g. stress).

- That gene mutations are changes to the base (nucleotide) sequence of DNA. These can affect protein function by altering the amino acid sequence (primary structure), and whether a protein is produced at all.

- That substitution mutations involve one base being swapped for another, insertion mutations involve one or more nucleotides being added, and deletion mutations involve one or more nucleotides being removed.

- How gene mutations can have neutral, beneficial or harmful effects on an organism.

Exam-style Questions

1 Which of the following statements is/are true?

Statement 1: The homeobox sequences found in Hox genes are highly conserved.

Statement 2: Mutations in Hox genes can cause developmental abnormalities.

Statement 3: Identical Hox genes are found in all living things.

A 1, 2 and 3

B Only 1 and 2

C Only 2 and 3

D Only 1

(1 mark)

2 Glucagon is a hormone involved in the regulation of the blood glucose level in humans. It controls protein activation in a cell via the secondary messenger cAMP.

(a) Glucagon is a protein.
How is the order of amino acids in glucagon determined?

(1 mark)

(b) Suggest how glucagon could control the activation of a protein via cAMP.

(2 marks)

(c) cAMP is also involved in the regulation of the *lac* operon in *E. coli*.

When the concentration of glucose is low, cAMP activates the protein CRP. CRP helps RNA polymerase bind to the promoter at the start of the operon.

Explain how this helps *E. coli* to continue respiring when the concentration of glucose is low, but lactose is present

(3 marks)

3 A mutation in the APC gene is found in the majority of colon cancers.
The mutation prevents the protein produced from carrying out its function.

(a) Mutations that result in a non-functioning APC protein are usually caused by **base deletions**.
Explain how the deletion of a single base could result in a non-functioning protein.

(3 marks)

(b) Explain why a single-base **substitution** in a gene may have a less serious effect on the gene's protein structure than a single-base deletion.

(2 marks)

(c) Mutations in the APC gene that lead to the development of colon cancer have a harmful effect on a person. Explain how other mutations may have a **neutral effect** on an organism.

(4 marks)

Learning Objectives:

- Understand the genetic basis of continuous and discontinuous variation, including reference to the number of genes that influence each type of variation.

- Be able to explain how sexual reproduction can lead to genetic variation within a species, including meiosis and the random fusion of gametes at fertilisation.

- Understand the contribution of both environmental and genetic factors to phenotypic variation.

- Recall examples of both genetic and environmental contributions to phenotypic variation, e.g. diet in animals and etiolation or chlorosis in plants as environmental examples.

Specification Reference 6.1.2

1. Types and Causes of Variation

You might remember learning about variation in Module 4... Here it is again, but you need to know it in a bit more detail now.

Continuous variation

Continuous variation is when the individuals in a population vary within a range — there are no distinct categories.

Examples

- Height — humans can be any height within a range (e.g. 139 cm, 175 cm, 185.9 cm, etc.), not just tall or short — see Figure 1.

- Waist circumference — humans can have any waist size within a range.

- Fur length — dogs can have any length of fur within a range.

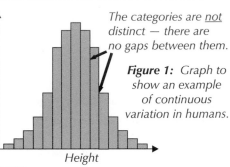

The categories are <u>not</u> distinct — there are no gaps between them.

Figure 1: *Graph to show an example of continuous variation in humans.*

Continuous variation can be shown by continuous data. Continuous data is quantitative — this means it has values that can be measured with a number.

Discontinuous variation

Discontinuous variation is when there are two or more distinct categories — each individual falls into only one of these categories, there are no intermediates.

Examples

- Blood group — humans can be group A, B, AB or O (see Figure 2).

- Violet flower colour — violets can either be coloured or white.

- Tongue-rolling ability — you can either roll your tongue or you can't.

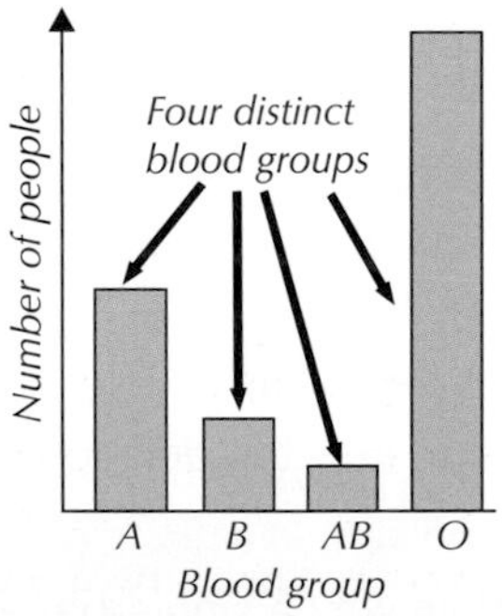

Four distinct blood groups

Figure 2: *Graph to show an example of discontinuous variation in humans.*

Discontinuous variation can be shown by qualitative data — this is data that doesn't contain any numbers.

Phenotypic variation

Phenotypic variation is the variation in an organism's **phenotype** (i.e. the characteristics it displays, see page 165). Phenotypic variation is influenced by different factors — see next page.

Figure 3: *Tongue-rolling ability is an example of a characteristic that shows discontinuous variation.*

Tip: Characteristics are sometimes described as phenotypic traits.

1. Genotype

Different species have different genes. Individuals of the same species have the same genes, but different **alleles** (versions of genes). The genes and alleles of an organism make up its genotype (see page 165).

Sexual reproduction leads to variation in genotypes within a species. **Meiosis** makes gametes with a unique assortment of alleles through crossing-over and the independent assortment of chromosomes. The random fusion of gametes during fertilisation also increases genetic variation in the offspring. Differences in genotype result in phenotypic variation.

─ Example ─────────────────────

Human blood group — there are three different blood group alleles, which result in four different blood groups.

Inherited characteristics that show continuous variation are usually influenced by many genes — these characteristics are said to be **polygenic**.

─ Example ─────────────────────

Human skin colour is polygenic — it comes in loads of different shades of colour.

Inherited characteristics that show discontinuous variation are usually influenced by only one gene (or a small number of genes). Characteristics controlled by only one gene are said to be **monogenic**.

─ Example ─────────────────────

Violet flower colour (either coloured or white) is controlled by only one gene.

Tip: You'll have covered how meiosis leads to genetic variation back in Module 2 — have a look back at your notes if you need a reminder of how it works.

Tip: 'Poly' means 'many' and 'mono' means 'one' — so 'polygenic' means 'many genes' and 'monogenic' means 'one gene'. Simple.

Tip: Blood group is also a monogenic characteristic. It's only controlled by one gene (there just happen to be a few different alleles of that gene — see page 171 for more on this).

2. The environment

Phenotypic variation can also be caused by differences in the environment, e.g. climate, food, lifestyle. Characteristics controlled by environmental factors can change over an organism's life.

─ Examples ─────────────────────

- Etiolation — this is when plants grow abnormally long and spindly because they're not getting enough light.

- Chlorosis — this is when plants don't produce enough chlorophyll and turn yellow (see Figure 4). It's caused by several environmental factors, e.g. a lack of magnesium in soil.

3. Genotype and the environment

Genotype tends to influence the characteristics an organism is born with, but environmental factors can influence how some characteristics develop. Most phenotypic variation is caused by the combination of genotype and environmental factors. Phenotypic variation influenced by both usually shows continuous variation.

─ Example 1 — Body mass in animals ─────────────

Body mass is partly genetic but it's also strongly influenced by environmental factors, like diet. For example, if your diet doesn't contain enough of the right nutrients, your body mass is likely to be lower than that determined by your genes. Body mass varies within a range, so it's continuous variation.

Figure 4: *Chlorosis of a camellia plant due to iron deficiency.*

Example 2 — Height of pea plants

Pea plants come in tall and dwarf forms (discontinuous variation, see Figure 5), which is determined by genotype. However, the exact height of the tall and dwarf plants varies (continuous variation) because of environmental factors (e.g. light intensity and water availability affect how tall a plant grows).

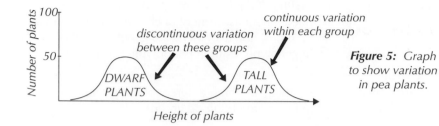

Figure 5: Graph to show variation in pea plants.

Practice Questions — Application

Tip: Monoamines are a type of chemical with one amine group (NH_2).

Q1 MAOA is an enzyme that breaks down monoamines in humans. Low levels of MAOA have been linked to mental health problems. MAOA production is controlled by a single gene, but taking anti-depressants or smoking tobacco can reduce the amount produced.

   a) Is MAOA production monogenic or polygenic?

   b) Patient X has mental health problems linked to low MAOA levels. Are these problems likely to be due to the patient's genotype, the environment or both? Explain your answer.

Q2 A study was conducted into how temperature affects the percentage germination of seeds of one type of plant. Seeds of three different genotypes of the plant were each grown at three different temperatures, and the mean percentage germination was recorded. The results are shown in the graph below.

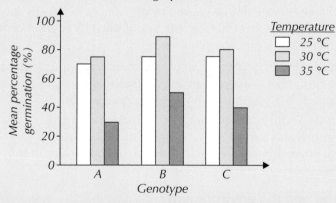

What can be concluded about the influence of genotype and environmental factors on the mean percentage germination of seeds? Give evidence from the study to support your answer.

Practice Questions — Fact Recall

Q1 Are traits that show continuous variation usually monogenic or polygenic?

Q2 What is etiolation?

Q3 What type of variation do traits that are influenced by both genotype and the environment tend to show?

2. Genetic Terms

Inheritance is all about how you got the genes you have and how likely you are to pass them on to your children. To help you understand the rest of this section, you really need to get to grips with the basic terms described below.

Basic terms and definitions

Genes and alleles

A **gene** is a sequence of bases on a DNA molecule that codes for a protein (polypeptide) which results in a characteristic.

You can have one or more versions of the same gene. These different versions are called **alleles**. The order of bases in each allele is slightly different — that's because each allele codes for different versions of the same characteristic. Alleles are represented using letters.

> **Tip:** 'Codes for' means 'contains the instructions for'.

> **Tip:** A base is a nitrogen-containing molecule that forms part of a DNA nucleotide.

Examples

- There are many different alleles for eye colour. The allele for brown eyes is shown using a B, and the allele for blue eyes uses b.
- Pea plants have a gene for seed shape. The allele for a round seed shape is shown using R, and the allele for wrinkled seed shape uses r.

Most plants and animals, including humans, have two alleles of each gene, one from each parent. That's because we inherit one copy of each chromosome of a pair from our parents. The allele of each gene is found at a fixed position, called a **locus**, on each chromosome in a pair (see Figure 1).

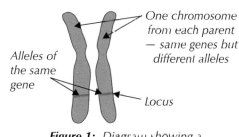

One chromosome from each parent — same genes but different alleles

Alleles of the same gene

Locus

Figure 1: Diagram showing a locus on a pair of chromosomes.

Genotype

The genotype of an organism is the alleles it has. This could be a list of all its alleles but usually it's just the alleles for one characteristic at a time.

Examples

- One person may have the genotype BB for eye colour and another person Bb.
- One pea plant might have the genotype RR for seed shape and another pea plant rr.

Phenotype

The phenotype of an organism is the characteristics the alleles produce.

Examples

- One person may have brown eyes and another may have blue eyes.
- One pea plant may have round seeds and another may have wrinkled seeds.

> **Tip:** The phenotype of an organism can't always be seen. E.g. your metabolic rate (how fast your metabolic reactions are) is a phenotype but you can't see it.

Homozygous and heterozygous

If an organism carries two copies of the same allele it's said to be homozygous. If an organism carries two different alleles then it's heterozygous.

Dominant and recessive alleles

An allele whose characteristic appears in the phenotype even when there's only one copy is called a dominant allele. Dominant alleles are shown by a capital letter. Recessive alleles are those whose characteristics only appear in the phenotype if two copies are present. They're shown by lower case letters.

Examples
- The allele for brown eyes, B, is dominant, so if a person's genotype is Bb or BB they'll have brown eyes. The allele for blue eyes, b, is recessive, so a person will only have blue eyes if their genotype is bb.
- The allele for round seed shape, R, is dominant, so if a pea plant's genotype is Rr or RR it will have round seeds. The allele for wrinkled seed shape, r, is recessive, so a pea plant will only have wrinkled seeds if its genotype is rr.

Codominant alleles

Some alleles are both expressed in the phenotype because neither one is recessive. They are said to be codominant alleles.

Examples
- Horses can have alleles for white hair or coloured hair. Neither allele is recessive, so a horse with one copy of each allele will have a roan coat — a coat with a mixture of white hairs and coloured hairs.
- The alleles for haemoglobin are codominant because they're both expressed in the phenotype (see page 169).

Figure 2: *A horse with a roan coat.*

Carrier

A carrier is a person carrying an allele which is not expressed in the phenotype but that can be passed on to offspring.

Example
Cystic fibrosis is an inherited disease caused by a mutation in the CFTR gene. It's a recessive disease, so both CFTR alleles have to be mutated for someone to get the disease. If someone has one mutated CFTR allele and one normal CFTR allele, they won't have cystic fibrosis but they will be a carrier of the disease.

Practice Questions — Application

Q1 In owl monkeys, the allele T codes for a tufted tail and t codes for a non-tufted tail. For each of the following genotypes, give the owl monkey's phenotype: A — Tt, B — TT, C — tt.

Q2 The yellow colour pea seed allele is dominant to the green allele.
- a) What would be the phenotype of a pea seed with the genotype Yy?
- b) Give the genotype of a homozygous pea seed that's yellow.
- c) Give the genotype of a green pea seed.

3. Genetic Diagrams — Monogenic Crosses

Learning Objective:

- Be able to use genetic diagrams to show patterns of inheritance, including monogenic inheritance and codominance.

Specification Reference 6.1.2

Genetic diagrams show how alleles could be passed on to the next generation.

What are genetic diagrams?

The body cells of individuals have two alleles for each gene. Gametes (sex cells) contain only one allele for each gene. When gametes from two parents fuse together, the alleles they contain form the genotype of the offspring produced.

Genetic diagrams show the possible genotypes of offspring, so they can be used to predict the genotypes and phenotypes of the offspring that would be produced if two parents are crossed (bred). You need to know how to use genetic diagrams to predict the results of various crosses, including **monogenic crosses**.

Tip: Monogenic inheritance is sometimes called monohybrid inheritance.

Monogenic inheritance

Monogenic inheritance is the inheritance of a characteristic controlled by a single gene. Monogenic crosses show the likelihood of the different alleles of that gene (and so different versions of the characteristic) being inherited by offspring of particular parents. The example below shows how wing length can be inherited in fruit flies.

Figure 1a: Photo of a fruit fly with normal wings.

— **Example** —

The allele for normal wings is dominant, so it's shown by a capital letter N. Any flies that have even one N allele will have normal wings. The allele for vestigial (little) wings is recessive, so it's shown by the letter n. Only flies that have two n alleles will have vestigial wings.

The genetic diagram in Figure 2 shows a cross between one homozygous parent with normal wings (NN) and one homozygous parent with vestigial wings (nn). The normal winged parent can only produce gametes with the allele for normal wings (N). The vestigial winged parent can only produce gametes with the allele for vestigial wings (n).

Here's how to draw a genetic diagram for this cross:

Step 1: Make sure you're clear what the letters mean.

Step 2: Show the parents' genotype at the top.

Step 3: The middle circles show the possible gametes. Put one of each letter into a circle.

Step 4: The lines show all the possible ways the gametes could combine. Fill in the possible combinations in the bottom boxes.

Figure 1b: Photo of a fruit fly with vestigial wings.

N — normal wings allele

n — vestigial (little) wings allele

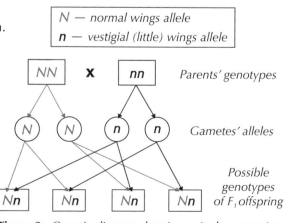

Parents' genotypes

Gametes' alleles

Possible genotypes of F₁ offspring

Tip: The first set of offspring is called the F_1 generation.

Figure 2: Genetic diagram showing a single generation monogenic cross between homozygous parents.

All offspring produced are heterozygous (Nn), as one allele is inherited from each parent.

Tip: A monogenic cross with two homozygous parents will <u>always</u> produce <u>all heterozygous</u> offspring in the F_1 generation.

The genetic diagram in Figure 3 shows a cross between two parents from the F_1 generation (both heterozygous). Just follow the same steps as on the previous page, but this time the gametes produced by each F_1 offspring may contain the allele for either normal (N) or vestigial wings (n).

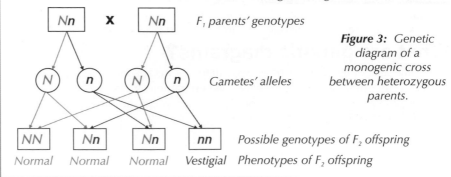

Figure 3: Genetic diagram of a monogenic cross between heterozygous parents.

Phenotypic ratios

The phenotypic ratio is the ratio of different phenotypes in the offspring. Genetic diagrams allow you to predict the phenotypic ratios in F_1 and F_2 offspring.

Example —— Maths Skills

Using the example above, there's a 75% chance the F_2 offspring will have the normal wings phenotype (genotype NN or Nn) and a 25% chance they'll have the vestigial wings phenotype (genotype nn). So you'd expect a 3 : 1 ratio of normal : vestigial wings in the offspring. This is the phenotypic ratio.

Usually whenever you do a monogenic cross with two heterozygous parents you get a 3 : 1 ratio of dominant : recessive characteristics. However, sometimes you won't get the expected (predicted) phenotypic ratio. This can be because of linkage (see pages 174-177) epistasis (see pages 179-181).

Punnett squares

A Punnett square is just another way of showing a genetic diagram. The Punnett squares below show the same crosses from p. 167 and above.

Example ——

Step 1: Work out the alleles the gametes would have.

Parents' genotypes

Gametes' alleles

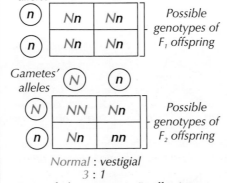

Normal : vestigial
3 : 1
Ratio of phenotypes in F_2 offspring

Step 2: Cross the parents' gametes to show the possible genotypes of the F_1 generation — all heterozygous, Nn.

Step 3: Cross the gametes of the F_1 generation to show the possible genotypes of the F_2 generation. The Punnett square shows a 75% chance that offspring will have normal wings and a 25% chance that they'll have vestigial wings, i.e. a 3 : 1 ratio.

Monogenic inheritance of codominant alleles

Occasionally, alleles show codominance — both alleles are expressed in the phenotype, and neither one is recessive. One example in humans is the allele for sickle-cell anaemia, a genetic disorder caused by a mutation in the haemoglobin gene. It causes red blood cells to be sickle (crescent) shaped.

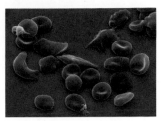

Figure 4: A coloured scanning electron micrograph (SEM) of normal red blood cells (red) and sickle-shaped cells (pink).

Example

People who are homozygous for normal haemoglobin ($H^N H^N$) don't have the disease. People who are homozygous for sickle haemoglobin ($H^S H^S$) have sickle-cell anaemia — all their blood cells are sickle shaped. People who are heterozygous ($H^N H^S$) have an in-between phenotype, called the sickle-cell trait — they have some normal haemoglobin and some sickle haemoglobin. The two alleles are codominant because they're both expressed in the phenotype.

The genetic diagram in Figure 5 shows the possible offspring from crossing two parents with sickle-cell trait (heterozygous).

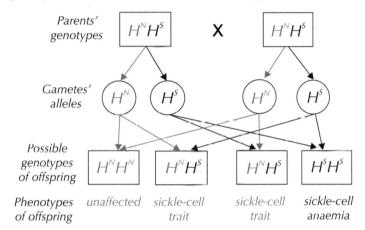

Figure 5: Genetic diagram showing a monogenic cross of codominant alleles.

This cross has produced a 1 : 2 : 1 phenotypic ratio of unaffected : sickle-cell trait : sickle-cell anaemia, or unaffected homozygous : heterozygous : disorder homozygous.

Usually, whenever you do a monogenic cross involving codominant alleles with two heterozygous parents, you get a 1 : 2 : 1 phenotypic ratio of homozygous for one allele : heterozygous : homozygous for the other allele.

Tip: When alleles show codominance they're represented in a slightly different way to normal — you show the main gene as a normal capital letter (H) and then the alleles as superscript capitals (H^S or H^N), because neither is recessive.

Tip: A codominant cross where one parent is homozygous for one allele and the other parent homozygous for the other allele will produce all heterozygous offspring in the F_1 generation. E.g. for the sickle-cell trait:

	H^N	H^N
H^S	$H^N H^S$	$H^N H^S$
H^S	$H^N H^S$	$H^N H^S$

Practice Questions — Application

Q1 The allele for tall pea plants is dominant over the allele for dwarf pea plants. Give the possible genotype(s) of offspring produced if a homozygous tall pea plant is crossed with a homozygous dwarf pea plant. Show your working.

Q2 In dogs, the allele for curly hair (H) is dominant over the allele for smooth hair (h). A cross between two dogs that are heterozygous for curly hair results in eight puppies. How many of those puppies would you expect to have curly hair? Show your working.

Tip: In these questions, where you're not given letters to use for a genetic diagram, just choose sensible ones yourself, e.g. T for tall dominant allele and t for dwarf recessive allele.

Exam Tip
If you're asked to find the probability of something, you can write it as a fraction (e.g. ¾), a decimal (e.g. 0.75) or a percentage (e.g. 75%).

Q3 A couple decide to have a child. One of the couple has sickle-cell anaemia (genotype H^SH^S) and the other is homozygous normal for the sickle-cell gene (genotype H^NH^N).

a) Draw a genetic diagram to show that the child will be a carrier of the sickle-cell allele (H^NH^S).

b) The child grows up and has children with an individual with the sickle-cell trait. What is the probability that any of these children will have sickle-cell anaemia? Show your working.

Q4 Polydactyly is a genetic disorder where a baby is born with extra fingers or toes. The disorder is caused by a dominant allele. What is the probability of a baby being born with the condition if a person heterozygous for the disorder and a person without the disorder have a child? Show your working.

Tip: Make sure you really know your definitions, especially homozygous, heterozygous, genotype and phenotype (see pages 165-166).

Q5 In one organism, the alleles for skin colour show codominance. Any organisms that are homozygous with blue alleles are blue in colour. Organisms that are homozygous with yellow alleles are yellow in colour. Heterozygous organisms are yellow and blue striped. What colour ratio of organisms would be produced if a heterozygous parent was crossed with a homozygous blue parent? Show your working.

Practice Questions — Fact Recall

Q1 What is monogenic inheritance?

Q2 Define the term 'phenotypic ratio'.

Q3 What are codominant alleles?

Q4 Predict the phenotypic ratio for:

a) a monogenic cross <u>not</u> involving codominant alleles with two heterozygous parents,

b) a monogenic cross involving codominant alleles with two heterozygous parents.

4. Genetic Diagrams — Multiple Allele and Dihybrid Crosses

Multiple allele crosses aren't much different to the monogenic crosses you've already come across. They still only involve one gene, it's just the gene can have more than two alleles. If you want to, you can also use genetic diagrams to look at the inheritance of two genes simultaneously — this is called a dihybrid cross.

Multiple allele crosses

Inheritance is more complicated when there are more than two alleles of the same gene (multiple alleles).

Example

In the ABO blood group system in humans there are three alleles for blood type:

- I^O is the allele for blood group O.
- I^A is the allele for blood group A.
- I^B is the allele for blood group B.

Allele I^O is recessive. Alleles I^A and I^B are codominant — people with genotype $I^A I^B$ will have blood group AB.

Figure 1 shows a cross between a heterozygous person with blood group A and a heterozygous person with blood group B.

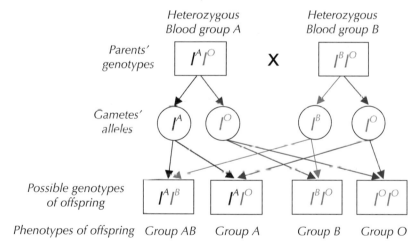

Parents' genotypes — Heterozygous Blood group A: $I^A I^O$ X Heterozygous Blood group B: $I^B I^O$

Gametes' alleles: I^A I^O I^B I^O

Possible genotypes of offspring: $I^A I^B$ $I^A I^O$ $I^B I^O$ $I^O I^O$

Phenotypes of offspring: Group AB, Group A, Group B, Group O

Figure 1: *Genetic diagram showing the inheritance of blood group.*

Any offspring could have one of four different blood groups (A, B, O or AB). So the expected phenotypic ratio is 1 : 1 : 1 : 1.

Tip: Recessive blood groups are normally really rare, but it just so happens that loads of people in Britain are descended from people who were $I^O I^O$, so O's really common.

Dihybrid crosses

Dihybrid inheritance is the inheritance of two characteristics, which are controlled by different genes. Each of the two genes will have different alleles. **Dihybrid crosses** can be used to show the likelihood of offspring inheriting certain combinations of the two characteristics from particular parents. The example on the next page is a dihybrid cross showing how seed shape and colour are inherited in pea plants.

Tip: Monogenic crosses (see p. 167) look at the inheritance of one characteristic only.

Figure 2: Pea seeds can be wrinkled or round.

Tip: See page 166 for a reminder of what dominant and recessive alleles are.

Tip: You could never get a gamete that contained both the alleles for a particular gene (e.g. Rr or Yy) because the homologous chromosomes that contain these alleles are separated during meiosis.

Tip: A dihybrid cross between a homozygous dominant parent and a homozygous recessive parent (e.g. RRYY × rryy) will produce all heterozygous offspring in the F_1 generation.

Example

As you saw on page 165, the gene for seed shape has two alleles. The allele for round seeds (R) is dominant and the allele for wrinkled seeds (r) is recessive. The seed colour gene also has two alleles. The allele for a yellow seed (Y) is dominant and the allele for a green seed (y) is recessive.

The genetic diagram in Figure 3 shows a cross between two heterozygous parents — both have round and yellow seeds (RrYy).

Here's how to draw a genetic diagram for this cross:

Step 1: Make sure you're clear what the letters mean.

R — round seeds	Y — yellow seeds
r — wrinkled seeds	y — green seeds

Step 2: Work out the alleles the gametes would have.

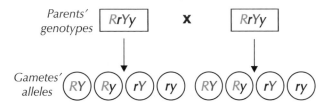

Step 3: Cross the parents' gametes to show the possible offspring.

	RY	Ry	rY	ry
RY	RRYY	RRYy	RrYY	RrYy
Ry	RRYy	RRyy	RrYy	Rryy
rY	RrYY	RrYy	rrYY	rrYy
ry	RrYy	Rryy	rrYy	rryy

Round and yellow seeds
= RRYY, RrYY, RrYy, RRYy = 9

Round and green seeds
= RRyy, Rryy = 3

Wrinkled and yellow seeds
= rrYY, rrYy = 3

Wrinkled and green seeds
= rryy = 1

Phenotypic ratio: 9 : 3 : 3 : 1

Figure 3: Genetic diagram showing a dihybrid cross between two heterozygous parents.

Usually, whenever you do a dihybrid cross with two heterozygous parents you get a 9 : 3 : 3 : 1 phenotypic ratio of dominant both : dominant first, recessive second : recessive first, dominant second : recessive both.

Practice Questions — Application

Q1 The striping pattern of cats can be determined by three alleles —
Ta for Abyssinian, T for the mackerel phenotype and tb for blotched.
Abyssinian is dominant to both of the other alleles, mackerel is
dominant to blotched only and blotched is recessive to all.
(So the dominance of the alleles is Ta > T > tb.)

Tip: Q1 involves a monogenic cross with multiple alleles.

What are the possible striping patterns of offspring if a TaT cat and a
tbtb cat breed together?

Q2 The colour of one species of moth is controlled by three alleles
— pale typical (m), darkly mottled insularia (M') and nearly
black melanic (M). The table below shows all possible genotype
combinations and their phenotypic outcomes.

Genotype	Phenotype
mm	Typical
MM	Melanic
M'M'	Insularia
mM	Melanic
mM'	Insularia
MM'	Melanic

a) Describe the dominance of the different alleles.

b) A homozygous melanic and a typical pale moth breed.
Show all the possible results of this cross.

Q3 In tomato plants, the allele for round fruit (F) is dominant to the allele
for pear-shaped fruit (f). The allele for red fruit colour (R) is dominant
to the allele for yellow fruit colour (r).

a) Two tomato plants, heterozygous for fruit shape and colour,
are crossed. Draw a Punnett square for this cross.

b) What is the expected ratio of round, red tomatoes to pear-shaped,
yellow tomatoes?

Q4 In cattle, the alleles for black colouring (B) and polled (no horns)
(P) are dominant and the alleles for red colouring (b) and horns (p)
are recessive.

a) A black bull with no horns (BBPP) is crossed with a red cow with
horns. What would the phenotypic ratio of the F₁ generation be?

b) Use a genetic diagram to show the expected phenotypic ratio in
the offspring of a cross between two heterozygous black cattle
with no horns.

Practice Questions — Fact Recall

Q1 How many genes are involved in a multiple allele cross?

Q2 What is dihybrid inheritance?

Q3 Predict the phenotypic ratio of the offspring for a dihybrid cross
<u>not</u> involving codominant alleles with two heterozygous parents.

Learning Objectives:

- Be able to explain linkage.
- Be able to use genetic diagrams to show patterns of inheritance, including sex linkage.
- Be able to use phenotypic ratios to identify linkage (autosomal and sex linkage).

Specification Reference 6.1.2

Tip: In mammals, males are <u>heterogametic</u> — they have two different kinds of sex chromosomes (X and Y). Females are <u>homogametic</u> — they have only one kind of sex chromosome (X).

Tip: Remember, a carrier is a person carrying an allele which is not expressed in the phenotype but that can be passed on to offspring. Males can't be carriers of X-linked disorders because they only have one copy of each chromosome, so if they have the allele they have the disease — whether it's recessive or not.

Tip: The faulty allele for colour vision is represented by a lower case 'n', so you know it's a recessive allele.

5. Linkage

There are two types of gene linkage, and they can both affect the phenotypic ratios of monogenic and dihybrid crosses. You can use this variation from the expected ratios to identify that genes are linked.

Inheritance of sex-linked characteristics

The genetic information for biological sex is carried on two sex chromosomes. In mammals, females have two X chromosomes (XX) and males have one X chromosome and one Y chromosome (XY).

Figure 1 is a genetic diagram that shows how sex is inherited. From this you can see that the probability of having male offspring is 50% and the probability of having female offspring is 50%.

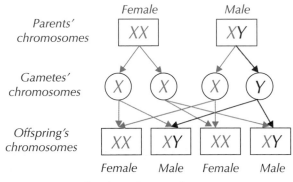

Figure 1: *Genetic diagram showing the inheritance of sex.*

Some characteristics are **sex-linked**. That means the alleles that code for them are located on a sex chromosome. The Y chromosome is smaller than the X chromosome and carries fewer genes. So most genes on the sex chromosomes are only carried on the X chromosome (called X-linked genes).

As males only have one X chromosome they often only have one allele for sex-linked genes. So because they only have one copy they express the characteristic of this allele even if it's recessive. This makes males more likely than females to show recessive phenotypes for genes that are sex-linked.

Genetic disorders caused by faulty alleles located on sex chromosomes include colour blindness and haemophilia. The faulty alleles for both of these disorders are carried on the X chromosome and so are called X-linked disorders. Y-linked disorders do exist but are less common.

┌─ **Example** ─────────────────────

Figure 2 on the next page shows a genetic diagram for colour blindness. Colour blindness is a sex-linked disorder caused by a faulty allele carried on the X chromosome. As it's sex-linked both the chromosome and the allele are represented in the genetic diagram, e.g. X^n, where X represents the X chromosome and n the faulty allele for colour vision. The Y chromosome doesn't have an allele for colour vision so is just represented by Y.

Females would need two copies of the recessive allele to be colour blind, while males only need one copy. This means colour blindness is much rarer in women than men. Females with one copy of the recessive allele are said to be **carriers**.

Here's how to draw a Punnett square for the sex-linked cross between a carrier female and an unaffected male:

Step 1: Make sure you're clear what the letters mean. You need to show X and Y chromosomes too this time. You usually show them as a capital X and Y and then have the genes as superscript letters.

Step 2: Work out the alleles the gametes would have.

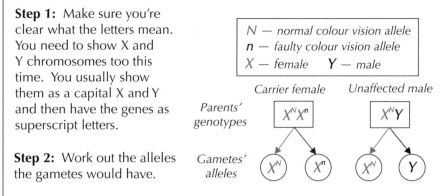

Exam Tip
Always read the question carefully — if it only asks you for the F_1 genotypes, don't write about anything else in your answer. It wastes time and you might lose marks.

Step 3: Cross the parents' gametes to show the possible offspring.

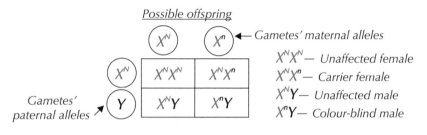

$X^N X^N$ — Unaffected female
$X^N X^n$ — Carrier female
$X^N Y$ — Unaffected male
$X^n Y$ — Colour-blind male

Figure 2: Punnett square showing the inheritance of colour-blindness.

Tip: This cross isn't any harder than the simple monogenic ones you saw on pages 167-169. Just follow the same steps to work out all the possible combinations of gametes and what they would mean.

In the example above there's a 3 : 1 ratio of offspring without colour blindness : offspring with colour-blindness. But when a female carrier and a male without colour-blindness have children (as in this example), only their male offspring are at risk of being colour-blind. So you can also say that there's a predicted 2 : 1 : 1 ratio — of female offspring without colour-blindness : male offspring without colour-blindness : male offspring with colour-blindness.

This ratio will change if a female carrier ($X^N X^n$) and a male with colour-blindness ($X^n Y$) have children. The predicted ratio will then be 1 : 1 — of offspring with colour-blindness : offspring without colour-blindness. The ratio will be the same for offspring of each sex (see Figure 3). You only end up with this predicted ratio for a monogenic F_2 cross with a sex-linked characteristic.

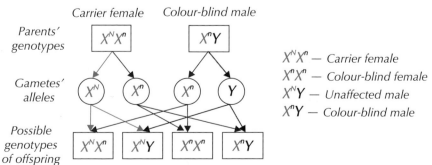

$X^N X^n$ — Carrier female
$X^n X^n$ — Colour-blind female
$X^N Y$ — Unaffected male
$X^n Y$ — Colour-blind male

Figure 3: Genetic diagram showing the inheritance of colour-blindness in an F_2 cross.

Tip: If a colour-blind female and an unaffected male had children, the predicted ratio of offspring without colour-blindness : offspring with colour-blindness would be 1 : 1 — all male offspring would be colour-blind, and all female offspring would be carriers.

Linkage of autosomal genes

Tip: Independent assortment is the random division of homologous (paired) chromosomes into separate daughter cells during meiosis. Crossing over is when two homologous chromosomes 'swap bits'. It happens in meiosis I before independent assortment. You'll have learnt about both of these in Year 1 of your course.

Autosome is the fancy name for any chromosome that isn't a sex chromosome. Autosomal genes are the genes located on the autosomes. Genes on the same autosome are said to be **linked** — that's because they'll stay together during the independent assortment of chromosomes in meiosis I, and their alleles will be passed on to the offspring together. The only reason this won't happen is if crossing over splits them up first. The closer together two genes are on the autosome, the more closely they are said to be linked. This is because crossing over is less likely to split them up.

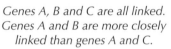

A pair of X-shaped autosomes.

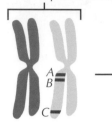
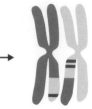

Genes A, B and C are all linked. Genes A and B are more closely linked than genes A and C.

Crossing over occurs.

Genes A and B stay together, but are split up from gene C.

Figure 4a: *Autosomal genes being split up during crossing over.*

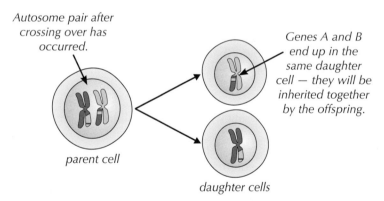

Autosome pair after crossing over has occurred.

Genes A and B end up in the same daughter cell — they will be inherited together by the offspring.

parent cell

daughter cells

Figure 4b: *Independent assortment of autosomes during meiosis I.*

If two genes are autosomally linked, you won't get the phenotypic ratio you expect in the offspring of a cross.

> **Example**
>
> In a dihybrid cross between two heterozygous parents you'd expect a 9 : 3 : 3 : 1 ratio in the offspring. Instead, the phenotypic ratio is more likely to be that expected for a monogenic cross between two heterozygous parents (3 : 1) because the two autosomally-linked alleles are inherited together. This means that a higher proportion of the offspring will have their parents' (heterozygous) genotype and phenotype.

Tip: There's more about the expected phenotypic ratios for dihybrid and monogenic crosses on pages 168 and 172.

So you can use the predicted phenotypic ratio to identify autosomal linkage — see next page.

A scientist was investigating autosomal linkage between the genes for eye colour and wing length in fruit flies. The gene for normal wings (N) is dominant to the gene for vestigial wings (n) and the gene for red eyes (R) is dominant to the gene for purple eyes (r).

The first cross the scientist carried out was between flies homozygous dominant for both normal wings and red eyes (NNRR) and flies homozygous recessive for both vestigial wings and purple eyes (nnrr). The resulting offspring were all heterozygous for normal wings and red eyes (NnRr).

The second cross the scientist carried out was between these offspring (NnRr) and the flies homozygous recessive for vestigial wings and purple eyes (nnrr). He expected a 1 : 1 : 1 : 1 ratio as shown in Figure 5:

Tip: Crossing the offspring with one of the parents is known as a back cross.

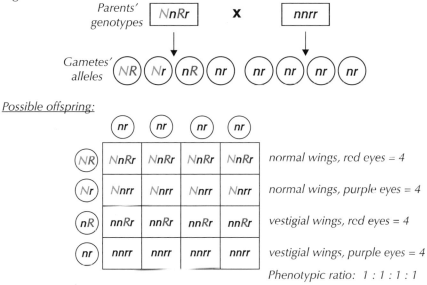

Tip: Watch out — a 1 : 1 : 1 : 1 ratio is expected here because the cross is between a <u>homozygous</u> parent and a <u>heterozygous</u> parent <u>not</u> two heterozygous parents (which would be a 9 : 3 : 3 : 1 ratio).

Figure 5: *Genetic diagram showing the expected phenotypic ratio for a dihybrid cross between one heterozygous parent and one homozygous parent.*

However, the results the scientist got for the NnRr × nnrr cross showed an 8 : 1 : 1 : 8 ratio, as in the table:

	Number of offspring
Normal wings, red eyes (NnRr)	1216
Normal wings, purple eyes (Nnrr)	152
Vestigial wings, red eyes (nnRr)	148
Vestigial wings, purple eyes (nnrr)	1184

Phenotypic ratio = 8 : 1 : 1 : 8

Tip: To give the ratio 1216 : 152 : 148 : 1184 in its simplest form, divide each number by the smallest number in the ratio (i.e. 148).

In order for the NnRr and nnrr genotypes to be so common in the offspring, the NR alleles and the nr alleles in the NnRr parent must have been linked. This means that the NnRr parent produced mostly NR and nr gametes. Some Nr and nR gametes were still made due to crossing over, but there were fewer Nnrr and nnRr offspring overall. As a result, a higher proportion of the offspring have their parents' phenotypes.

Exam Tip
In the exam you might get some genetic cross results that show linkage and have to explain them.

Q1 Fragile X syndrome is an X-linked dominant disorder. A male and female, each with Fragile X syndrome, have a child. The female is heterozygous for the disorder. Give the possible genotypes and phenotypes of the child.

Q2 Hypertrichosis pinnae (extremely hairy ears) was once thought to be a Y-linked characteristic. If this were true, why might a father with 'bald' ears whose child has hairy ears, be suspicious of his wife?

Q3 Duchenne muscular dystrophy is a form of muscular dystrophy that causes muscle breakdown and difficulties walking and breathing. It is caused by a recessive X-linked allele. What is the probability of having a child with Duchenne muscular dystrophy if a normal male has a child with a carrier female?

Q4 In corn plants, the allele for glossy leaves (G) is dominant to the gene for normal leaves (g) and the gene for branching of ears (B) is dominant to the gene for no branching (b). A cross is carried out between a plant that is heterozygous for glossy leaves and branching of ears (GgBb) and a plant that is homozygous recessive for normal leaves and no branching (ggbb).

a) Use a genetic diagram to work out the expected phenotypic ratio in the offspring.

b) The results of the cross are shown in the table below.

	Number of offspring
Glossy leaves, lots of branching (GgBb)	126
Glossy leaves, no branching (Ggbb)	81
Normal leaves, lots of branching (ggBb)	74
Normal leaves, no branching (ggbb)	133

What is the observed phenotypic ratio in the offspring?

c) Suggest why the observed ratio differs from the expected ratio.

Figure 6: *A photo showing normal leaves and no branching in two ears of corn.*

Q1 What is the probability of having a female child?

Q2 Some characteristics are sex-linked. What does this mean?

Q3 Why are X-linked disorders more common in males than females?

Q4 What is an autosome?

Q5 Why are genes on the same autosome said to be linked?

6. Epistasis

Just like linkage, epistasis affects the phenotypic ratios of dihybrid crosses.

What is epistasis?

Many different genes can control the same characteristic — they interact to form the phenotype. This can be because the allele of one gene masks (blocks) the expression of the alleles of other genes — this is called **epistasis**.

┌─ **Example 1 — Widow's peak** ─────────────────────

In humans a widow's peak (see Figure 1) is controlled by one gene and baldness by others. If you have the alleles that code for baldness, it doesn't matter whether you have the allele for a widow's peak or not, as you have no hair. The baldness genes are epistatic to the widow's peak gene, as the baldness genes mask the expression of the widow's peak gene.

└──

┌─ **Example 2 — Flower colour** ────────────────────

Flower pigment in a plant is controlled by two genes. Gene 1 codes for a yellow pigment (Y is the dominant yellow allele) and gene 2 codes for an enzyme that turns the yellow pigment orange (R is the dominant orange allele). If you don't have the Y allele it won't matter if you have the R allele or not as the flower will be colourless. Gene 1 is epistatic to gene 2 as it can mask the expression of gene 2.

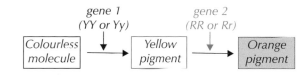

└──

Phenotypic ratios for epistatic genes

Crosses involving epistatic genes don't result in the expected phenotypic ratios, e.g. if you cross two heterozygous orange flowered plants (YyRr) from the example above you wouldn't get the expected 9 : 3 : 3 : 1 phenotypic ratio for a normal dihybrid cross.

The phenotypic ratio you would expect to get from a dihybrid cross involving an epistatic allele depends on whether the epistatic allele is recessive or dominant.

Recessive epistatic alleles

If the epistatic allele is recessive then two copies of it will mask (block) the expression of the other gene. If you cross a homozygous recessive parent with a homozygous dominant parent you will produce a 9 : 3 : 4 phenotypic ratio of dominant both : dominant epistatic, recessive other : recessive epistatic in the F_2 generation.

┌─ **Example** ──────────────────────────────────────

The flower colour example above is an example of a recessive epistatic allele. If a plant is homozygous recessive for the epistatic gene (yy) then it will be colourless, masking the expression of the orange gene. So if you cross homozygous parents you should get a 9 : 3 : 4 ratio of orange : yellow : white in the F_2 generation. You can check the phenotypic ratio is right using a genetic diagram — see Figure 2 on the next page.

└──

Learning Objectives:

- Be able to explain epistasis.
- Be able to use phenotypic ratios to identify epistasis.

Specification Reference 6.1.2

Figure 1: *A man with a widow's peak (a V-shaped hair growth). If this man were bald, you wouldn't be able to tell whether he had a widow's peak or not.*

Tip: Epistatic genes are usually at different loci (different positions on chromosomes).

Tip: Remember the F_1 generation is the first generation and the F_2 generation is the second generation.

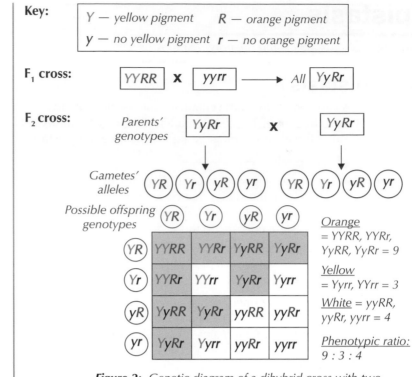

Key:

Y — yellow pigment	R — orange pigment
y — no yellow pigment	r — no orange pigment

F₁ cross: $\boxed{YYRR}$ **X** $\boxed{yyrr}$ ⟶ All $\boxed{YyRr}$

F₂ cross:

Parents' genotypes: $\boxed{YyRr}$ **X** $\boxed{YyRr}$

Gametes' alleles: (YR) (Yr) (yR) (yr)   (YR) (Yr) (yR) (yr)

Possible offspring genotypes

	(YR)	(Yr)	(yR)	(yr)
(YR)	YYRR	YYRr	YyRR	YyRr
(Yr)	YYRr	YYrr	YyRr	Yyrr
(yR)	YyRR	YyRr	yyRR	yyRr
(yr)	YyRr	Yyrr	yyRr	yyrr

Orange = YYRR, YYRr, YyRR, YyRr = 9

Yellow = Yyrr, YYrr = 3

White = yyRR, yyRr, yyrr = 4

Phenotypic ratio: 9 : 3 : 4

Figure 2: *Genetic diagram of a dihybrid cross with two heterozygous parents, involving a recessive epistatic gene.*

Tip: All of the F₁ offspring have to have the genotype YyRr because the only gametes you can get from the parents are YR and yr.

Tip: You should be familiar with Punnett squares by now but if not, see page 168 for a recap.

Tip: This is a dihybrid cross because you're looking at the inheritance of two genes.

Dominant epistatic alleles

If the epistatic allele is dominant, then having at least one copy of it will mask (block) the expression of the other gene. Crossing a homozygous recessive parent with a homozygous dominant parent will produce a 12 : 3 : 1 phenotypic ratio of dominant epistatic : recessive epistatic, dominant other : recessive both in the F₂ generation.

Exam Tip: Make sure you know the difference between dominant and recessive epistatic alleles. The phenotypic ratios you'd expect to get are different for each.

┌─ **Example** ─────────────

Squash colour is controlled by two genes — the colour epistatic gene (W/w) and the yellow gene (Y/y). The no-colour, white allele (W) is dominant over the coloured allele (w), so WW or Ww will be white and ww will be coloured. The yellow gene has the dominant yellow allele (Y) and the recessive green allele (y). So if the plant has at least one W, then the squash will be white, masking the expression of the yellow gene.

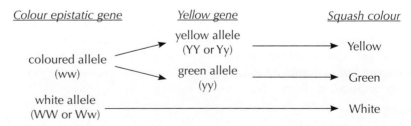

Colour epistatic gene	*Yellow gene*	*Squash colour*
	yellow allele (YY or Yy)	⟶ Yellow
coloured allele (ww)		
	green allele (yy)	⟶ Green
white allele (WW or Ww)		⟶ White

Figure 3: *Diagram to show how squash colour is controlled by two genes.*

So if you cross wwyy with WWYY, you'll get a 12 : 3 : 1 ratio of white : yellow : green in the F₂ generation. The genetic diagram to prove it is shown in Figure 5 (see next page).

Figure 4: *These squash are yellow in colour so they must have the genotype wwYY or wwYy.*

Key:

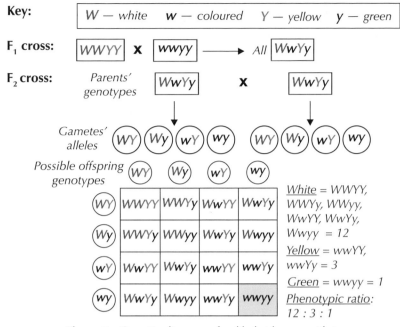

W — white w — coloured Y — yellow y — green

F_1 cross: $WWYY$ **x** $wwyy$ ⟶ All $WwYy$

F_2 cross: Parents' genotypes $WwYy$ **x** $WwYy$

Gametes' alleles: WY Wy wY wy WY Wy wY wy

Possible offspring genotypes: WY Wy wY wy

	WY	Wy	wY	wy
WY	$WWYY$	$WWYy$	$WwYY$	$WwYy$
Wy	$WWYy$	$WWyy$	$WwYy$	$Wwyy$
wY	$WwYY$	$WwYy$	$wwYY$	$wwYy$
wy	$WwYy$	$Wwyy$	$wwYy$	$wwyy$

<u>White</u> = $WWYY$, $WWYy$, $WWyy$, $WwYY$, $WwYy$, $Wwyy$ = 12

<u>Yellow</u> = $wwYY$, $wwYy$ = 3

<u>Green</u> = $wwyy$ = 1

<u>Phenotypic ratio</u>: $12 : 3 : 1$

Figure 5: *Genetic diagram of a dihybrid cross with two heterozygous parents, involving a dominant epistatic gene.*

Exam Tip

If you set your crosses out like this in the exam, it'll help you keep track of what you're doing and it'll help the examiner follow your working out.

Practice Questions — Application

Q1 Coat colour in Labrador retrievers is controlled by two genes. Gene 1 controls whether the dog can express dark pigment in its coat (E) or not (e). Gene 1 is epistatic over gene 2, which controls whether the dark pigment is black (B) or chocolate (b). Dogs that can't express dark pigment in their coat are yellow (golden) in colour.

a) Write down all the possible genotypes for:
   i) a black Labrador,   ii) a chocolate Labrador,
   iii) a yellow Labrador.

b) Describe and explain the phenotypic ratio produced in the F_2 generation if a black Labrador retriever (EEBB) breeds with a yellow Labrador retriever (eebb).

Figure 6: *Chocolate and black coated Labrador retrievers.*

Q2 Petal colour in a species of flower is controlled by this pathway:

gene 1   gene 2

White pigment ⊣→ Red pigment →→ Purple pigment

Gene 1 codes for a protein that prevents the formation of the red pigment. This means the dominant allele for gene 1 (W) causes the petals to be white and the recessive allele (w) causes red pigment to be made. Gene 2 codes for a protein that turns the red pigment into purple pigment. This means the dominant allele for gene 2 (P), causes the petals to be purple and the recessive allele (p) causes the petals to stay red. When a white flower (WWPP) is crossed with a red flower (wwpp), 48 white flowers, 12 purple flowers and 4 red flowers are produced in the F_2 generation.

a) Is this an example of dominant or recessive epistasis?

b) Explain the phenotypic ratio shown by the cross.

c) Draw a genetic diagram to show this cross.

Learning Objective:

- Be able to use the chi-squared (χ^2) test to determine the significance of the difference between observed and expected results.
  Specification Reference 6.1.2

7. The Chi-Squared Test

OK, it's time for a bit of maths. The chi-squared test can be a bit tricky to get your head around, but it might pop up in the exam so make sure you spend some time working through the next few pages.

What is the chi-squared test?

The chi-squared (χ^2) test is a statistical test that's used to see if the results of an experiment support a theory. First, the theory is used to predict a result — this is called the expected result. Then, the experiment is carried out and the actual result is recorded — this is called the observed result.

Tip: A theory is a possible explanation for something and a hypothesis is a specific testable statement. See page 1 for more on this.

To see if the results support the theory you have to make a hypothesis called the **null hypothesis**. The null hypothesis is always that there's no significant difference between the observed and expected results. Your experimental result will usually be a bit different from what you expect, but you need to know if the difference is just due to chance, or because your theory is wrong. The χ^2 test is then carried out and the outcome either supports or rejects the null hypothesis.

Using the chi-squared test

You can use the χ^2 test in genetics to test theories about the inheritance of characteristics.

Tip: See pages 167-169 for a recap on monogenic inheritance.

┌─ **Example — inheritance of wing length experiment** ─

Theory: Wing length in fruit flies is controlled by a single gene with two alleles (monogenic inheritance). The dominant allele (N) gives normal wings, and the recessive allele (n) gives vestigial wings.

Expected results: With monogenic inheritance, if you cross a homozygous dominant parent with a homozygous recessive parent, you'd expect a 3 : 1 phenotypic ratio of normal : vestigial wings in the F_2 generation.

Observed results: The experiment (of crossing a homozygous dominant parent with a homozygous recessive parent) is carried out on fruit flies and the number of offspring in the F_2 generation with normal and vestigial wings is counted.

Null hypothesis: There's no significant difference between the observed and expected results.

Chi-squared test: To find out if the results are significant you first need to calculate the **chi-squared value** (see below) and then compare it to the **critical value** (see page 184). If the χ^2 test shows the observed and expected results are not significantly different, then we are unable to reject the null hypothesis — the data supports the theory that wing length is controlled by monogenic inheritance.

Figure 1: *Karl Pearson — the English statistician who developed the chi-squared test.*

Calculating the chi-squared value

Chi-squared (χ^2) is calculated using this formula:

$$\chi^2 = \sum \frac{(O - E)^2}{E}$$

O = observed result
E = expected result
$\sum$ = the sum of...

Exam Tip
You don't need to learn the formula for chi-squared — it'll be given to you in the exam.

The best way to understand the χ^2 test is to work through an example — there's one for testing the wing length of fruit flies, as explained above, on the next page.

Homozygous dominant flies (NN) are crossed with homozygous recessive flies (nn) and 160 offspring are produced in the F_2 generation.

1. First the number of offspring expected (E) for each phenotype (out of a total of 160) is worked out using this equation:

   | E = total no. of offspring ÷ ratio total × predicted ratio |

   A 3 : 1 phenotypic ratio of normal : vestigial wings is expected, so the ratio total is 3 + 1 = 4. Here are the expected results:

Phenotype	Ratio	Expected result (E)
Normal wings	3	160 ÷ 4 × 3 = 120
Vestigial wings	1	160 ÷ 4 × 1 = 40

Tip: This isn't the only way to work out the expected results. If you're taught a different way in class, stick with whichever method you find easiest.

2. Then the actual number of offspring observed with each phenotype (out of the 160 offspring) is recorded, e.g. 111 with normal wings:

Phenotype	Ratio	Expected result (E)	Observed result (O)
Normal wings	3	120	111
Vestigial wings	1	40	49

3. The results are used to work out χ^2, taking it one step at a time:

   a. First calculate O – E (subtract the expected result from the observed result) for each phenotype.

Phenotype	Ratio	Expected result (E)	Observed result (O)	O – E
Normal wings	3	120	111	111 – 120 = –9
Vestigial wings	1	40	49	49 – 40 = 9

   b. Then the resulting numbers are squared:

Phenotype	Ratio	Expected result (E)	Observed result (O)	O – E	$(O – E)^2$
Normal wings	3	120	111	–9	$–9^2 = 81$
Vestigial wings	1	40	49	9	$9^2 = 81$

Tip: Don't forget — if you multiply a negative number by a negative number you get a positive number. So $–9^2$ ($–9 × –9$) is 81 and not –81.

   c. These figures are divided by the expected results:

Phenotype	Ratio	Expected result (E)	Observed result (O)	O – E	$(O – E)^2$	$\dfrac{(O – E)^2}{E}$
Normal wings	3	120	111	–9	81	81 ÷ 120 = 0.675
Vestigial wings	1	40	49	9	81	81 ÷ 40 = 2.025

Exam Tip
Make sure you divide $(O – E)^2$ by E and not O. It's easy to get these two mixed up when you're under pressure in the exam.

   d. Finally, the numbers are added together to get χ^2.

Phenotype	Ratio	Expected result (E)	Observed result (O)	O – E	$(O – E)^2$	$\dfrac{(O – E)^2}{E}$
Normal wings	3	120	111	–9	81	0.675
Vestigial wings	1	40	49	9	81	2.025

   $$\sum \frac{(O – E)^2}{E} = 0.675 + 2.025 = \boxed{2.7}$$

Tip: Remember you need to work out $(O – E)^2 ÷ E$ for each phenotype first, then add all the numbers together.

The critical value

To find out whether there is a significant difference between your observed and expected results you need to compare your χ^2 value to a critical value. The critical value is the value of χ^2 that corresponds to a 0.05 (5%) level of probability that the difference between the observed and expected results is due to chance.

Finding the critical value

In the exam you might be given the critical value or asked to work it out from a table.

Example — Maths Skills

Figure 2 below is a chi-squared table — this shows a range of probabilities that correspond to different critical values for different **degrees of freedom** (explained below). Biologists normally use a **probability level** (P value) of 0.05 (5%), so you only need to look in that column.

Abridged from Statistical Tables for Biological, Agricultural and Medical Research (6th ed.) © 1963 R.A Fisher and F. Yates. Reprinted with permission of Pearson Education Limited.

degrees of freedom	no. of classes	Critical values					
1	2	0.46	1.64	2.71	3.84	6.64	10.83
2	3	1.39	3.22	4.61	5.99	9.21	13.82
3	4	2.37	4.64	6.25	7.82	11.34	16.27
4	5	3.36	5.99	7.78	9.49	13.28	18.47
probability that result is due to chance only		0.50 (50%)	0.20 (20%)	0.10 (10%)	0.05 (5%)	0.01 (1%)	0.001 (0.1%)

Figure 2: A chi-squared table.

In order to find the critical value for the wing length experiment:

- First, the degrees of freedom for the experiment are worked out — this is the number of classes (number of phenotypes) minus one. There were two phenotypes, so the degrees of freedom = 2 − 1 = **1**.

- Next, the critical value corresponding to the degrees of freedom (1 in this case) and a probability level of 0.05 is found in the table. By following the arrows in Figure 2 you can see that the critical value is **3.84**.

Comparing the χ^2 value to the critical value

If your χ^2 value is larger than (or equal to) the critical value, then there is a significant difference between the observed and expected results (something other than chance is causing the difference) — and the null hypothesis can be rejected. If your χ^2 value is smaller than the critical value, then there is no significant difference between the observed and expected results — the null hypothesis can't be rejected. This is summarised in Figure 3.

> χ^2 value ≥ critical value = rejection of the null hypothesis
> χ^2 value < critical value = failure to reject the null hypothesis

Figure 3: Possible outcomes of a chi-squared test.

Example — Maths Skills

The chi-squared value of 2.7 is smaller than the critical value of 3.84. This means that there's no significant difference between the observed and expected results. We've failed to reject the null hypothesis — so the theory that wing length in fruit flies is controlled by monogenic inheritance is supported.

Exam Tip
The table of critical values you get given in the exam might look a bit different to this, but don't panic. It'll still contain all the information you need to answer the question.

Tip: Remember, the two phenotypes for the wing length experiment are normal wings and vestigial wings.

Tip: In this kind of statistical test, you can never prove that the null hypothesis is true — you can only 'fail to reject it'. This just means that the evidence doesn't give you a reason to think the null hypothesis is wrong.

Tip: If the χ^2 value had been bigger than 3.84 then something else must have been affecting wing length — like epistasis or sex linkage.

Practice Questions — Application

Q1 The critical value for a chi-squared test is 5.99. Explain whether or not the difference between the observed and expected results would be significant if the calculated chi-squared value was:

a) 6.20,   b) 4.85.

Q2 Fruit flies can have grey bodies or ebony bodies. The allele for grey bodies is dominant over the allele for ebony bodies. If two heterozygous parents are crossed, you would expect a 3 : 1 phenotypic ratio of grey : ebony offspring. When this cross was carried out, 64 offspring were produced, 45 of which had grey bodies and the rest were ebony. Copy and complete the table below to calculate the chi-squared value for this experiment.

Phenotype	Ratio	Expected result (E)	Observed result (O)	O – E	$(O - E)^2$	$\dfrac{(O - E)^2}{E}$
Grey body	3		45			
Ebony body	1					

$$\chi^2 = \Sigma \frac{(O - E)^2}{E} = \boxed{}$$

For the following questions, you may need to use the χ^2 table below:

Degrees of freedom	Probability (p)					
	0.50	0.20	0.10	0.05	0.01	0.001
1	0.46	1.64	2.71	3.84	6.64	10.83
2	1.39	3.22	4.61	5.99	9.21	13.82
3	2.37	4.64	6.25	7.82	11.34	16.27
4	3.36	5.99	7.78	9.49	13.28	18.47

probability ← levels

critical values

Q3 A student is looking at the inheritance of pea shape (round vs. wrinkled) and pea colour (green vs. yellow) in pea plants. His theory is that this is a simple case of dihybrid inheritance with no linkage or epistasis involved. He predicts that if this is the case, when two heterozygous plants are crossed, there will be a 9 : 3 : 3 : 1 ratio in the offspring. To test his theory, the student carries out this cross and looks at the phenotypes of the 128 offspring produced.

Some of his results are shown in the table below. His null hypothesis is that there is no significant difference between the observed and expected results.

a) Copy and complete the table to calculate χ^2 for this experiment:

Phenotype	Ratio	Expected result (E)	Observed result (O)	O – E	$(O - E)^2$	$\dfrac{(O - E)^2}{E}$
Round, green	9		74			
Round, yellow	3		21			
Wrinkled, green	3					
Wrinkled, yellow	1		7			

$$\chi^2 = \Sigma \frac{(O - E)^2}{E} = \boxed{}$$

b) Find the critical value for this experiment and explain whether the null hypothesis can be rejected or not.

Exam Tip
You won't always be told the observed number of offspring for both phenotypes. You can work out the number of offspring for the phenotype you don't know by taking the number you do know away from the total.

Tip: Remember the degrees of freedom are just the number of classes minus one (n − 1).

Exam Tip
In the exam, you could be given a table like this to fill in. If you're not given a table, the easiest way to calculate χ^2 would be to draw a table like this yourself and work through it step by step.

Tip: Remember to check whether the ratio and number of offspring of each phenotype in the question refer to the F_1 or the F_2 generation.

Exam Tip
You can take a calculator in the exam to help you do these kinds of questions.

Tip: There's more about recessive epistasis on pages 179-180.

Q4 A scientist comes up with the following theory:

> 'Height in plants is controlled by a single gene with two alleles. The dominant allele gives tall plants. The recessive allele gives dwarf plants.'

The scientist predicts that if this theory is true, when a homozygous recessive plant is crossed with a homozygous dominant plant you will get a 3 : 1 ratio of tall : dwarf in the F_2 generation. The scientist then comes up with a null hypothesis and carries out the cross. Of the 52 F_2 offspring produced, 9 were dwarf.

a) What should the scientist's null hypothesis be?

b) The formula for calculating chi-squared is:

$$\chi^2 = \sum \frac{(O - E)^2}{E}$$

Use the chi-squared test to explain whether or not the results of the scientist's experiment support his theory.

Q5 A flower can have red, white or pink flowers. If this is an example of codominance and two heterozygous plants were crossed, you would expect a 1 : 2 : 1 ratio of red : pink : white flowers in the offspring. This cross was performed and of the 160 offspring produced, 92 had pink flowers, 24 had red flowers and 44 had white flowers. The null hypothesis is that there is no significant difference between the observed and expected results.

a) The formula for calculating chi-squared is:

$$\chi^2 = \sum \frac{(O - E)^2}{E}$$

Use the chi-squared test to show that this is unlikely to be an example of codominance.

b) If the determination of flower colour in this plant involved recessive epistasis a 9 : 3 : 4 phenotypic ratio of pink flowers : red flowers : white flowers would be expected. Using the chi-squared test, show that recessive epistasis is likely to be involved. (The null hypothesis is that there is no significant difference between the observed and expected results.)

Section Summary

Make sure you know...

- That characteristics which show continuous variation are usually polygenic (influenced by many genes), while characteristics that display discontinuous variation are usually monogenic (influenced by one gene).

- That both genotype and the environment contribute to phenotypic variation.

- That genetic variation is generated during meiosis via crossing-over and the independent assortment of chromosomes, and during fertilisation via the random fusion of gametes.

- That examples of environmental contributions to phenotypic variation include diet in animals, and that etiolation and chlorosis in plants are variations in phenotype caused by environmental factors.

- That there can be one or more versions of the same gene and that these are called alleles.

- That most plants and animals have two alleles for each gene and that each one is found at a fixed position (called a locus) on each chromosome in a pair.

- That the genotype of an organism is what alleles it has and that the phenotype of an organism is the characteristics the alleles produce.

- That if an organism has two different alleles for the same characteristic it's heterozygous, but if it has two copies of the same allele it's homozygous.

- That an allele can be dominant (its characteristic is always shown in the phenotype), recessive (its characteristic is only shown in the phenotype if there are two copies of it) or codominant (where two alleles are both shown in the phenotype).

- That a carrier is a person carrying an allele which is not expressed in the phenotype but that can be passed on to offspring.

- How to use genetic diagrams to show the inheritance of a single gene (monogenic inheritance) and the inheritance of codominant alleles.

- That the phenotypic ratio is the ratio of phenotypes in the offspring and that the typical phenotypic ratio for a monogenic cross between two heterozygous parents is 3 : 1 of dominant : recessive characteristic and the typical phenotypic ratio for a cross between two heterozygous parents involving codominant alleles is 1 : 2 : 1 of homozygous for one allele : heterozygous : homozygous for the other allele.

- How to use genetic diagrams showing crosses involving multiple alleles and showing the inheritance of two characteristics controlled by different genes (dihybrid inheritance).

- That a typical phenotypic ratio for a dihybrid cross between two heterozygous parents is 9 : 3 : 3 : 1 (dominant both : dominant first, recessive second : recessive first, dominant second : recessive both).

- How to use genetic diagrams to show the inheritance of sex-linked characteristics (the alleles that code for them are located on sex chromosomes) and recognise that sex linkage alters expected phenotypic ratios in the offspring of crosses.

- How to identify genes linked on autosomes (chromosomes that aren't sex chromosomes) and recognise that autosomal linkage alters expected phenotypic ratios in the offspring of crosses.

- That epistasis is when the allele of one gene masks the expression of the alleles of other genes.

- What recessive epistasis is and that when the epistatic allele is recessive, crossing a homozygous recessive parent with a homozygous dominant parent will produce a 9 : 3 : 4 phenotypic ratio of dominant both : dominant epistatic, recessive other : recessive epistatic in the F_2 generation.

- What dominant epistasis is and that when the epistatic allele is dominant, crossing a homozygous recessive parent with a homozygous dominant parent will produce a 12 : 3 : 1 phenotypic ratio of dominant epistatic : recessive epistatic, dominant other : recessive both in the F_2 generation.

- How to calculate the chi-squared (χ^2) value for an experiment, how to find the critical value from a chi-squared table and how to use these values to determine whether the difference between observed and expected results is significant or not, and whether or not to reject the null hypothesis.

1 In mice, the allele for wild-type speckled coat colour, agouti (A), is dominant to the allele for solid coloured fur (a).

(a) Several pairs of heterozygous agouti mice are crossed, producing 256 offspring.

Assuming this is a normal case of monogenic inheritance, with no linkage involved, how many of the offspring would you expect to have the agouti coat colour?

(1 mark)

(b) The alleles for coat colour (A and a) are actually controlled by another gene (P). If a mouse is homozygous recessive for this gene, it is unable to produce any pigmentation and so will be albino.

Give the possible genotype(s) that will produce the albino phenotype.

(1 mark)

(c) A student produces a genetic diagram to show the phenotypic ratio produced in the F_2 generation if a homozygous dominant mouse (PPAA) breeds with a homozygous recessive mouse (ppaa). His results are shown in **Table 1.1** below.

Table 1.1

	PA	**pA**	**Pa**	**pa**
PA	PPAA	PpAA	PPAa	PpAa
pA	PpAA	ppAA	PpAa	ppAa
Pa	PPAa	PpAa	PPaa	Ppaa
pa	PpAa	ppAa	Ppaa	ppaa

The student concludes that this cross produces a phenotypic ratio of 9 : 3 : 3 : 1. This is incorrect. Give the phenotypic ratio that would be expected from this cross and explain why the student's conclusion is wrong.

(3 marks)

2 Yeast cells can convert substance 1 to substance 3 via the enzyme pathway shown in **Fig. 2.1**. Two different gene loci control the pathway and each has two alleles. Having the dominant versions of alleles A and B means that the yeast cell will produce enzymes A and B as shown in **Fig. 2.1**.

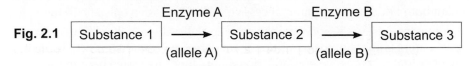

Fig. 2.1

Yeast cells that lack either enzyme A or enzyme B cannot convert substance 1 to substance 3 and so cannot grow in media containing substance 1.

(a) Complete **Table 2.1** by putting a tick (✓) or a cross (✗) in the correct boxes below to show whether or not yeast cells with the following genotypes could grow on substance 1. The first one has been done for you

Table 2.1

Genotype	Growth on substance 1
AaBb	✓
aaBb	
AAbb	
AABb	

(1 mark)

(b) Some of the cells that could not grow on substance 1 will grow if supplied with substance 2. Suggest why (with reference to their genotype).

(3 marks)

(c) Yeast cells with genotype AaBb were crossed with yeast cells homozygous recessive for both alleles. Draw a genetic diagram to show the expected ratio of offspring genotypes for this cross. Predict the percentage of F_1 cells that would not be able to grow in medium containing substance 1.

(4 marks)

3 Haemophilia is a sex-linked genetic disorder. It is caused by a faulty allele on the X-chromosome. The faulty allele (X^h) is recessive to the normal allele (X^H). A study was carried out into the inheritance of haemophilia. The phenotypes of children in families where the mother was a carrier of the disease (genotype $X^H X^h$) and the father was a haemophiliac (genotype $X^h Y$) were recorded.

(a) Draw a genetic diagram to show why a 1 : 1 : 1 : 1 phenotypic ratio of haemophiliac male : haemophiliac female : carrier female : unaffected male was expected in the results of this study.

(3 marks)

(b) Of the 272 children in this study, 130 were boys and 142 were girls.
61 of the boys and 70 of the girls had haemophilia.
A chi-squared test was used to analyse the results.

(i) Calculate the chi-squared value (χ^2) for this study.

$$\chi^2 = \sum \frac{(O - E)^2}{E}$$

O = observed result
E = expected result

(3 marks)

(ii) Use your calculated value of χ^2 and **Table 3.1** to determine whether or not the difference between the observed and expected results is significant.

Degrees of freedom	Probability (P)					
	0.50	0.20	0.10	0.05	0.01	0.001
1	0.46	1.64	2.71	3.84	6.64	10.83
2	1.39	3.22	4.61	5.99	9.21	13.82
3	2.37	4.64	6.25	7.82	11.34	16.27

Table 3.1

(1 mark)

Tip: A population is a group of organisms of the same species living in a particular area.

Tip: Genetic variation is generated by meiosis (see page 163) and mutations.

Tip: A selection pressure is anything that affects an organism's chance of survival and reproduction.

Exam Tip
If you're asked to describe the process of natural selection in the exam, it's important to make it clear that it takes place <u>over many generations</u>.

1. Evolution by Natural Selection and Genetic Drift

You might remember evolution from Module 4. It's caused by the variation in alleles within a species.

Alleles and evolution

The complete range of alleles present in a population is called the **gene pool**. How often an allele occurs in a population is called the **allele frequency**. It's usually given as a percentage of the total population, e.g. 35%, or a decimal, e.g. 0.35. The frequency of an allele in a population changes over time — this is evolution.

Evolution by natural selection

Evolution may take place by the process of natural selection. Here's how it works:

- Individuals within a population vary because they have different alleles. New alleles are usually generated by **mutations** in genes.

- Predation, disease and competition (selection pressures) create a struggle for survival.

- Because individuals vary, some are better adapted to the selection pressures than others.

- Individuals that have an allele that increases their chance of survival (an advantageous allele) are more likely to survive, reproduce and pass on the advantageous allele than individuals with other alleles.

- This means that a greater proportion of the next generation inherit the advantageous allele.

- They, in turn, are more likely to survive, reproduce and pass on their genes. So the frequency of the advantageous allele increases from generation to generation.

An allele is only advantageous with the right selection pressure. Without a selection pressure, natural selection won't take place.

Evolution and the environment

Whether the environment is changing or stable affects which characteristics are selected for by natural selection.

Selection in a stable environment

When the environment isn't changing much, individuals with alleles for characteristics towards the middle of the range are more likely to survive and reproduce. This is called **stabilising selection** and it reduces the range of possible phenotypes.

Example

In any mammal population there's a range of fur length. In a stable climate, having fur at the extremes of this range reduces the chances of surviving as it's harder to maintain the right body temperature, so mammals with very short or very long fur have a selective disadvantage. Mammals with alleles for average fur length are the most likely to survive, reproduce and pass on their alleles. These mammals have a selective advantage, so these alleles for average fur length increase in frequency.

Over time, the proportion of the population with average fur length increases and the range of fur lengths decreases — as shown in Figure 1. In the offspring graph the range of fur lengths has decreased, which results in a narrower graph. The proportion with average length fur has increased, resulting in a taller graph in the average fur length region.

Tip: The breeding population is just the animals that are surviving, reproducing and passing on their alleles.

Exam Tip
Here the data is shown as a graph, but you could be given a table of data in your exam.

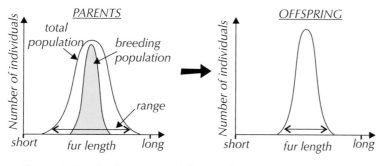

Figure 1: Graphs that show stabilising selection across generations.

Selection in a changing environment

When there's a change in the environment, individuals with alleles for characteristics of an extreme type are more likely to survive and reproduce. This is called **directional selection**.

Tip: If a species can't adapt to changes in its environment, then its numbers may decrease and it may become extinct.

Example

If the environment becomes very cold, individual mammals with alleles for long fur length will find it easier to maintain the right body temperature than animals with short fur length. They have a selective advantage, so they're more likely to survive, reproduce and pass on their alleles. Over time the frequency of alleles for long fur length increases — see Figure 2. In the offspring graph, the average fur length (dotted line) has moved towards the extreme, longer end.

Tip: With data that shows <u>stabilising</u> selection, the mean <u>stays</u> in the middle. With data that shows <u>directional</u> selection, the mean moves in one <u>direction</u> or the other.

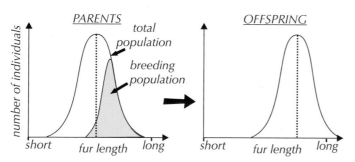

Figure 2: Graphs that show directional selection across generations.

Evolution via genetic drift

Natural selection is just one process by which evolution occurs.
Evolution also occurs due to genetic drift — this just means that instead of environmental factors affecting which individuals survive, breed and pass on their alleles, chance dictates which alleles are passed on.
Here's how it works:

- Individuals within a population show variation in their genotypes (e.g. A and B, see Figure 3).

- By chance, the allele for one genotype (B) is passed on to the offspring more often than others. So the number of individuals with the allele increases.

- If by chance the same allele is passed on more often again and again, it can lead to evolution as the allele becomes more common in the population.

Figure 3: Diagram to show genetic drift in a population.

Exam Tip
Don't confuse genetic drift with natural selection in the exam. In natural selection, characteristics become more common if they increase an organism's likelihood of survival. In genetic drift, they become more common by chance.

Genetic drift and population size

Natural selection and genetic drift work alongside each other to drive evolution, but one process can drive evolution more than the other depending on the population size. Evolution by genetic drift usually has a greater effect in smaller populations where chance has a greater influence. In larger populations any chance variations in allele frequency tend to even out across the whole population.

Tip: Genetic drift tends to cause the genetic diversity of a population to decrease. Lack of genetic diversity may make species less able to adapt to future changes in their environment, so genetic drift can be a problem for small populations.

─ **Example — the evolution of human blood groups** ──────

Different Native American tribes show different blood group frequencies. For example, Blackfoot Indians are mainly group A, but Navajos are mainly group O. Blood group doesn't affect survival or reproduction, so the differences aren't due to evolution by natural selection. In the past, human populations were much smaller and were often found in isolated groups. The blood group differences were due to evolution by genetic drift — by chance the allele for blood group O was passed on more often in the Navajo tribe, so over time this allele and blood group became more common.

Genetic bottlenecks

A genetic bottleneck is an event (such as a natural disaster) that causes a big reduction in a population's size, leading to a reduction in the gene pool. Evolution by genetic drift has a greater effect if there's a genetic bottleneck.

Tip: The gene pool is the complete range of alleles in a population.

Tip: Disease and habitat destruction by humans can also act as genetic bottlenecks.

─ **Example** ─────────────────────────────

The mice in a large population are either black or grey. The coat colour doesn't affect their survival or reproduction. A large flood hits the population and the only survivors are grey mice and one black mouse. Grey becomes the most common colour due to genetic drift (see Figure 4 on the next page).

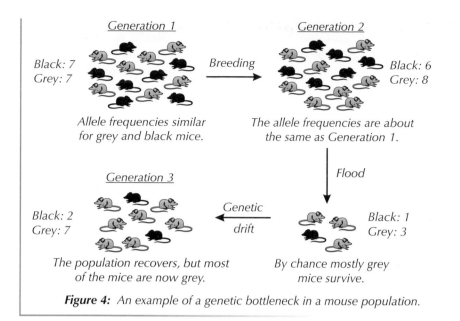

Generation 1

Black: 7
Grey: 7

Breeding

Generation 2

Black: 6
Grey: 8

Allele frequencies similar for grey and black mice.

The allele frequencies are about the same as Generation 1.

Flood

Tip: The flood is the genetic bottleneck here — it's significantly reduced the size of the mouse population.

Generation 3

Black: 2
Grey: 7

Genetic drift

Black: 1
Grey: 3

The population recovers, but most of the mice are now grey.

By chance mostly grey mice survive.

Figure 4: *An example of a genetic bottleneck in a mouse population.*

The founder effect

The founder effect describes what happens when just a few organisms from a population start a new population and there are only a small number of different alleles in the initial gene pool. Here's how it works:

- Individuals within a population show variation in their genotypes (see Figure 5).
- Some of these individuals start a new population. By chance these individuals mostly have one particular genotype (e.g. the blue genotype).
- Without any further 'gene flow' (i.e. the introduction of new alleles from outside the population) the new population will grow with reduced genetic variation. As the population is small, it's more heavily influenced by genetic drift than a larger population.

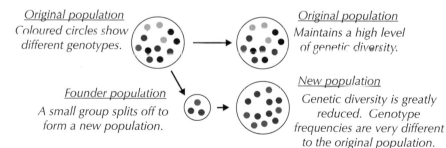

Original population
Coloured circles show different genotypes.

Original population
Maintains a high level of genetic diversity.

Founder population
A small group splits off to form a new population.

New population
Genetic diversity is greatly reduced. Genotype frequencies are very different to the original population.

Figure 5: *Diagram illustrating the founder effect.*

Tip: The brown genotype in Figure 5 could represent carriers of a genetic disorder. It's easy to see why the founder effect can lead to an unusually high incidence of a certain genetic disorder within a population, if the allele for it is present in the founding population.

The founder effect can occur as a result of migration leading to geographical separation or if a new colony is separated from the original population for another reason, such as religion.

Example

The Amish population of North America are all descended from a small number of Swiss who migrated there. The population shows little genetic diversity. They have remained isolated from the surrounding population due to their religious beliefs, so few new alleles have been introduced. The population has an unusually high incidence of certain genetic disorders.

Practice Questions — Application

Q1 Flowers of a plant species can be purple, pink or white. Each colour is coded for by a different allele. The graphs below show the frequencies of these alleles in two populations of the plant species.

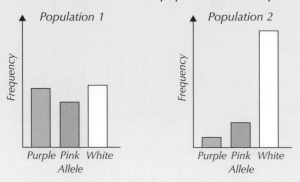

a) Describe the differences in allele frequencies between the two populations.

b) Explain how genetic drift could have led to the allele frequencies shown in Population 2.

c) Which is likely to be the smaller population, 1 or 2? Give a reason for your answer.

Q2 The frequency of an allele involved in fur colouring was calculated for two populations of woodland mammal found in the north and south of a large forest. The results are shown in the table below. In 1999 a fire destroyed thousands of square miles of trees in the north of the forest.

a) The allele frequency for the southern population peaked in 2000. Suggest an explanation for this.

b) The allele is involved in the production of dark fur. Use this information to explain how natural selection might have accounted for the results for the northern population.

	Allele frequency	
Year	North	South
1994	0.31	0.17
1996	0.33	0.17
1998	0.33	0.19
2000	0.48	0.32
2002	0.52	0.24

Tip: Take your time looking at any data you're given — make sure you really understand what the table in Q2 is showing you before you attempt to answer the questions.

Tip: To help you answer Q2 b), think about how the fire might change the forest environment.

Practice Questions — Fact Recall

Q1 Explain what is meant by the following terms:
   a) gene pool,
   b) allele frequency.

Q2 How are allele frequency and evolution related?

Q3 Explain why variation is needed for evolution to take place.

Q4 How does a stable environment affect selection?

Q5 What is a genetic bottleneck and how does it influence evolution?

Q6 Explain why the founder effect can lead to an increased incidence of genetic disease.

2. The Hardy-Weinberg Principle

Learning Objective:

- Be able to use the equations for the Hardy-Weinberg principle ($p + q = 1$ and $p^2 + 2pq + q^2 = 1$) to calculate allele frequencies in populations.

Specification Reference 6.1.2

A little bit of maths now... but I promise it's not too bad. Basically, you can work out allele and genotype frequencies for a whole population — which is more useful than it sounds.

What is the Hardy-Weinberg principle?

The Hardy-Weinberg principle is a mathematical model which predicts that the frequencies of alleles in a population won't change from one generation to the next. But this prediction is only true under certain conditions:

- It has to be a large population where there's no immigration, emigration, mutations or natural selection (see page 190).

- There needs to be random mating — all possible genotypes can breed with all others.

The Hardy-Weinberg equations (see below) are based on this principle. They can be used to estimate the frequency of particular alleles and genotypes within populations. If frequencies do change between generations in a large population then immigration, emigration, natural selection or mutations have happened.

The Hardy-Weinberg equations

There are two Hardy-Weinberg equations — one is used for working out allele frequency and the other one is usually used when you're dealing with genotype frequencies.

Allele frequency

The total frequency of all possible alleles for a characteristic in a certain population is 1.0. So the frequencies of the individual alleles (the dominant one and the recessive one) must add up to 1.0. Here's that idea in an equation:

$$p + q = 1$$

Where...

p = the frequency of the dominant allele

q = the frequency of the recessive allele

Tip: If the frequencies for two alleles add up to <u>more than one</u>, they're not alleles for the same gene (characteristic). If they come to <u>less than one</u>, there are more than two alleles for that gene.

Genotype frequency

The total frequency of all possible genotypes for one characteristic in a certain population is 1.0. So the frequencies of the individual genotypes must add up to 1.0. But remember there are three genotypes — homozygous recessive, homozygous dominant and heterozygous. Here's the second equation:

$$p^2 + 2pq + q^2 = 1$$

Where...

p^2 = frequency of homozygous dominant genotype

$2pq$ = frequency of heterozygous genotype

q^2 = frequency of homozygous recessive genotype

Tip: Remember, homozygous dominant means two copies of the dominant allele (e.g. BB), homozygous recessive means two copies of the recessive allele (e.g. bb) and heterozygous means one copy of each allele (e.g. Bb). See pages 165-166.

Uses of the Hardy-Weinberg principle

The best way to understand how to use the principle and the equations is to follow through some examples — like the ones on the next page...

Predicting allele frequency

You can figure out the frequency of one allele if you know the frequency of the other:

Example — Maths Skills

- A species of plant has either red or white flowers. Allele R (red) is dominant and allele r (white) is recessive. If the frequency of R is 0.4 in Population X, what is the frequency of r?
- You know the frequency of one allele and just need to find the frequency of the other using $p + q = 1$ (where p = dominant allele, R, and q = recessive allele, r). So:

$$p + q = 1$$
$$R + r = 1$$
$$0.4 + r = 1$$
$$r = 1 - 0.4 = 0.6$$

So the frequency of the r allele in Population X is 0.6.

You can also figure out allele frequencies if you're given information about genotype (or phenotype) frequencies:

Example — Maths Skills

- There are two alleles for flower colour (R and r), so there are three possible genotypes — RR, Rr and rr. If the frequency of genotype RR is 0.56 in Population Y, what is the allele frequency of r?
- You know that RR is the homozygous dominant genotype, so RR = p^2. You also know that the allele frequency for R = p, so:

$$p^2 = 0.56$$
$$p = \sqrt{0.56} = 0.75, \text{ so } R = 0.75$$

You also know that $p + q = 1$, where p = the dominant allele, R, and q = the recessive allele, r. So:

$$p + q = 1$$
$$R + r = 1$$
$$0.75 + r = 1$$
$$r = 1 - 0.75 = 0.25$$

So the frequency of the r allele (white) in Population Y is 0.25.

Tip: Remember, genotype is the alleles an organism has (e.g. Rr) and phenotype is the characteristics the alleles produce (e.g. red flowers). See page 165 for more.

Exam Tip
You'll be allowed to take a calculator into the exam to help you with calculations like these.

Predicting genotype frequency

Here you're after genotype, so it's p^2, q^2 or $2pq$ you need to find:

Example — Maths Skills

- If there are two alleles for flower colour (R and r), there are three possible genotypes — RR, Rr and rr. In Population Z, the frequency of genotype RR is 0.34 and the frequency of genotype Rr is 0.27. Find the frequency of rr in Population Z.
- $p^2 + 2pq + q^2 = 1$, where p^2 = homozygous dominant genotype, RR, $2pq$ = heterozygous genotype, Rr, and q^2 = homozygous recessive genotype, rr. So:

$$p^2 + 2pq + q^2 = 1$$
$$RR + Rr + rr = 1$$
$$0.34 + 0.27 + rr = 1$$
$$rr = 1 - 0.34 - 0.27 = 0.39$$

So the frequency of the rr genotype in Population Z is 0.39.

Tip: The more examples you practise, the more confident you'll be at working out allele and genotype frequencies when it comes to your exam.

Predicting the percentage of a population that has a certain genotype

You're looking at genotype again, so it's ultimately something to do with p^2, q^2 or $2pq$. But you might have to use a combination of equations to get there:

Example — Maths Skills

- The frequency of cystic fibrosis (genotype ff) in the UK is currently approximately 1 birth in every 2500. Use this information to estimate the percentage of people in the UK that are cystic fibrosis carriers (Ff).
- To do this you need to find the frequency of the heterozygous genotype Ff, i.e. $2pq$, using both equations. (You can't just use the big one as you only know one of the three genotypes — q^2.)

First calculate q:

Frequency of cystic fibrosis (homozygous recessive, ff) is 1 in 2500

$$\text{ff} = q^2 = \frac{1}{2500} = 0.0004. \text{ So } q = \sqrt{0.0004} = 0.02$$

Next calculate p:

Use $p + q = 1$, rearranged: $p = 1 - q = 1 - 0.02 = 0.98$

Then calculate $2pq$:

$$2pq = 2 \times p \times q = 2 \times 0.98 \times 0.02 = 0.039$$

The frequency of genotype Ff is 0.039, so the percentage of the UK population that are carriers is 0.039 × 100 = 3.9%.

Exam Tip
It's easier than it might seem to decide which equation to use.
If you're given one allele frequency and asked to find the other it's the simple equation.
If you know two out of the three genotype frequencies, you can find the other frequency using the big equation.
For anything else you'll probably need to use a combination of equations.

Tip: There's more on carriers on page 166.

Practice Questions — Application

Q1 In a human population, the allele frequency for the recessive albino allele is measured over generations as shown in the table below.

a) Calculate the frequency of the pigmented (non-albino) allele in generation 1.

b) Calculate the frequency of the heterozygous genotype in generation 1.

c) Does the Hardy-Weinberg principle apply to this population? Explain your answer.

Generation	*Allele frequency*
1	*0.10*
4	*0.07*
7	*0.03*

Q2 ADA deficiency is an inherited metabolic disorder caused by a recessive allele. The recessive allele frequency in a population is 0.16. What is the frequency of the homozygous dominant genotype in the same population?

Q3 Seed texture in pea plants is controlled by two alleles, the dominant round allele and the recessive wrinkled allele. 31% of a population have wrinkled seeds. What percentage of the population have a heterozygous genotype?

Practice Questions — Fact Recall

Q1 Describe the Hardy-Weinberg principle and the conditions under which it is true.

Q2 Write down the two Hardy-Weinberg equations and describe what each component represents.

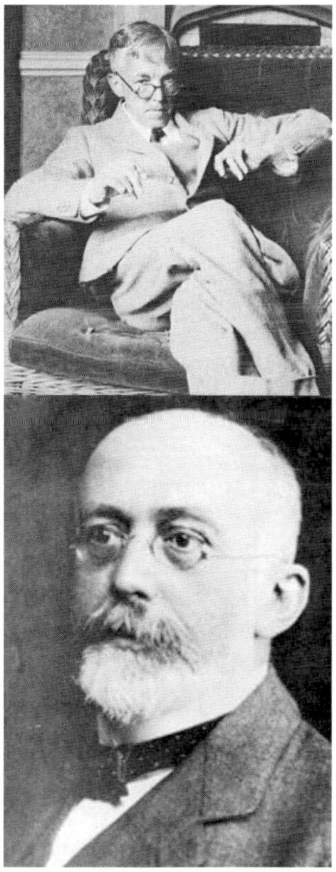

Figure 1: *G H Hardy (top) and Wilhelm Weinberg (bottom) actually came up with the ideas behind the Hardy-Weinberg principle independently from one another.*

Learning Objectives:

- Understand the principles of artificial selection and its uses, including examples of selective breeding in plants and animals.

- Understand the importance of maintaining a resource of genetic material for use in selective breeding, including wild types.

- Understand the ethical considerations surrounding the use of artificial selection, including a consideration of the more extreme examples of the use of artificial selection to 'improve' domestic species, e.g. dog breeds.

Specification Reference 6.1.2

Tip: Artificial selection is also called selective breeding.

Figure 1: The large ears of Triticum aestivum.

3. Artificial Selection

Selection for particular characteristics happens naturally in populations as a result of environmental factors — but it can also happen artificially when humans get involved...

What is artificial selection?

Artificial selection is when humans select individuals in a population to breed together to get desirable traits. Here are two examples:

1. Modern dairy cattle

Modern dairy cows have been produced through artificial selection. One of the characteristics that has been selected for is a high milk yield. Here's how it's done:

- Farmers select a female with a very high milk yield and a male whose mother had a very high milk yield and breed these two together.
- Then they select the offspring with the highest milk yields and breed them together.
- This is continued over several generations until a very high milk-yielding cow is produced.

Other characteristics selected for in dairy cows include:

- a high milk quality (rich and creamy),
- a long lactation period (so the cow produces milk for longer),
- large udders (to make milking easier),
- resistance to mastitis (inflammation of the udders) and other diseases,
- a calm temperament.

Artificial selection has been taking place for hundreds of years but it's been made much easier by modern techniques, e.g. artificial insemination and IVF give farmers more control over which cows reproduce. Animal cloning (see pages 234-237) allows farmers to produce genetically identical copies of their best cows, so they can be certain of the offspring's characteristics.

2. Bread wheat

Bread wheat (*Triticum aestivum*) is the plant from which flour is produced for bread-making. It produces a high yield of wheat because of artificial selection by humans:

- Wheat plants with a high wheat yield (e.g. large ears) are bred together.
- The offspring with the highest yields are then bred together.
- This is continued over several generations to produce a plant that has a very high yield.

Large ears ✕ Large ears → Breed → Very large ears

Other characteristics selected for in bread wheat include:

- a higher tolerance of the cold than other wheat varieties,
- short stalks (so they don't collapse under the weight of the ears),
- uniform stalk heights (to make harvesting easier).

Techniques such as plant cloning (see pages 230-233) can be useful in the artificial selection of crop plants.

Problems with artificial selection

Artificial selection is really useful, but it has downsides too.

Reducing the gene pool

Artificial selection means that only organisms with similar traits and therefore similar alleles are bred together. This leads to a reduction in the number of alleles in the gene pool. A reduced gene pool could cause us problems in the future — for example, if a new disease appears, there's less chance of the alleles that could offer resistance to that disease being present in the population. Artificial selection could also mean that potentially useful alleles are accidentally lost from the population when other alleles are being selected for.

This means it's important to maintain resources of genetic material for use in the future, for example by preserving the original 'wild type' organisms that haven't undergone any artificial selection.

Problems for organisms

Artificial selection can exaggerate certain traits, leading to health problems for the organisms involved. A reduced gene pool can also result in an increased incidence of genetic disease.

Figure 2: *Pugs and Dalmatians can both suffer health problems as a result of selective breeding.*

> **Examples**
>
> Modern pedigree dog breeds are all descended from a single wolf-like ancestor. Each breed has gone through many generations of artificial selection to produce the dogs we know today. Pedigree dogs such as Pugs and French Bulldogs have been bred to have flat, squashed up faces. This trait has become so exaggerated that many of these dogs now suffer breathing problems as a result.
>
> There's a high incidence of hereditary deafness in certain dog breeds, including Dalmatians and English Bull Terriers. The cause of this is not fully understood, but there is evidence to suggest that deafness is linked to genes affecting pigmentation in these dogs.

Problems like these mean that there are ethical issues surrounding the use of artificial selection. For example, many people don't think it's fair to keep artificially selecting traits in dogs that cause them health problems.

Practice Questions — Fact Recall

Q1 Define artificial selection.

Q2 a) Describe how large udders may have been selected for in modern dairy cows.

   b) Apart from large udders, give one other characteristic that could be artificially selected for in dairy cows.

Q3 Outline an example of selective breeding in plants.

Q4 Describe two potential problems associated with selective breeding.

Tip: There are ethical arguments for artificial selection too — it can make food production more efficient, which means more people can be fed using fewer resources, and it makes food production cheaper, which is important in parts of the world where people struggle to afford food. Make sure you can weigh up the benefits and the costs of artificial selection.

Tip: Geographical isolation is also known as ecological isolation.

Exam Tip

It's important to use the correct terminology in the exam, so make sure you understand and can use terms such as 'allele frequency', 'geographical isolation', 'allopatric speciation' and 'sympatric speciation' (coming up on the next page).

4. Speciation

The next few pages cover what a species is and how a new one is formed...

What is speciation?

A **species** is defined as a group of similar organisms that can reproduce to give fertile offspring. Speciation is the development of a new species. It occurs when populations of the same species become **reproductively isolated** — changes in allele frequencies cause changes in phenotype that mean they can no longer breed together to produce fertile offspring.

Allopatric speciation

Populations can become reproductively isolated through a combination of geographical isolation and natural selection — this is called **allopatric speciation**. Geographical isolation happens when a physical barrier, e.g. a flood or an earthquake, divides a population of a species, causing some individuals to become separated from the main population. Populations that are geographically isolated will experience slightly different conditions. For example, there might be a different climate on each side of the physical barrier. Because the environment is different for each population, different characteristics will become more common due to natural selection (because there are different selection pressures):

- Because different characteristics will be advantageous on each side, the allele frequencies will change in each population, e.g. if one allele is more advantageous on one side of the barrier, the frequency of that allele on that side will increase.
- Mutations will take place independently in each population, also changing the allele frequencies.
- The changes in allele frequencies will lead to changes in phenotype frequencies, e.g. the advantageous characteristics (phenotypes) will become more common on that side.

Eventually, individuals from different populations will have changed so much that they won't be able to breed with one another to produce fertile offspring — they'll have become reproductively isolated. The two groups will have become separate species — see Figure 2.

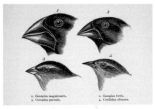

Figure 1: *Four species of 'Darwin's finches'. These are often seen as a classic example of speciation.*

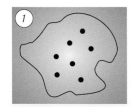

Population of individuals
● = individual organism

Populations adapt to new environments.

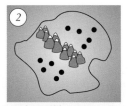

Physical barriers stop interbreeding between populations.

Allele and phenotype frequency change leading to the development of new species.

Figure 2: *Diagram showing how geographical isolation could lead to reproductive isolation and so speciation.*

How does reproductive isolation occur?

Reproductive isolation occurs because the changes in the alleles and phenotypes of the two populations prevent them from successfully breeding together. These changes include:

- Seasonal changes — individuals from the same population develop different flowering or mating seasons, or become sexually active at different times of the year.
- Mechanical changes — changes in genitalia prevent successful mating.
- Behavioural changes — a group of individuals develop courtship rituals that aren't attractive to the main population.

Sympatric speciation

A population doesn't have to become geographically isolated to become reproductively isolated. Random mutations could occur within a population, resulting in the changes mentioned above, preventing members of that population breeding with other members of the species. Speciation without geographical isolation is called sympatric speciation.

It's generally thought that sympatric speciation is pretty rare, as it's difficult for a section of a population to become completely reproductively isolated from the rest of the population without being geographically isolated too (as is the case with allopatric speciation).

Example

Most eukaryotic organisms are diploid — they have two sets of homologous (matched) chromosomes in their cells. Sometimes, mutations can occur that increase the number of chromosomes. This is known as polyploidy. Individuals with different numbers of chromosomes can't reproduce sexually to give fertile offspring — so if a polyploid organism emerges in a diploid population, the polyploid organism will be reproductively isolated from the diploid organisms. If the polyploid organism then reproduces asexually, a new species could develop. Polyploidy can only lead to speciation if it doesn't prove fatal to the organism and more polyploid organisms can be produced. It's more common in plants than animals.

Tip: Don't confuse geographical isolation with reproductive isolation. Populations that are geographically isolated are physically separated, but may still be able to reproduce if brought back together. Geographical isolation can lead to reproductive isolation if natural selection significantly changes the allele frequencies in the two separated populations.

Tip: Reproductive isolation is necessary for sympatric or allopatric speciation to take place.

Tip: Polyploidy can be a mechanism of reproductive isolation.

Exam Tip
Make sure you're clear on the difference between sympatric and allopatric speciation, and can remember which is which. If it helps, you could think of **S**ympatric speciation happening in the **S**ame place, and **A**llopatric speciation occurring in populations that are **A**way from each other.

Practice Questions — Application

Q1 African elephants have been traditionally classified as one species, *Loxodonta africana*. However, recent research suggests that there are actually two separate species of African elephant, one living in a savannah (grassland) habitat and one living in forested areas. The two populations are thought to have separated from each other several million years ago when a drier climate caused some elephants to move out of the forests and onto the savannah.

Using your knowledge of speciation, describe how the two separate species of African elephant may have evolved.

Q2 *Rhagoletis pomonella* is a species of fly from North America. Historically, *R. pomonella* flies laid their eggs in hawthorn fruits, but when apples were introduced to North America, some started to lay their eggs inside apples. There are now two separate populations of *R. pomonella* — one laying its eggs inside apples and the other laying its eggs inside hawthorn fruits. The flies only tend to mate on fruit of the same species that they hatched in. Some scientists think this could be the beginning of speciation.

a) Describe how you could test whether the two populations of *R. pomonella* had become different species.

b) What kind of speciation would this be an example of? Explain your answer.

Practice Questions — Fact Recall

Q1 Explain what is meant by the following terms:
a) reproductive isolation,
b) geographic isolation,
c) speciation.

Q2 Describe the difference between allopatric speciation and sympatric speciation.

Q3 Suggest three changes that could lead to a population becoming reproductively isolated.

Section Summary

Make sure you know...

- That evolution is a change in allele frequencies in a population over time, and can occur due to natural selection and genetic drift.

- Why variation is essential for natural selection — because organisms vary, some individuals will be better adapted to selection pressures than others. These organisms are more likely to survive, reproduce and pass on their beneficial alleles than others. This will increase the frequency of the beneficial allele in the population over many generations.

- That in a stable environment, selection will favour alleles for characteristics towards the middle of the range (stabilising selection).

- That in a changing environment, selection will favour alleles for characteristics of an extreme type (directional selection).

- That in evolution by genetic drift, alleles become more common in a population by chance.

- That genetic drift has a bigger effect in small populations than in large populations.

- That genetic bottlenecks occur when a population shrinks rapidly, e.g. due to a natural disaster.

- That the founder effect describes what happens when a few organisms from a population start a new population so there is only a small number of different alleles in the initial gene pool.

- That genetic bottlenecks and the founder effect make populations more susceptible to genetic drift.

- That the Hardy-Weinberg principle predicts that allele frequencies in a population won't change between one generation and the next, provided that certain conditions are met.

- How to use the Hardy-Weinberg equations ($p + q = 1$ and $p^2 + 2pq + q^2 = 1$) to calculate allele and genotype frequencies.

- How artificial selection is used to produce plants and animals with desirable traits.

- Why preserving 'wild type' organisms is important for maintaining resources of genetic material for use in the future.

- That there are ethical considerations concerning the use of artificial selection.

- That speciation is the development of a new species and it happens when populations of the same species become reproductively isolated (unable to interbreed to produce fertile offspring).

- That allopatric speciation can occur when populations of the same species are geographically isolated and differences in the gene pools develop that eventually lead to reproductive isolation.

- That sympatric speciation occurs when a random mutation causes reproductive isolation without geographic isolation.

- The different ways in which reproductive isolation can occur.

1   A species of insectivorous bird usually breeds in mid-April, although there is variation between individuals in breeding date. Individuals that breed earlier in the year have difficulties finding sufficient food to feed their young, and the offspring of individuals that breed later are less likely to survive the following winter.

(a)   State the kind of selection that is acting on this species.

(1 mark)

(b)   It is thought that climate change may cause the insects that this species feeds on to increase in abundance earlier in the year. Describe and explain the possible effect of this selective pressure on the bird species.

(2 marks)

2   Chickens that are farmed for their meat are known as broiler chickens. Broiler chickens grow faster than normal chickens, so can be slaughtered at a younger age, are more efficient at converting food into body mass, and produce a higher proportion of breast meat. However, their rapid growth to large sizes means broiler chickens are more vulnerable to cardiovascular problems than normal chickens, and can have problems with walking.

(a) (i)   State the name of the process by which farmers developed broiler chickens from normal chickens.

(1 mark)

(ii)   Describe how this process may have occurred.

(2 marks)

(b)   Discuss the ethical issues around the development of broiler chickens for meat.

(3 marks)

3   A forest is home to a population of a species of flightless beetle. A new motorway is built, separating an area of woodland from the main body of the forest, and isolating a small population of the beetle from the larger population in the main forest. The beetles will not cross open spaces, due to increased visibility to predators, so the motorway acts as a barrier between the two populations. There is no immigration into either woodland from the wider area.

Scientists study the two populations, collecting data on the size and colour of individuals, and how likely they are to survive (which they estimate from recapture rates). Over time, they notice that the beetles in the small fragment of woodland have evolved to become significantly smaller than the beetles in the main body of the forest. The size of the beetles in the main body of the forest remains unchanged.

(a)   Suggest two possible mechanisms for this evolutionary change.

(2 marks)

(b)   Describe how the scientists could distinguish between these two mechanisms using the data they have collected.

(2 marks)

4   The Amish population of North America descended from a small group of migrants. They live isolated from the surrounding population, and it is rare for people to migrate into the Amish community.

The Amish population has an unusually high incidence of genetic disorders, including a rare form of dwarfism called Ellis-van Creveld syndrome, which can lead to health problems and death in childhood.

(a)   Ellis-van Creveld syndrome is caused by a recessive allele (e). In some Amish communities, the frequency of Ellis-van Creveld syndrome may be as high as 5 births in every 1000.
The Hardy-Weinberg equations are:

$$p + q = 1$$
$$p^2 + 2pq + q^2 = 1$$

Use the Hardy-Weinberg equations to calculate the percentage of these communities that are **carriers** of Ellis-van Creveld syndrome (genotype Ee). Show your working. Give your answer to **two decimal places**.

(2 marks)

(b)   What process is likely to have led to the high frequency of the Ellis-van Creveld allele in some Amish communities? Give a reason for your answer.

(2 marks)

5   In the early 1970s, ten lizards of the species *Podarcis sicula* were introduced to the island of Pod Mrcaru in the Adriatic Sea from the nearby island of Pod Kopiste. Pod Mrcaru has denser vegetation than Pod Kopiste.

Thirty-six years later, researchers returned to the islands. They found that *P. sicula* on Pod Kopiste ate a diet mainly consisting of insects, whilst the diet of *P. sicula* on Pod Mrcaru had changed to include a high proportion of plant material. The *P. sicula* lizards on Pod Mrcaru had larger heads than the *P. sicula* on Pod Kopiste, and were able to bite with more force. *P. sicula* lizards on Pod Mrcaru had also developed chambers in their intestines, which are associated with fermenting cellulose in order to produce fatty acids, and which were absent in *P. sicula* from Pod Kopiste.

(a)*   Explain how the differences between lizards on the two islands may have arisen in the 36 years since their introduction to Pod Mrcaru.

(9 marks)

(b)   It is possible that these changes may be early stages of speciation.

(i)   State the name for this kind of speciation.

(1 mark)

(ii)   State what would need to occur for these two populations to become separate species.

(1 mark)

* The quality of your response will be assessed in this question.

Learning Objectives:

- Understand the principles of the polymerase chain reaction (PCR) and its application in DNA analysis.
- Understand the use of restriction enzymes.
- Understand the principles and uses of electrophoresis for separating nucleic acid fragments or proteins.
- Know how to carry out electrophoresis (PAG6).

Specification Reference 6.1.3

1. Common Techniques

There are many techniques that can be used to do things like copy, cut out and separate fragments of DNA. This allows us to study and alter genes. You might not get much opportunity to use the techniques involved, but you do need to know the theory behind a few of the more common ones...

Techniques for studying genes

There are lots of techniques used to study genes and their function — you need to learn some of these techniques for the exam. They include:

- The polymerase chain reaction (PCR) (see below).
- Cutting out DNA fragments using restriction enzymes (see p. 207-208).
- Gel electrophoresis (see pages 208-209).

These techniques are also used in DNA profiling (see page 211), genetic engineering (see pages 212-213), gene therapy (see pages 218-219) and DNA sequencing (see pages 220-225).

The polymerase chain reaction

The polymerase chain reaction (PCR) can be used to select a fragment of DNA (containing the gene or bit of DNA you're interested in) and amplify it to produce millions of copies in just a few hours. PCR has several stages and is repeated over and over to make lots of copies. Here's how it works:

Tip: The techniques described over the next few pages will turn up again in the rest of the section, so make sure you're familiar with them now.

Step 1

A reaction mixture is set up that contains the DNA sample, free nucleotides, **primers** and **DNA polymerase**. Primers are short pieces of DNA that are complementary to the bases at the start of the fragment you want. DNA polymerase is an enzyme that creates new DNA strands.

Tip: We've only shown very small pieces of DNA to make the diagrams easier to follow, but real genes are much longer. (Real primers are longer too, but not as big as genes.)

Step 2

The DNA mixture is heated to 95 °C to break the hydrogen bonds between the two strands of DNA. DNA polymerase doesn't denature even at this high temperature — this is important as it means many cycles of PCR can be carried out without having to use new enzymes each time. The mixture is then cooled to 50-65 °C so that the primers can bind (anneal) to the strands.

Tip: DNA polymerase is called a <u>thermostable</u> enzyme because it doesn't denature at high temperatures.

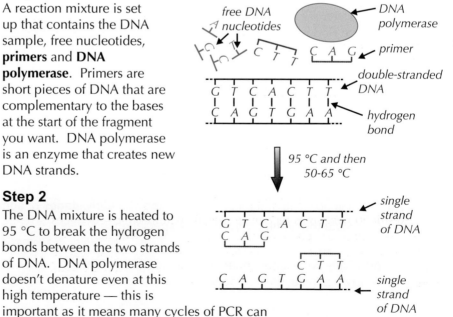

Step 3

The reaction mixture is heated to 72 °C, so DNA polymerase can work. The DNA polymerase lines up free DNA nucleotides alongside each template strand. Complementary base pairing means new complementary strands are formed.

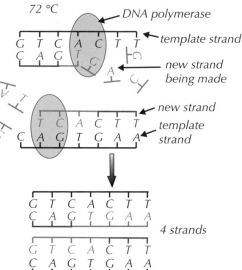

Step 4

Two new copies of the fragment of DNA are formed and one cycle of PCR is complete. Then the cycle starts again — the mixture is heated to 95 °C and this time all four strands (two original and two new) are used as templates.

Figure 1: Scientist using a programmable PCR machine.

As shown below, each PCR cycle doubles the amount of DNA, e.g. 1st cycle = 2 × 2 = 4 DNA fragments, 2nd cycle = 4 × 2 = 8 DNA fragments and so on.

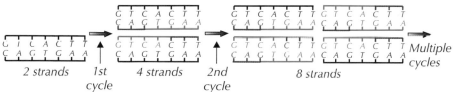

Tip: PCR produces lots of identical copies of DNA, so it can be used to clone genes outside of a living organism — this is called *in vitro* cloning.

Using restriction enzymes

As well as PCR, another way to get a DNA fragment from an organism's DNA is by using restriction enzymes. Here's how they work:

Some sections of DNA have **palindromic sequences** of nucleotides. These sequences consist of antiparallel base pairs (base pairs that read the same in opposite directions) — see Figure 2.

Tip: Restriction enzymes are also known as restriction endonucleases.

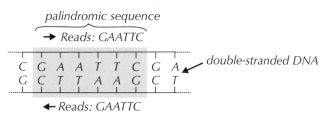

Figure 2: A palindromic DNA sequence.

Restriction enzymes recognise specific palindromic sequences (known as **recognition sequences**) and cut (digest) the DNA at these places. Different restriction enzymes cut at different specific recognition sequences, because the shape of the recognition sequence is complementary to an enzyme's active site.

Tip: Remember, the active site is where an enzyme's substrate binds. In this case, the recognition sequence is the substrate molecule.

- Examples
  - The restriction enzyme *Eco*RI cuts at GAATTC.
  - The restriction enzyme *Hind*III cuts at AAGCTT.

If recognition sequences are present at either side of the DNA fragment you want, you can use restriction enzymes to separate it from the rest of the DNA — see Figure 3. The DNA sample is incubated with the specific restriction enzyme, which cuts the DNA fragment via a hydrolysis reaction. Sometimes the cut leaves **sticky ends** — small tails of unpaired bases at each end of the fragment. Sticky ends can be used to bind (anneal) the DNA fragment to another piece of DNA that has sticky ends with complementary sequences (there's more about this on pages 212-213).

Tip: You won't always find the same restriction enzyme site either side of the fragment you want. E.g. you might get an *Eco*RI site on one side and a *Hind*III on the other, so you'd have to incubate the DNA sample with both enzymes to cut the piece you're after.

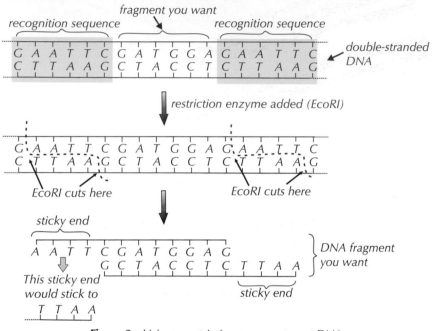

Figure 3: Using a restriction enzyme to cut DNA.

Tip: You'll need to carry out a risk assessment before doing any electrophoresis. It should include making sure your hands are dry before handling any electrical equipment.

Electrophoresis

Electrophoresis is a procedure that uses an electrical current to separate out DNA fragments, RNA fragments or proteins depending on their size. Here's how you can carry out electrophoresis in the lab using samples of fragmented DNA — there are three main stages involved.

Stage 1

Electrophoresis is commonly performed using agarose gel that has been poured into a gel tray and left to solidify. A row of wells is created at one end of the gel. To perform electrophoresis, firstly you need to put the gel tray into a gel box (or tank). You need to make sure the end of the gel tray with the wells is closest to the negative electrode on the gel box. Then add buffer solution to the reservoirs at the sides of the gel box so that the surface of the gel becomes covered in the buffer solution (see Figure 4).

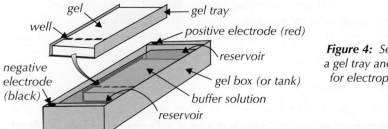

Figure 4: Setting up a gel tray and gel box for electrophoresis.

Stage 2

Take your fragmented DNA samples and, using a micropipette, add the same volume of loading dye to each — loading dye helps the samples to sink to the bottom of the wells and makes them easier to see.

Next add a set volume (e.g. 10 μl) of a DNA sample to the first well. You have to be really careful when adding the samples to the wells — make sure the tip of your micropipette is in the buffer solution and just above the opening of the well (see Figure 5). Don't stick the tip of the micropipette too far into the well or you could pierce the bottom of it.

Figure 6: *A scientist loading a DNA sample into a gel.*

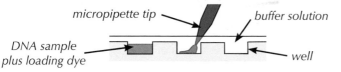

Figure 5: *Adding the DNA samples (with loading dye) to the wells in the gel.*

Then repeat this process and add the same volume of each of your other DNA samples to other wells in the gel. Use a clean micropipette tip each time. Make sure you record which DNA sample you have added to each well.

Tip: Electrophoresis forms the basis of DNA profiling — a process that can be used to determine how closely related (genetically similar) two or more organisms are.

Stage 3

Put the lid on the gel box and connect the leads from the gel box to the power supply. Then turn on the power supply and set it to the required voltage, e.g. 100 V. This causes an electrical current to be passed through the gel.

DNA fragments are negatively charged, so they'll move through the gel towards the positive electrode at the far end of the gel (called the anode). Small DNA fragments move faster and travel further through the gel, so the DNA fragments will separate according to size.

Let the gel run for about 30 minutes (or until the dye is about 2 cm from the end of the gel), then turn off the power supply. Remove the gel tray from the gel box and tip off any excess buffer solution. Wearing gloves, stain the DNA fragments by covering the surface of the gel with a staining solution then rinsing the gel with water. The bands of the different DNA fragments will now be visible (see Figure 7).

Tip: The size (length) of DNA fragments is measured in bases, e.g. ATCC = 4 bases or base pairs (bp) or nucleotides, 1000 bases is one kilobase (1 kb).

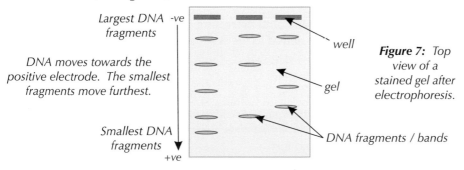

Figure 7: *Top view of a stained gel after electrophoresis.*

Electrophoresis with RNA fragments and proteins

Electrophoresis can be carried out on RNA fragments following the same basic method as for DNA fragments.

However, proteins can be positively charged or negatively charged so, before they undergo electrophoresis, they're mixed with a chemical that denatures the proteins so they all have the same charge. Electrophoresis of proteins has many uses, e.g. to identify the proteins present in urine or blood samples, which may help to diagnose disease.

Practice Questions — Application

Q1 The following DNA fragment is being copied using PCR. The arrows mark the start of each DNA strand.

Start

```
G  C  A  T  A  C  C  G  T  A  A  T  G  G
C  G  T  A  T  G  G  C  A  T  T  A  C  C
```

Start

a) The scientist carrying out the PCR uses primers that are four bases long. Give the sequences of the primers he will need to use to copy the DNA fragment.

b) The scientist carries out six cycles of PCR. How many single strands of DNA will he have once the six cycles are complete?

Q2 Using information from the table below, describe and explain how restriction enzymes could be used to cut this DNA sequence:

CAGGATCCTCCTTACATAGTGAATTCATGC

Restriction enzyme	Recognition sequence
BamHI	GGATCC
HindIII	AAGCTT
EcoRI	GAATTC

Tip: Restriction enzymes are used a lot in gene technology to cut DNA fragments, so make sure you can answer Q2 — they'll pop up again, I promise.

Q3 Below is part of a method for carrying out electrophoresis. A tray containing a prepared gel has already been added to a gel box and covered with buffer solution.

- Using a micropipette, add the same volume of loading dye to each DNA sample.
- Add 10 µl of each DNA sample (plus loading dye) to each well in the gel, so there is one sample in each well.
- Record which DNA sample has been added to each well.

a) Why is loading dye added to the DNA samples?

b) Describe how you could make sure that the DNA sample is successfully transferred to the well without being contaminated.

c) What are the next steps needed to make the DNA fragments move through the gel?

Practice Questions — Fact Recall

Q1 What does PCR stand for?

Q2 Explain what is meant by the term 'palindromic sequence'.

Q3 What are sticky ends? Why are they useful?

Q4 Where would the longest DNA fragments be found in a gel — at the top (near the negative electrode) or at the bottom (near the positive electrode)?

Q5 What do you need to do to samples of proteins before they can undergo electrophoresis?

Q6 Give an example of a use for the electrophoresis of proteins.

2. DNA Profiling

Techniques for studying genes and their functions are actually very useful...

Learning Objective:

- Know the principles of DNA profiling and its uses, including in forensics and analysis of disease risk.

Specification Reference 6.1.3

What are DNA profiles?

Some of an organism's genome (all the genetic material in an organism) consists of repetitive, non-coding base sequences — sequences that don't code for proteins and repeat over and over (sometimes thousands of times). The number of times these non-coding sequences are repeated differs from person to person, so the length of these sequences in nucleotides differs too.

The number of times a sequence is repeated at different, specific places (loci) in a person's genome (and so the number of nucleotides there) can be analysed using electrophoresis. This creates a DNA profile. The probability of two individuals having the same DNA profile is very low because the chance of two individuals having the same number of sequence repeats at each locus in DNA is very low.

Use in forensic science

Forensic scientists use DNA profiling to compare samples of DNA collected from crime scenes (e.g. DNA from blood, semen, skin cells, saliva, hair etc.) to samples of DNA from possible suspects, to link them to crime scenes. The DNA is isolated from all the collected samples (from the crime scene and from the suspects). PCR (see pages 206-207) is used to amplify multiple areas containing different sequence repeats — primers are used to bind to either side of these repeats and so the whole repeat is amplified. The PCR products are run on an electrophoresis gel and the DNA profiles produced are compared to see if any match (i.e. if they have the same pattern of bands on the gel). If the samples match, it links a person to the crime scene.

Tip: Electrophoresis could also be used in this way to see if two DNA samples have come from the same species (i.e. the more similar the pattern of bands, the more likely the samples are from the same species).

Example

This gel shows that the DNA profile from suspect C matches that from the crime scene, linking them to the crime scene. All four bands match, so suspect C has the same number of repeats (nucleotides) at four different places.

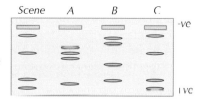

Use in medical diagnosis

In medical diagnosis, a DNA profile can refer to a unique pattern of several alleles. It can be used to analyse the risk of genetic disorders. It's useful when the specific mutation isn't known or where several mutations could have caused the disorder, because it identifies a broader, altered genetic pattern.

Tip: In DNA profiling in the UK, the results from ten different loci (plural for locus) are analysed. The chances of two DNA profiles matching by chance is up to 1 in a billion.

Example

Preimplantation genetic haplotyping (PGH) screens embryos created by IVF for genetic disorders before they're implanted into the uterus. The faulty regions of the parents' DNA are used to produce DNA profiles, which are compared to the DNA profile of the embryo. If the profiles match, the embryo has inherited the disorder. It can be used to screen for cystic fibrosis, Huntington's disease etc.

Practice Question — Fact Recall

Q1 Describe how DNA profiling can be used in forensic science.

3. Genetic Engineering

Genetic engineering uses gene technologies to alter organisms' DNA.

What is genetic engineering?

Genetic engineering is the manipulation of an organism's DNA. Organisms that have had their DNA altered by genetic engineering are called **transformed organisms**. These organisms have **recombinant DNA** — DNA formed by joining together DNA from different sources.

Genetic engineering involves extracting a gene from one organism and then inserting it into another organism (often one that's a different species). Genes can also be manufactured (e.g. by PCR) instead of extracted from an organism. The organism with the inserted gene will then produce the protein coded for by that gene.

An organism that has been genetically engineered to include a gene from a different species is sometimes called a **transgenic organism**. There's more on transgenic organisms on pages 214-216.

Genetic engineering — the process

You need to know how genetic engineering is carried out. There are three parts to the process:

Part 1 — Obtaining DNA containing the desired gene

The first step is to get hold of a DNA fragment that contains the desired gene (i.e. the gene you're interested in). The fragment can be isolated from another organism using restriction enzymes.

Part 2 — Making recombinant DNA

The next step is to insert the DNA fragment into **vector DNA** — a vector is something that's used to transfer DNA into a cell. Vectors can be **plasmids** (small, circular molecules of DNA in bacteria) or **bacteriophages** (viruses that infect bacteria). The vector DNA is isolated, then restriction enzymes and **DNA ligase** (an enzyme) are used to stick the DNA fragment and vector DNA together. Here's how it works:

Step 1

The vector DNA is isolated.

Step 2

The vector DNA is cut open using the same restriction enzyme that was used to isolate the DNA fragment containing the desired gene. This means that the sticky ends of the vector DNA are complementary to the sticky ends of the DNA fragment containing the gene.

Step 3

The vector DNA and DNA fragment are mixed together with DNA ligase. DNA ligase joins the sugar-phosphate backbones of the two bits of DNA. This process is called ligation.

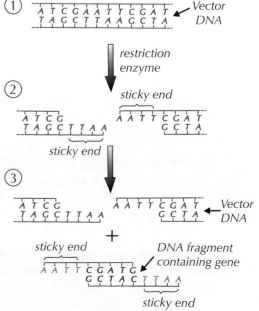

Step 4

The new combination of bases in the DNA (vector DNA + DNA fragment) is called recombinant DNA.

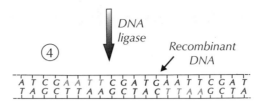

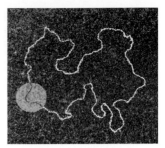

Figure 1: *Recombinant plasmid DNA. The DNA fragment containing the desired gene is highlighted red.*

Part 3 — Transforming cells

The vector with the recombinant DNA is used to transfer the gene into the bacterial cells (called **host cells**). If a plasmid vector is used, the host cells have to be persuaded to take in the plasmid vector and its DNA.

┌ **Example** ───

A suspension of the bacterial cells is mixed with the plasmid vector and placed in a machine called an electroporator. The machine is switched on and an electrical field is created in the mixture, which increases the permeability of the bacterial cell membranes and allows them to take in the plasmids. This technique is called **electroporation**.

With a bacteriophage vector, the bacteriophage will infect the host bacterium by injecting its DNA into it — see Figure 2. The phage DNA (with the desired gene in it) then integrates into the bacterial DNA.

Cells that take up the vectors containing the desired gene are genetically engineered, so are called transformed.

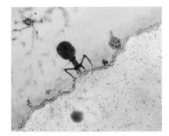

Figure 2: *This isn't an alien spaceship — it's actually a bacteriophage (orange) injecting its viral DNA into an* E. coli *bacterium (blue).*

Practice Question — Application

Q1 A scientist is studying the role of a protein in cancer progression. He transformed some *E. coli* cells with recombinant DNA containing the gene that codes for this protein.

a) A DNA fragment containing the desired gene was made using restriction enzymes. Describe and explain how the recombinant DNA was produced using this fragment.

b) Name a technique that could be used to increase the likelihood of the *E. coli* cells taking up the recombinant DNA.

Practice Questions — Fact Recall

Q1 What is genetic engineering?

Q2 What is the name given to DNA that has been formed by joining together DNA fragments from different sources?

Q3 a) Describe the role of a vector in genetic engineering.

b) Give two different types of vectors.

Q4 Explain why it is important to cut open the vector DNA with the same restriction enzyme that was used to isolate the DNA fragment containing the desired gene.

Q5 Describe the role of DNA ligase in genetic engineering.

- Understand the
  positive and negative
  ethical issues relating
  to the genetic
  manipulation of
  animals, plants and
  microorganisms
  including:

  - insect resistance
    in genetically
    modified soya,
    'pharming' (i.e.
    genetically modified
    animals to produce
    pharmaceuticals)
    and genetically
    modified pathogens
    for research,

  - issues relating
    to patenting and
    technology transfer,
    e.g. making
    genetically modified
    seed available to
    poor farmers.

  **Specification
  Reference 6.1.3**

4. Genetically Modified Organisms

Genetic engineering can be used to produce transformed organisms. These organisms are made to benefit humans in different ways. However, there can be negative ethical issues with this type of technology...

Creating insect-resistant plants

One way in which plants can be genetically manipulated is by having a gene inserted into their cells which makes them resistant to insect pests.

Example

Soybeans are an important food source across the world, but yields of soybeans can be greatly reduced by insect pests that feed on the soybean plants.

Scientists have successfully genetically modified soybean plants to include a gene originally found in the bacteria *Bacillus thuringiensis* (Bt). The gene codes for a protein that is toxic to some of the insects that feed on soybean plants.

Step 1

To genetically modify a soybean plant, the desired gene can be isolated from Bt using restriction enzymes and inserted into a plasmid taken from the bacterium *Agrobacterium tumefaciens*.

Step 2

The plasmid is put back into *A. tumefaciens*.

Step 3

The soybean plant cells are then deliberately infected with the transformed bacteria. The desired gene gets inserted into the soybean plant cells' DNA, creating a genetically modified (GM) plant.

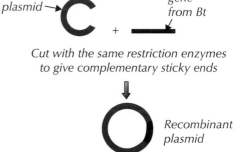

plasmid → C + gene from Bt

Cut with the same restriction enzymes to give complementary sticky ends

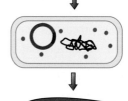

Recombinant plasmid

The plasmid is put back into A. tumefaciens

A. tumefaciens infects soybean plant cells

Tip: Genetically
modified organisms
are also known as
genetically engineered
or transformed
organisms.

Ethical issues

There are positive ethical issues concerning GM soybean plants — for example, they will reduce the amount of chemical pesticides that farmers use on their crops, which can harm the environment. GM plants can also be designed to be more nutritious.

But there are also negative ethical issues to consider. For example, farming GM soybean plants may encourage monoculture (where only one type of crop is planted). Monoculture decreases biodiversity and could leave the whole crop vulnerable to disease, because all the plants are genetically identical. There is also a risk that GM soybean plants could interbreed with wild plants creating 'superweeds' — weeds that are resistant to herbicides.

HOW
SCIENCE
WORKS

Tip: Biodiversity
describes the variety
of living organisms in
an area. Monoculture
reduces biodiversity by
reducing the number of
plant species in an area.
This in turn reduces the
number of other species,
e.g. insects, that the area
can support.

Producing drugs from animals

Many pharmaceuticals (medicinal drugs) are produced using genetically modified organisms, such as animals. This is called 'pharming'.

Example

Hereditary antithrombin deficiency is a disorder that makes blood clots more likely to form in the body. The risk of developing blood clots in people with this disorder can be reduced with infusions of the protein antithrombin.

Scientists have developed a way to produce high yields of this protein using goats (see Figure 1).

1. DNA fragments that code for production of human antithrombin in the mammary glands are extracted.

2. The DNA fragments are injected into a goat embryo.

3. The embryo is implanted into a female goat.

4. When the offspring is born it is tested to see if it can produce the antithrombin protein.

5. If it does, selective breeding is used to produce a herd of goats that produce antithrombin in their milk.

The protein is extracted from the milk and used to produce a drug (ATryn®) that can be given to people with hereditary antithrombin deficiency.

Figure 1: Diagram to show how antithrombin is produced from goats.

DNA fragments → goat embryo → female goat → offspring tested for making antithrombin → selective breeding → herd

Figure 2: Milk from genetically modified cows, created to produce human growth hormone.

Ethical issues

There are positive ethical issues with 'pharming'— drugs made this way can be made in large quantities compared to other methods of production. This can make them more available to more people.

HOW SCIENCE WORKS

However, the creation of genetically modified animals raises negative ethical issues. For example, there is concern that manipulating an animal's genes could cause harmful side-effects for the animal, and that using an animal in this way is enforcing the idea that animals are merely 'assets' that can be treated however we choose.

Using pathogens for research

Scientists are carrying out research into genetically engineered pathogens (microorganisms that cause disease, such as viruses) in order to find treatments for disease.

Example

Scientists found that tumour cells have receptors on their membranes for the poliovirus — so the poliovirus will recognise and attack them. By genetically engineering the poliovirus to inactivate the genes that cause poliomyelitis, scientists can use it to attack and kill cancer cells without causing disease. This may lead to a treatment for cancer.

Tip: Poliomyelitis is the disease caused by the poliovirus.

Ethical issues

The genetic modification of pathogens to help cure disease has obvious positive ethical issues — for example, it could mean that previously untreatable diseases can now be treated, reducing the suffering they would cause. However, there are many possible negative ethical issues as well:

- Some people are worried that the scientists researching the pathogens could become infected with the live pathogen and potentially cause a mass outbreak of disease.

- Some people are concerned that the genetically modified version of a pathogen could revert back to its original form and cause an outbreak of disease.

- Some people worry that in the wrong hands, knowledge of how to genetically engineer dangerous pathogens could be used maliciously to create agents for biowarfare.

Researchers using live pathogens have to follow strict protocols, which makes the chance of any of these things happening very, very low.

Tip: Biowarfare means deliberately attacking humans or other organisms using biological substances that can poison or cause disease.

Ownership of GM organisms

Many scientists around the world are working on techniques to improve and advance genetic engineering. Scientists working for different institutions often share their knowledge and skills in this field so that, globally, beneficial genetically modified products can be created at a faster rate. The sharing of knowledge, skills and technology like this is called **technology transfer**.

Although they share information, a group of scientists or the company they work for may want to obtain legal protection for their genetically modified products, e.g. by getting a patent. This means, by law, they can control who uses the product and how for a set period of time.

Ethical issues

This raises some positive ethical issues — it means that the owner of the patent will get money generated from selling the product. This encourages scientists to compete to be the first to come up with a new, beneficial genetic engineering idea, so we get genetically engineered products faster.

But the process raises many negative ethical issues too. For example, farmers in poorer countries may not be able to afford patented genetically modified seeds. Even if they can afford seeds for one year, some patents mean that they are not legally allowed to plant and grow any of the seeds from that crop without paying again. Many people think this is unfair and that the big companies that own the patents should relax the rules to help farmers in poorer countries.

Figure 3: Genetically modified cotton (Bt cotton), created to be resistant to insect pests, such as the cotton bollworm, is now widely grown in India.

Practice Questions — Application

Q1 Golden Rice is a variety of transformed rice. It contains one gene from maize and one gene from a soil bacterium, which together enable the rice to produce beta-carotene. The beta-carotene is used by our bodies to produce vitamin A.

a) Explain how Golden Rice could have been created.

b) Suggest how Golden Rice may benefit humans.

Q2 People with Type 1 diabetes need to inject insulin to regulate their blood glucose concentration. Insulin used to be obtained from the pancreases of dead animals, such as pigs. However, the technology is now available to use genetically engineered bacteria to manufacture human insulin.

Suggest some positive ethical issues raised by the production of genetically modified insulin.

Q3 A 'pharming' company own the patent for the production of various human proteins in the milk of farm animals. They have produced genetically modified sheep that make the protein alpha-1-antitrypsin. This protein is lacking in sufferers of some lung diseases, such as hereditary emphysema.

a) Explain how the sheep could have been genetically modified to produce the protein.

b) Suggest why the company have taken out a patent for making the product.

Tip: The bacterium *A. tumefaciens* is a tool used to produce many transformed plants because of how it can transfer DNA into plant cells.

***Figure 4:** Genetically modified Golden Rice (right) compared to normal white rice (left).*

Practice Questions — Fact Recall

Q1 a) Why have scientists genetically modified soybean plants to be resistant to insect pests?

b) Which bacterium is the gene in the genetically modified soybean plants taken from?

c) Explain how the gene makes the plant insect-resistant.

Q2 a) What is pharming?

b) Discuss the ethical issues surrounding pharming.

Q3 Give one advantage of carrying out research into genetically engineered pathogens.

Q4 What is meant by the term 'technology transfer'?

Q5 Give one negative issue faced by farmers in poor countries who farm with genetically modified seeds.

Exam Tip
If you're asked to discuss the ethical issues surrounding genetic engineering in the exam, make sure you think about both sides of the debate. That means writing about both the positive and negative ethical issues.

5. Gene Therapy

There is a chance that in the future we'll be able to treat genetic disorders at the source — by using gene therapy to alter the mutations that have caused them.

How does gene therapy work?

Genetic disorders are inherited disorders caused by abnormal genes or chromosomes, e.g. cystic fibrosis. Gene therapy could be used to cure these disorders — it isn't being used widely yet but there is a form of somatic gene therapy available, and other treatments are undergoing clinical trials.

Gene therapy involves altering alleles inside cells to cure genetic disorders. How you do this depends on whether the disorder is caused by a mutated dominant allele or two mutated recessive alleles.

- If it's caused by two mutated recessive alleles you can add a working dominant allele to make up for them — you 'supplement' the faulty ones.
- If it's caused by a mutated dominant allele you can 'silence' the dominant allele (e.g. by sticking a bit of DNA in the middle of the allele so it doesn't work any more).

To get the 'new' allele (DNA) inside the cell, the allele is inserted into cells using vectors (see pages 212-213). A range of different vectors can be used, e.g. altered viruses, plasmids or liposomes (spheres made of lipid).

Types of gene therapy

There are two types of gene therapy:

1. Somatic therapy

This involves altering the alleles in body cells, particularly the cells that are most affected by the disorder.

— Example —

Cystic fibrosis (CF) is a genetic disorder that's very damaging to the respiratory system, so somatic therapy for CF targets the epithelial cells lining the lungs.

Somatic therapy doesn't affect the individual's sex cells (sperm or eggs) though, so any offspring could still inherit the disease.

2. Germ line therapy

This involves altering the alleles in the sex cells. This means that every cell of any offspring produced from these cells will be affected by the gene therapy and they won't inherit the disease. Germ line therapy in humans is currently illegal though.

Positive ethical issues of gene therapy

There are positive ethical issues surrounding gene therapy:

- Gene therapy could prolong the lives of people with life-threatening genetic disorders.
- Gene therapy could give people with genetic disorders a better quality of life if it helps to ease symptoms.
- Germ line therapy would allow the carriers of genetic disorders to conceive a baby without that disorder.
- Germ line therapy could decrease the number of people that suffer from genetic disorders and cancer, which is beneficial for individuals and society as a whole (as fewer people will require treatment).

Negative ethical issues of gene therapy

There are also negative ethical issues surrounding gene therapy:

- The technology could potentially be used in ways other than for medical treatment, such as for treating the cosmetic effects of ageing.

- There's the potential to do more harm than good by using the technology (e.g. risk of overexpression of genes — see below).

- There's concern that gene therapy is expensive — some people believe that health service resources could be better spent on other treatments that have passed clinical trials.

> **Tip:** Gene expression is when genes are transcribed and translated into proteins (see pages 150-152). If a gene is overexpressed, this means that too much of the protein it codes for gets made.

Disadvantages of gene therapy

There other potential disadvantages of gene therapy too:

- The body could identify vectors as foreign bodies and start an immune response against them.

- An allele could be inserted into the wrong place in the DNA, possibly causing more problems, e.g. cancer.

- An inserted allele could get overexpressed, producing too much of the missing protein, and so causing other problems.

- The effects of the treatment may be short-lived in somatic therapy.

- The patient might have to undergo multiple treatments with somatic therapy.

- It might be difficult to get the allele into specific body cells.

Practice Questions — Application

Haemophilia B is caused by a mutation in the gene for the blood clotting factor IX (FIX). Sufferers usually have FIX levels less than 1% of normal values, causing frequent bleeding and often early death. Increasing levels to greater than 1% can greatly improve patient health. Treatment usually involves FIX injections multiple times a week, which is expensive and inconvenient. A trial has investigated the use of somatic gene therapy to treat haemophilia B. Six patients were injected with a virus carrying the normal FIX gene. Some results are shown on the right.

Q1 Explain the role of the virus.

Q2 Calculate the average maximum FIX level after gene therapy.

Q3 Was the trial a success? Give evidence to support your answer.

Q4 Describe the positive ethical issues of this treatment.

Patient	Maximum FIX level (% of normal) after therapy
1	2
2	2
3	3
4	4
5	8
6	12

Practice Questions — Fact Recall

Q1 Define the term 'gene therapy'.

Q2 Describe the difference between somatic gene therapy and germ line gene therapy.

- Understand the
  principles of DNA
  sequencing and the
  development of new
  DNA sequencing
  techniques,
  including the rapid
  advancements of the
  techniques used in
  sequencing, which
  have increased the
  speed of sequencing
  and allowed whole
  genome sequencing,
  e.g. high-throughput
  sequencing.

- Understand how
  gene sequencing
  has allowed for the
  sequences of amino
  acids in polypeptides
  to be predicted.

- Understand how
  gene sequencing
  has allowed for the
  development of
  synthetic biology.

- Understand how
  gene sequencing has
  allowed for genome-
  wide comparisons
  between individuals
  and between species.

- Understand how
  bioinformatics and
  computational biology
  are contributing
  to biological
  research into
  genotype-phenotype
  relationships,
  epidemiology
  and searching
  for evolutionary
  relationships.

  **Specification
  Reference 6.1.3**

Tip: In this example,
A* can't be added at,
e.g., point 3 because A
doesn't pair with G in
complementary base
pairing.

6. Sequencing Genes and Genomes

*Gene sequencing means finding out the order of bases in a gene.
Genome sequencing means finding out the order of bases in all of an
organism's DNA.*

DNA sequencing

DNA can be sequenced by the **chain termination method** — this was one of
the first methods used to determine the order of bases in a section of DNA
(gene). Here's how it works:

Step 1

A mixture of the following is added to four separate tubes:

- A single-stranded DNA template — the DNA to be sequenced.
- DNA polymerase — the enzyme that joins DNA nucleotides together.
- Lots of DNA primer — short pieces of DNA (see page 206).
- Free nucleotides — lots of free A, T, C and G nucleotides.
- A fluorescently-labelled modified nucleotide — like a regular nucleotide,
  but once it's added to a DNA strand, no more bases are added after it.
  A different modified nucleotide is added to each tube (these are called
  A*, T*, C*, G*).

Step 2

The tubes undergo PCR (see pages 206-207), which produces many strands
of DNA. The strands are different lengths because each one terminates at a
different point depending on where the modified nucleotide was added.
For example, look at Figure 1 below — in tube A (with the modified adenine
nucleotide A*) sometimes A* is added to the DNA at point 4 instead of A,
stopping the addition of any more bases (the strand is terminated). Sometimes
A is added at point 4, then A* is added at point 5. Sometimes A is added at
point 4, A again at point 5, G at point 6 and A* is added at point 7. So strands
of three different lengths (4 bases, 5 bases and 7 bases) all ending in A* are
produced.

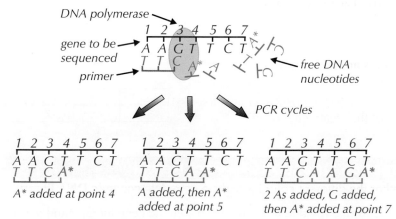

Figure 1: *DNA sequencing example showing what happens in
Tube A, which contains A*.*

Step 3

The DNA fragments in each tube are separated by electrophoresis and visualised under UV light (because of the fluorescent label). The complementary base sequence can be read from the gel (see Figure 2). The smallest nucleotide (e.g. one base) is at the bottom of the gel. Each band after this represents one more base added. So by reading the bands from the bottom of the gel upwards, you can build up the DNA sequence one base at a time.

Tip: Remember, the smallest (shortest) DNA fragments travel the furthest through the gel — towards the positive electrode.

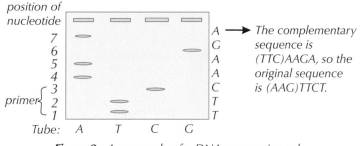

position of nucleotide

7
6
5
4
3
primer { 2
1

Tube: A T C G

A → The complementary sequence is (TTC)AAGA, so the original sequence is (AAG)TTCT.
G
A
A
C
T
T

Figure 2: An example of a DNA sequencing gel.

Figure 3: An actual DNA sequencing gel being analysed under UV light.

Genome sequencing

The chain-termination method can only be used for DNA fragments up to about 750 bp long. So if you want to sequence the entire genome (all the DNA) of an organism using this method, you need to chop it up into smaller pieces first. The smaller pieces are sequenced and then put back in order to give the sequence of the whole genome. Here's how it's done:

Step 1

A genome is cut into smaller fragments (about 100 000 bp) using restriction enzymes — see Figure 4a.

Step 2

The fragments are inserted into **bacterial artificial chromosomes** (**BACs**) — these are man-made plasmids. Each fragment is inserted into a different BAC.

Step 3

The BACs are then inserted into bacteria — each bacterium contains a BAC with a different DNA fragment.

G C T G T C C T C C A G C G — Entire genome

① Restriction enzymes

G C T G I C C — T C C A G C G — Different DNA fragments

② One DNA fragment into one BAC

③ One BAC into one bacterium

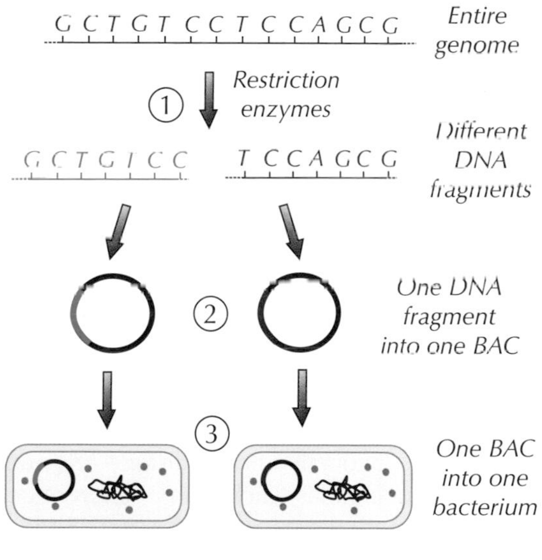

Figure 4a: Genome sequencing — the first three stages.

Tip: Genomes vary massively in size — the human genome is about 3 billion bases long, the zebra fish genome is about 1 billion bp, and the HIV genome is only around 9700 bp long. The size of the genome equates roughly to the number of genes. So humans have about 21 000 genes, zebra fish have about 16 000 genes and HIV has 9 genes.

Step 4

The bacteria divide, creating colonies of cloned (identical) cells that all contain a specific DNA fragment — see Figure 4b (on the next page). Together the different colonies make a complete **genomic DNA library**.

Step 5

DNA is extracted from each colony and cut up using restriction enzymes, producing overlapping pieces of DNA.

Step 6
Each piece of DNA is sequenced, using the chain-termination method.

Step 7
The pieces are put back in order to give the full sequence from that BAC (using powerful computer systems).

Step 8
Finally the DNA fragments from all the BACs are put back in order, by computers, to complete the entire genome.

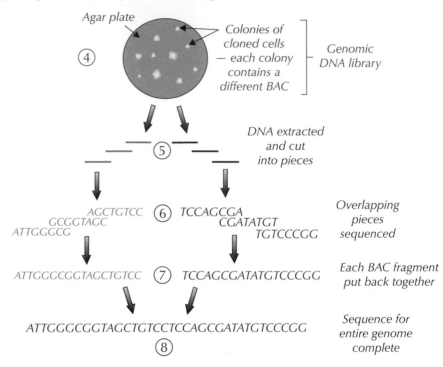

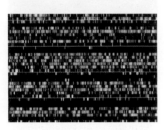

Figure 5: *Computer screen display of part of the human genome sequence. The four different bases are represented by bands of different colours.*

Figure 4b: *Genome sequencing — the final five stages.*

Advances in sequencing

Continued research and improvements in modern technology have led to rapid advancements in the field of gene sequencing. The chain-termination technique described on the previous two pages is still commonly used but it has become automated and is faster — nowadays the tube contains all the modified nucleotides, each with a different coloured fluorescent label, and a machine reads the sequence for you. So instead of running a gel manually and determining the sequence from that, the sequence is read automatically by a computer (see Figure 6).

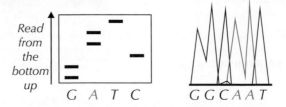

Figure 6: *A DNA sequencing gel (left) and an automated DNA sequence computer read-out (right).*

Further advances in the field have also led to **high-throughput sequencing** — techniques that can sequence a lot faster than original methods (e.g. up to 1000 times more bases in a given time), at a fraction of the cost. For example, the chain-termination technique has been made high-throughput by new technology allowing up to 384 sequences to be run in parallel.

There are several other, newer methods of high-throughput sequencing being used too, some of which don't use electrophoresis.

Example — Pyrosequencing

High-throughput pyrosequencing is a recently developed technique.

Step 1
A section of DNA is cut into fragments, split into single strands and then a strand from each fragment is attached to a small bead.

Step 2
PCR is used to amplify the DNA fragments on each bead.

Step 3
Then each bead is put into a separate well.

Step 4
Next, free nucleotides added to the wells attach to the DNA strands via complementary base pairing. The four different types of nucleotides are added to the wells one after the other, over and over again for 100 cycles.

Step 5
The wells also contain specific enzymes, which cause light to be emitted when a nucleotide is added to the DNA strand. More than one nucleotide can be added at a time if the bases are the same, so the intensity of the light can vary.

Step 6
Computers analyse the occurrence and intensities of the light emitted in the different wells, after each type of nucleotide is added, and process this information to interpret the DNA sequence.

This technique can sequence around 400 million bases in a ten-hour period (which is super fast compared to older techniques).

Figure 7: *These high-throughput DNA sequencers can sequence 400-600 million bases over a 10-hour run. This makes them very useful for sequencing the entire genome of an organism.*

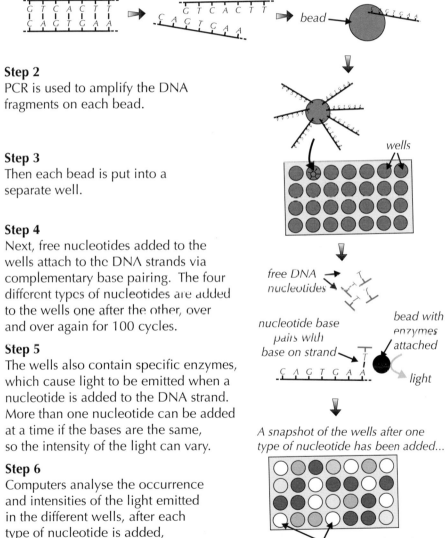

wells

free DNA nucleotides

nucleotide base pairs with base on strand

bead with enzymes attached

light

A snapshot of the wells after one type of nucleotide has been added...

bright spots indicate where the nucleotide joins the DNA strand

With newer, faster techniques such as pyrosequencing available, scientists can now sequence whole genomes much more quickly.

Sequencing and synthetic biology

You might remember from Module 2 that amino acids are coded for by triplets of bases in a gene. This means that by sequencing a gene, the sequence of amino acids that a gene codes for and so the primary structure of a polypeptide can be predicted. This has allowed us to create biological molecules from scratch and so has led to the development of an area of biology called 'synthetic biology'.

Synthetic biology is a large field that includes building biological systems from artificially made molecules (e.g. proteins) to see whether they work in the way we think they do, and redesigning biological systems to perform better and include new molecules. It also includes designing new biological systems and molecules that don't exist in the natural world, but could be useful to humans, e.g. energy products (fuels) and drug products.

Tip: Synthetic biology is different from genetic engineering — genetic engineering involves the direct transfer of DNA from one organism to another, whereas in synthetic biology DNA is created from scratch.

┌ **Example** ──────────────────────

Artemisinin is an antimalarial drug — until recently we got artemisinin by extracting it from a plant. Using synthetic biology, scientists have created all the genes responsible for producing a precursor to artemisinin. They've successfully inserted these genes into yeast cells, so we can now use yeast to help produce artemisinin.

Sequencing and comparing genomes

Gene sequences and whole genome sequences can be compared between organisms of different species and between organisms of the same species. This is a complicated process which is made easier with the use of computers — it involves **computational biology** (using computers to study biology, e.g. to create computer simulations and mathematical models) and **bioinformatics** (developing and using computer software that can analyse, organise and store biological data).

There are many reasons why biological research can involve comparison of gene sequences and genomes:

Studying genotype-phenotype relationships

Sometimes it's useful to be able to predict an organism's phenotype by analysing its genotype.

┌ **Example** ──────────────────────

Marfan syndrome is a genetic disorder caused by a mutation of the FBN1 gene. The position and nature of the mutation on the gene affects what symptoms a person with Marfan syndrome will experience (e.g. they could get a number of problems associated with their vision, cardiovascular system or muscles). Scientists have sequenced the FBN1 gene of many people with Marfan syndrome and documented this along with details of their phenotype. Bioinformatics has allowed the scientists to compare all the data and identify genotype-phenotype correlations — this could help in the treatment of Marfan syndrome by using gene sequencing to predict what health problems the person is likely to face.

Epidemiological studies

Epidemiology is the study of health and disease within a population — it considers the distribution of a disease, its causes and its effects. Some gene mutations have been linked to a greater risk of disease (e.g. mutations in the BRCA1 gene are linked to breast cancer). Computerised comparisons between the genomes of people that have a disease and those that don't can be used to detect particular mutations that could be responsible for the increased risk of disease.

Understanding evolutionary relationships

All organisms evolved from shared common ancestors (relatives). Closely related species evolved away from each other more recently and so share more DNA. Whole genomes of different species can be sequenced and then analysed using computer software to tell us how closely related different species are. E.g. the genomes of humans and chimpanzees are about 94% similar. Comparing the genomes of members of the same species can also tell us about evolutionary relationships.

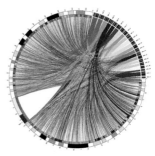

Figure 8: A circular genome map used to visually compare the sequence of one human chromosome with the entire mouse genome. The coloured lines connect genes that have evolved from common ancestor genes.

┌ **Example** ──────────────────────────────

When different groups of early humans separated and moved to different parts of the world, their genomes changed in slightly different ways. By using computers to compare the genomes of people from different parts of the world, it's possible to build up a picture of early human migration.

└───────────────────────────────────

Practice Question — Application

Scientists have found a large femur (thigh) bone from an unknown animal species in a swamp. They decide to sequence the bone's DNA, so they can establish what species the bone came from.

Q1 a) The scientists use a non-automated method to sequence the bone's DNA that involves four separate test tubes. What do they need to add to each tube?

  b) Describe the next steps the scientists need to take to sequence the bone's DNA.

The DNA sequencing gel obtained from the DNA of the bone and three reference samples are shown below.

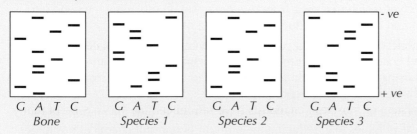

| G A T C | G A T C | G A T C | G A T C |
| Bone | Species 1 | Species 2 | Species 3 |

Tip: Remember that the sequence that you can read from the gel is the complementary sequence to the original reference sample of DNA.

  c) Give the original DNA sequence of the reference sample from Species 1.

  d) Which species did the bone come from? Explain your answer.

Q1 The chain termination method can be used to sequence DNA.

    a) What do you need to do before you can use this method to sequence an entire genome? Explain why.

    b) When sequencing an entire genome in this way, what are the man-made plasmids called that the DNA fragments are inserted into?

Q2 a) What are high-throughput sequencing techniques?

    b) Name a high-throughput sequencing technique.

Q3 Describe how DNA sequencing has allowed the development of synthetic biology.

Q4 Give two fields of biology where computers are used to aid the comparison of gene and genome sequences.

Q5 Describe how DNA sequencing can be used in epidemiological studies.

Q6 How can DNA sequencing help us understand evolutionary relationships between species?

Section Summary

Make sure you know...

- That millions of identical copies of a DNA fragment can be made using the polymerase chain reaction (PCR).

- That fragments of DNA can be isolated using restriction enzymes. These enzymes recognise and cut DNA at different, specific palindromic sequences (called recognition sequences).

- That DNA fragments, RNA fragments or proteins can be run on an electrophoresis gel to separate them according to size (length).

- How to carry out electrophoresis.

- That an organism's genome contains repetitive, non-coding base sequences.

- That electrophoresis can be used to analyse the number of times a non-coding sequence is repeated in a person's genome, creating a DNA profile for that individual. DNA profiles can be used in forensics and to analyse the risk of genetic disorders.

- That genetic engineering involves isolating a gene from one organism, and placing the gene into another organism, using a vector, and that it produces transformed organisms.

- The techniques involved in genetic engineering — using restriction enzymes to isolate a DNA fragment containing a desired gene, creating recombinant DNA from the DNA fragment and vector DNA using DNA ligase, and using electroporation to get bacteria to take up the vector and produce transformed cells (cells that have taken up the recombinant DNA).

- That soybean plants can be genetically modified to be resistant to insects, and the ethical issues relating to this, including positive issues (e.g. reducing the amount of harmful chemical pesticides used on the crops) and negative issues (e.g. encouraging monoculture, which decreases biodiversity).

- How 'pharming' (producing drugs from genetically modified organisms, such as animals) works, and the ethical issues relating to this, including positive issues (e.g. being able to make the drugs more available by producing them in large quantities) and negative issues (e.g. that the manipulation of an animal's genes could cause harmful side-effects for the animal).

- That pathogens are genetically engineered for research into treatments for disease, and the ethical issues relating to this, including positive issues (e.g. the ability to treat previously untreated diseases) and negative issues (e.g. the possibility of a mass outbreak of the disease).

- What technology transfer is, and why scientists or companies may patent genetically modified products.

- The ethical issues surrounding patenting and technology transfer, including the issues of making genetically modified seed available to farmers in poorer countries.

- That gene therapy involves altering defective alleles inside body cells (somatic gene therapy) or sex cells (germ line gene therapy), to attempt to treat or cure genetic disorders.

- The positive and negative ethical issues raised by gene therapy.

- That DNA sequencing is used to determine the order of bases in a section of DNA (e.g. a fragment of a gene) and that the chain termination method is one way this can be carried out.

- That whole genomes can be sequenced using bacterial artificial chromosomes (BACs) and the chain termination method.

- That advancements in sequencing techniques, such as high-throughput sequencing, have increased the speed of sequencing so that whole genome sequencing can happen much more quickly.

- That gene sequencing allows the amino sequences of amino acids to be predicted.

- That gene sequencing has allowed for the development of synthetic biology in which biological molecules can be made from scratch.

- That the results of whole genome sequencing can be used to compare genomes between and within species.

- How computational biology and bioinformatics are contributing to biological research into genotype-phenotype relationships, epidemiology and the understanding of evolutionary relationships.

Exam-style Questions

1 The following steps describe processes involved in genetic engineering.
They are **not** in the correct order.

  1 DNA ligase joins the sugar-phosphate backbones together.

  2 The desired DNA fragment is isolated using restriction enzymes.

  3 The plasmid is cut open using restriction enzymes.

  4 The bacterial cells take in the plasmid.

  5 Bacterial cells are mixed with the plasmid and placed in an electroporator.

  6 The DNA fragment and plasmid are mixed together with DNA ligase.

  Which of these is the correct order for producing genetically engineered cells?

  A 5, 3, 2, 1, 4, 6

  B 2, 3, 6, 1, 5 ,4

  C 5, 4, 6, 3, 2, 1

  D 2, 5, 4, 3, 6, 1

(1 mark)

2 A prize-winning racehorse has been stolen from its stables. Police suspect it has been taken to a stud farm where it has previously gone to breed. The police have obtained DNA samples from four similar-looking horses at the stud farm and used them to produce DNA profiles to compare against a DNA profile from the stolen animal. The DNA profiles are shown in **Fig. 2.1**.

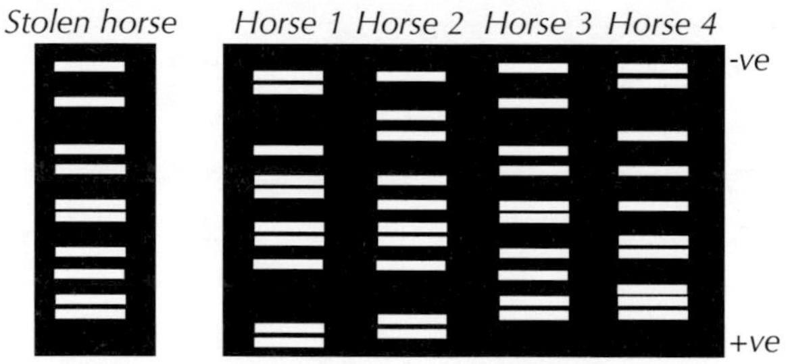

Fig. 2.1

(a) Describe and explain how the DNA profiles have been produced from the DNA samples.

(4 marks)

(b) Use your understanding of the biology behind DNA profiling technology to explain why the chances of two DNA profiles matching by chance are so small.

(3 marks)

(c) Is the stolen animal at the stud farm? Explain your answer.

(1 mark)

(d) Give **one** other use for DNA profiling technology other than in forensic science.

(1 mark)

3 An organic soybean farmer is concerned that his crop of non-GM soybean plants may have become cross-contaminated with a gene (called a transgene) from nearby GM soybean plants. One way to find out if the farmer's soybean plants contain the transgene is to first take a DNA sample from one of his plants and then use PCR to obtain DNA fragments of the region of DNA that would contain the transgene.

(a) Explain how the process of PCR works.

(5 marks)

The next step is to compare the DNA fragments produced to those from a sample of the GM soybean plant tissue, using gel electrophoresis. The GM soybean plant acts as a positive control.

(b) What would the gel show if the farmer's soybean plant did have the transgene?

(1 mark)

(c) What could be used as a negative control in this experiment?

(1 mark)

(d) Apart from cross-contamination, suggest and explain **one** other negative ethical issue associated with growing genetically modified plants.

(2 marks)

4 A study was carried out to investigate the effectiveness of gene therapy in patients with X-linked severe combined immunodeficiency disease (SCID). SCID is an inherited disorder that affects the immune system. It is caused by a mutation in the IL2RG gene.

Ten patients were treated with a virus vector carrying a correct version of the IL2RG gene. After gene transfer, the patients' immune systems were monitored for at least three years and noted as functional (good) or not. Their health was also monitored for the same time. **Fig. 4.1** shows the results.

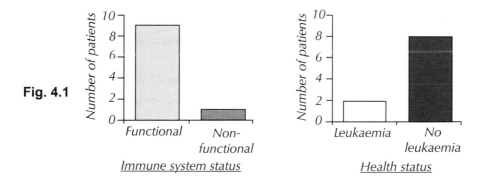

Fig. 4.1

(a) Besides viruses, give **one** other example of a type of vector they could have used.

(1 mark)

(b) (i) Describe the results shown in **Fig. 4.1**.

(2 marks)

(ii) Suggest **two** ways the study could be improved.

(2 marks)

(c) Outline **one** negative issue that may be raised by using gene therapy.

(1 mark)

Figure 1: *Stolons (runners) of strawberry plants.*

Tip: Farmers can use cloning methods to ensure they get uniform crops — as clones are genetically identical, any beneficial characteristics will be present in each crop plant.

1. Plant Cloning

Some plants produce clones naturally, but they can also be cloned artificially.

What is cloning?

Cloning is the process of producing genetically identical cells or organisms from the cells of an existing organism. Cloning can occur naturally in some plants and animals, but it can also be carried out artificially.

Vegetative propagation

Some plants can produce natural clones by vegetative propagation — this is the production of plant clones from non-reproductive tissues, e.g. roots, leaves and stems. It's a type of asexual reproduction. There are many different natural vegetative propagation methods used by plants:

Examples

- Rhizomes — These are stem structures that grow horizontally underground away from the parent plant. They have 'nodes' from which new shoots and roots can develop. An example of a plant that uses rhizomes is bamboo.

- Stolons — Also called runners, these are pretty similar to rhizomes. The main difference is that they grow above the ground, on the surface of the soil. New shoots and roots can either develop from nodes (like in rhizomes) or form at the end of the stolon. An example of a plant that uses stolons is the strawberry (see Figure 1).

- Suckers — These are shoots that grow from sucker buds (undeveloped shoots) present on the shallow roots of a parent plant. An example of a plant that uses suckers is the elm tree.

- Tubers — These are large underground plant structures that act as a food store for the plant. They're covered in 'eyes'. Each eye is able to sprout and form a new plant. An example of a plant that uses tubers is the potato.

- Bulbs — These are also underground food stores used by some plants. New bulbs are able to develop from the original bulb and form new individual plants. An example of a plant that uses bulbs is the onion.

Vegetative propagation in horticulture and agriculture

Horticulturists (plant growers) and farmers can exploit a plant's natural ability to produce clones. By manipulating the way in which a plant grows, they can induce vegetative propagation, so they get natural clones of the parent plant. There are several different methods they can use to do this:

Examples

- They can take cuttings (see next page).

- They can use grafting — joining the shoot of one plant to the growing stem and root of another plant.

- They can use layering — bending a stem of a growing plant downwards so it enters the soil and grows into a new plant.

Producing clones from cuttings

Growing plants from cuttings is a really simple way to make clones of a parent plant. You need to know how to dissect plant material in order to produce clones using this method.

Here's how a cutting can be taken and grown from a stem:

1. Use a scalpel or sharp secateurs to take a cutting, between 5 cm and 10 cm long, from the end of a stem of your parent plant.

2. Remove the leaves from the lower end of your cutting (if there are any), leaving just one at the tip.

3. Dip the lower end of the cutting in rooting powder, which contains hormones that induce root formation.

4. Then plant your cutting in a pot containing a suitable growth medium (e.g. well-drained compost).

5. Provide your cutting with a warm and moist environment by either covering the whole pot with a plastic bag or by putting it in a propagator (a specialised piece of kit that provides these conditions — see Figure 3).

6. When your cutting has formed its own roots and is strong enough, you can plant it elsewhere to continue growing.

> **Tip:** Make sure you assess any risks before you start this experiment. Be particularly careful with sharp tools (e.g. scalpels) and be aware that some plants (e.g. chrysanthemums) can be irritants to skin, so it's best that you wear gloves if handling plants like these.

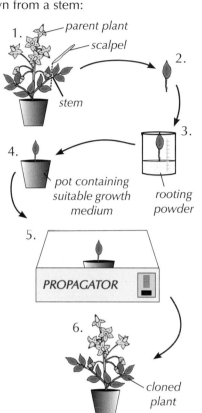

Figure 2: Example of how to produce a cloned plant from a stem cutting.

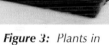

Figure 3: Plants in a propagator.

You can also take cuttings from other parts of a plant, such as a root or leaf:

Examples

- To take a root cutting, cut a piece of root from the plant with a straight cut using a scalpel or secateurs. Then remove the uncut end of the root with a slanted cut. Dip the end of the cutting in rooting powder and plant it in a suitable growth medium. Then follow steps 5 and 6 from the method above.

- A popular type of leaf cutting (known as a split vein cutting) involves removing a complete leaf and scoring the large veins on the lower leaf surface using a scalpel (see Figure 4). You then put it on top of the growth medium with the broken veins facing down and then follow steps 5 and 6 from above. A new plant should form from each break in the veins.

Figure 4: How to prepare a leaf for a split vein cutting.

Tissue culture

Tissue culture is an artificial way of cloning plants — i.e. it's different from vegetative propagation, which is regarded as a 'natural' way to produce clones. Here's how tissue culture is carried out:

Tip: Take a look back at what you learnt about stem cells in Module 2.

1. Cells are taken from the original plant that's going to be cloned. Cells from the stem and root tips are used because they're stem cells — like in humans, plant stem cells can develop into any type of cell.

2. The cells are sterilised to kill any microorganisms — bacteria and fungi compete for nutrients with the plant cells, which decreases their growth rate.

Tip: Plant hormones are included to help promote plant growth.

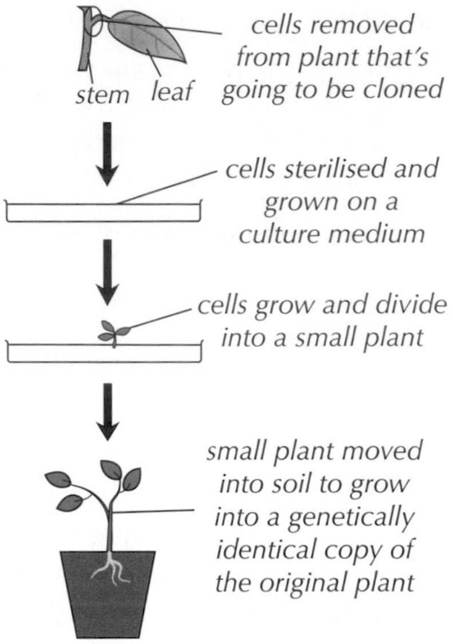

3. The cells are placed on a culture medium containing organic nutrients (like glucose and amino acids) and a high concentration of plant hormones (such as auxins, see p. 98). This is carried out under aseptic conditions (see p. 246). The cells divide to produce a mass of undifferentiated cells. The mass can be subdivided to produce lots of plants very quickly (see below).

cells removed from plant that's going to be cloned

stem   leaf

cells sterilised and grown on a culture medium

cells grow and divide into a small plant

small plant moved into soil to grow into a genetically identical copy of the original plant

Figure 5: *The process of using tissue culture to clone a plant.*

4. When the cells have divided and grown into a small plant they're taken out of the medium and planted in soil — they'll develop into plants that are genetically identical to the original plant.

Uses of tissue culture

Tissue culture is used to clone plants that don't readily reproduce or are endangered or rare.

Example

A number of British orchid species are now endangered in the UK. It's very difficult to reproduce orchids using seeds because it can take a long time for the plants to produce flowers, they have a very specialised mechanism of pollination and the seeds usually need a specific fungus present in order to germinate. But many have been successfully reproduced using tissue culture.

Figure 6: *A lady's slipper orchid — one of the species of orchid which is critically endangered in the UK.*

It's also used to grow whole plants from genetically engineered plant cells.

Tip: See pages 212-213 for lots more on genetic engineering.

Micropropagation

Micropropagation is when tissue culture is used to produce lots of cloned plants very quickly. Cells are taken from developing cloned plants and subcultured (grown on another fresh culture medium) — repeating this process creates large numbers of clones (see Figure 8). This technique is used extensively in horticulture and agriculture, e.g. to produce fields full of a crop that has been genetically engineered to be pest-resistant.

Figure 7: *Micropropagation.*

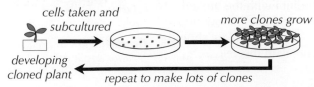

cells taken and subcultured

more clones grow

developing cloned plant

repeat to make lots of clones

Figure 8: *Micropropagation of cloned plants.*

Arguments for and against artificial plant cloning

You need to be able to evaluate the uses of tissue culture in agriculture and horticulture — this handy list of arguments for and against tissue culture should help you.

Arguments for

- Desirable genetic characteristics (e.g. high fruit production) are always passed on to clones. This doesn't always happen when plants reproduce sexually.

- Tissue culture allows plants to be reproduced in any season because the environment is controlled.

- Less space is required by tissue culture than would be needed to produce the same number of plants by conventional growing methods.

- It produces lots of plants quickly compared to the time it would take to grow them from seeds.

Arguments against

- Undesirable genetic characteristics (e.g. producing fruit with lots of seeds) are always passed on to clones.

- Cloned plant populations have no genetic variability, so a single disease could kill them all.

- Production costs of tissue culture are very high due to high energy use and the training of skilled workers, so it's unsuitable for small scale production.

- Contamination by microorganisms during tissue culture can be disastrous and result in complete loss of the plants being cultured.

Tip: Agriculture and horticulture both involve cultivating plants — agriculture generally relates to farming (i.e. using land to grow crops for human use or consumption) whereas horticulture can involve the cultivation of any plant for any purpose, but usually on a smaller scale, e.g. for gardening.

Tip: The advantages and disadvantages of cloning plants are similar to the advantages and disadvantages of cloning animals, which are covered on pages 236-237.

Practice Questions — Application

Q1 A florist has discovered a wild flower that has an unusual pattern on its petals. She wants to reproduce the flower so she can sell it.

   a) Name and briefly describe a method which could be used to produce a large number of clones of the plant very quickly.

   b) Explain why producing clones of the plant might be better than reproducing the flower sexually.

Q2 Strawberry plants can reproduce by vegetative propagation. When they are growing well, runners extend from their stems.

   Gardeners can use the runners to reproduce their strawberry plants. Give two disadvantages of reproducing strawberry plants in this way, rather than from seeds.

Tip: To help you answer Q2, think about whether using seeds is an example of asexual or sexual reproduction.

Practice Questions — Fact Recall

Q1 What is vegetative propagation?

Q2 Suggest a method for providing a warm and moist environment for a cutting once it has been transferred to a pot of growth medium.

Q3 Name three parts of a plant that can be dissected to produce a cutting.

Q4 Give two situations where cloning a plant using tissue culture might be useful.

- Know how natural
  clones are produced
  in animal species,
  e.g. twins formed by
  embryo splitting.
- Know how artificial
  clones in animals
  can be produced
  by artificial embryo
  twinning or by
  enucleation and
  somatic cell nuclear
  transfer (SCNT).
- Know the arguments
  for and against
  artificial cloning in
  animals, and be able
  to evaluate the uses
  of animal cloning
  (including examples
  of cloning used
  in agriculture and
  medicine, and issues
  of longevity of cloned
  animals).

  **Specification
  Reference 6.2.1**

Tip: The process could
also be done using an
early embryo extracted
from a pregnant animal,
rather than using an
embryo created in a lab.

Tip: Artificial embryo
twinning and SCNT (see
next page) involve the
clone developing inside
a surrogate animal.
The vast majority of
animals that have been
successfully cloned are
mammals — scientists
would need to adapt
the methods to clone
animals that don't
naturally develop inside
a parent (e.g. birds,
reptiles).

2. Animal Cloning

*Scientists have been able to clone animals for quite a while now, but the
process has advantages and disadvantages. Read on to find out more...*

Natural animal clones

Animal clones can be produced naturally as a result of sexual reproduction.
During sexual reproduction, once an egg has been fertilised, it's possible for it
to split during the very early stages of development and develop into multiple
embryos with the same genetic information. The embryos can develop as
normal to produce offspring that are all genetically identical — they are
clones. For example, identical twins are natural clones.

Artificial animal clones

It's possible for scientists to produce clones of animals. You need to know
how animals can be artificially cloned using the artificial embryo twinning
and somatic cell nuclear transfer methods.

Artificial embryo twinning

This type of artificial cloning is similar to what happens when animal clones
form naturally. Figure 1 shows how this is done in cows, but the same
technique can be used for other animals:

1. An egg cell is extracted from a female cow and fertilised in a Petri dish.
2. The fertilised egg is left to divide at least once, forming an embryo *in vitro*
   (outside a living organism).
3. Next, the individual cells from the embryo are separated and each is put
   into a separate Petri dish. Each cell divides and develops normally, so an
   embryo forms in each Petri dish.
4. The embryos are then implanted into female cows, which act as surrogate
   mothers.
5. The embryos continue to develop inside the surrogate cows, and eventually
   the offspring are born. They're all genetically identical to each other.

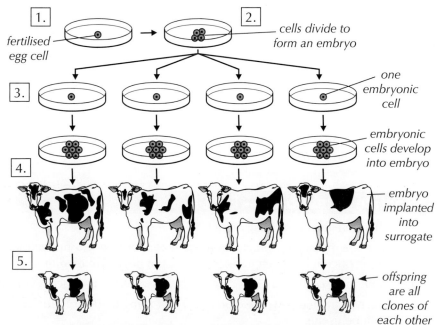

Figure 1: The process of artificial embryo twinning.

Somatic cell nuclear transfer (SCNT)

This method is a bit more high-tech than artificial embryo twinning. Figure 3 shows how it's done with sheep (but again the principles are the same for other animals):

1. A **somatic cell** (any cell that isn't a reproductive cell) is taken from sheep A. The nucleus is extracted and kept.

2. An oocyte (immature egg cell) is taken from sheep B. Its nucleus is removed to form an **enucleated** oocyte.

3. The nucleus from sheep A is inserted into the enucleated oocyte — the oocyte from sheep B now contains the genetic information from sheep A.

4. The nucleus and the enucleated oocyte are fused together and stimulated to divide (e.g. by electrofusion, where an electrical current is applied). This produces an embryo.

5. Then the embryo is implanted into a surrogate mother and eventually a lamb is born that's a clone of sheep A.

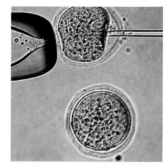

Figure 2: *Nuclear transfer — here the nucleus of an adult mouse cell is being injected into an enucleated mouse oocyte (top, centre).*

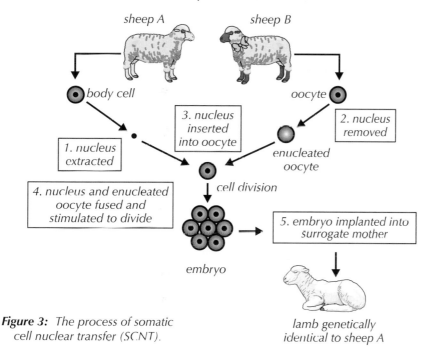

Figure 3: *The process of somatic cell nuclear transfer (SCNT).*

Tip: Producing a clone by SCNT can involve up to three different sheep (the nucleus donor, the egg donor and the surrogate mother), but the clone will only have genetic information from the nucleus donor.

Uses of animal cloning

Animal cloning has many uses. Here are a few to take a look at:

- Scientists use cloned animals for research purposes.

┌ **Example** ─────────

In the field of medicine they can test new drugs on cloned animals. They're all genetically identical, so the variables that come from genetic differences (e.g. the likelihood of developing cancer) are removed.

- Cloning can be used in agriculture so farmers can increase the number of animals with desirable characteristics to breed from.

┌ **Example** ─────────

A prize-winning cow with high milk production could be cloned.

- Animals that have been genetically modified (see page 215) to produce a useful substance that they wouldn't normally produce could be cloned to produce lots of identical animals that all produce the same substance.

Example

A goat that has been genetically modified to produce a beneficial protein in its milk could be cloned.

- Cloning can also be used to save endangered animals from extinction by cloning new individuals.

Example

The European mouflon is a species of wild sheep which is currently endangered. Scientists have successfully cloned a European mouflon and it's hoped that this could help save the species.

Figure 4: *Two wild mouflon in Austria.*

Cloning doesn't have to be used to make whole animals. Sometimes scientists only want the cloned **embryonic stem cells**. These cells are harvested from young embryos and have the potential to become any cell type, so scientists think they could be used to replace damaged tissues in a range of diseases, e.g. heart disease, spinal cord injuries, degenerative brain disorders like Parkinson's disease. If replacement tissue is made from cloned embryonic stem cells that are genetically identical to the patient's own cells, it won't be rejected by their immune system.

Arguments for and against animal cloning

You might have to evaluate the uses of animal cloning, so you need to be aware of the arguments for and against the process:

Arguments for

- Desirable genetic characteristics are always passed on to clones (e.g. high milk production in cows). This doesn't always happen with sexual reproduction because of processes such as independent assortment and crossing-over, which generate genetic variation during meiosis. So if a farmer had a cow that produced a lot of milk, the only way he could guarantee that his calves would also produce a lot of milk would be to clone the cow.

- Infertile animals can be reproduced, so if a farmer's prize winning cow was infertile for any reason, they could still reproduce it.
- Animals can be cloned at any time — you wouldn't have to wait until a breeding season to get new animals.
- Increasing the population of endangered species helps to preserve biodiversity.
- Cloning can help us develop new treatments for disease, which could mean less suffering for some people.

Arguments against

- Animal cloning is very difficult, time-consuming and expensive.
- There's no genetic variability in cloned populations, so undesirable genetic characteristics (e.g. a weak immune system) are always passed on to clones. This means that all of the cloned animals in a population are susceptible to the same diseases. Potentially, a single disease could wipe them all out.

- Some evidence suggests that clones may not live as long as natural offspring. Some think this is unethical.

Example

Dolly the sheep was a clone generated by somatic cell nuclear transfer. It took 277 nuclear transfer attempts before Dolly was finally born, which shows just how difficult it is to successfully clone an animal. The average life expectancy of sheep the same breed as Dolly is 11-12 years but Dolly had to be put down at the age of six after developing a lung disease and arthritis.

Figure 5: *Dolly the sheep.*

- Using cloned human embryos as a source of stem cells is controversial. The embryos are usually destroyed after the embryonic stem cells have been harvested — some people believe that doing this is destroying a human life.

Tip: Reproductive cloning of humans (to produce a full human being) is currently illegal in the UK. Cloning to produce a source of stem cells is allowed under licence. There's more on how society uses science to make decisions on page 4.

Practice Questions — Application

Q1 A scientist wants to clone some mice for use in a drug trial.

a) Describe how he could use artificial embryo twinning to produce several cloned mice.

b) Suggest why cloned mice are wanted for the drug trial, rather than mice produced via sexual reproduction.

Q2 The diagram below shows the early stages of a process used to clone a dog:

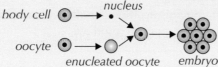

a) What is this process called?

b) Describe what would happen in the rest of this process.

Practice Questions — Fact Recall

Q1 Explain how natural animal clones occur.

Q2 Explain why animal clones may be used in agriculture.

Q3 Other than agriculture, give an example of how cloned animals may be useful.

Q4 Give three arguments for and three arguments against animal cloning.

Tip: Remember — enzymes are proteins that catalyse reactions in living organisms.

Tip: You can find out how isolated enzymes are used in biotechnology on page 250.

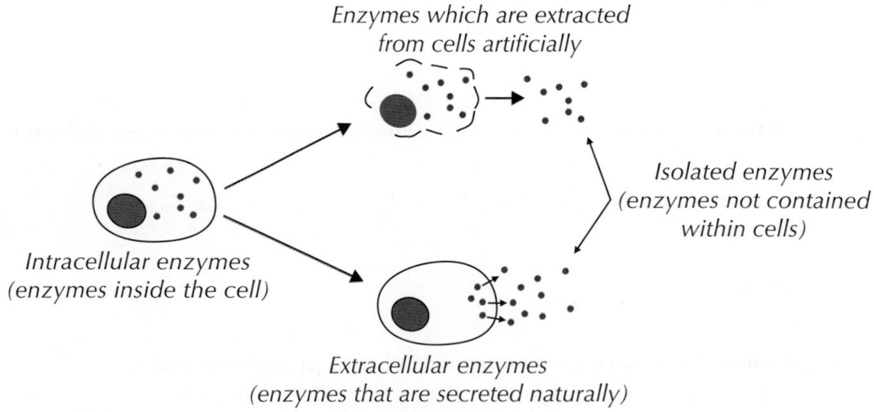

3. Biotechnology — The Use of Microorganisms

The biotechnology industry is pretty big these days — it's used to produce loads of useful products. This topic looks at what biotechnology is and how microorganisms can be used in biotechnological processes.

What is biotechnology?

Biotechnology is the industrial use of living organisms (or parts of living organisms, see below) to produce food, drugs and other products.

The living organisms used are mostly microorganisms (bacteria and fungi). Here are a few reasons why:

- Their ideal growth conditions can be easily created — microorganisms will generally grow successfully as long as they have the right nutrients, temperature, pH, moisture levels and availability of gases (e.g. some need oxygen).

- Due to their short life-cycle, they grow rapidly under the right conditions, so products can be made quickly.

- They can grow on a range of inexpensive materials — this makes them economical to use.

- They can be grown at any time of the year.

Enzymes in biotechnology

As well as whole living organisms, biotechnology also uses parts of living organisms (such as enzymes) to make products.

┌─ **Example** ─────────────────────────────

Lactase (the enzyme that breaks down lactose) is prepared from *Aspergillus* fungi and is used in the production of lactose-free products (see page 250).

Enzymes used in industry can be contained within the cells of microorganisms — these are called intracellular enzymes. Enzymes are also used that aren't contained within cells — these are called isolated enzymes. Some are secreted naturally by microorganisms (called extracellular enzymes), but others have to be extracted. Naturally secreted enzymes are cheaper to use because it can be expensive to extract enzymes from cells.

Enzymes which are extracted from cells artificially

Isolated enzymes (enzymes not contained within cells)

Intracellular enzymes (enzymes inside the cell)

Extracellular enzymes (enzymes that are secreted naturally)

Figure 1: *The different types of enzyme used in the biotechnology industry.*

Uses of microorganisms in biotechnology

Microorganisms are used in a wide variety of industrial processes.
You need to know how microorganisms are used in the following processes:

Brewing (making beer)

To make beer, yeast (e.g. *Saccharomyces cerevisiae*) is added to a type of grain (such as barley) and other ingredients. The yeast respires anaerobically using the glucose from the grain and produces ethanol (alcohol) and CO_2. (When anaerobic respiration produces ethanol, the process is called fermentation.)

Baking

Yeast is also the organism that makes bread rise. The CO_2 produced by fermentation of sugars in the dough makes sure it doesn't stay flat.
Many flat breads, like tortillas, are made without yeast.

Cheese making

Cheese production used to rely on a substance called rennet. Rennet contains the enzyme chymosin, which clots the milk — a key process in cheese making. Traditionally we used to get chymosin by extracting rennet from the lining of calves' stomachs, but now chymosin can be obtained from yeast cells that have been genetically modified to produce the enzyme. Cheese making also involves lactic acid bacteria (e.g. *Lactobacillus* and *Streptococcus*). These bacteria convert the lactose in milk into lactic acid, which makes it turn sour and contributes to it solidifying. The production of blue cheeses also involves the addition of fungi to make the characteristic blue veins.

Figure 2: *Rennet being added to milk to make cheese.*

Yoghurt production

Just like cheese making, yoghurt production involves the use of lactic acid bacteria to clot the milk and cause it to thicken. This creates a basic yoghurt product and then any flavours and colours are added.

Penicillin production

In times of stress, fungi from the *Penicillium* genus produce an antibiotic, penicillin, to stop bacteria from growing and competing for resources. Penicillin is one of the most common antibiotics used in medicine, so we produce it on a massive scale. The fungus (usually *Penicillium chrysogenum*) is grown under stress in industrial fermenters (see page 242) and the penicillin produced is collected and processed to be used in medicine.

Figure 3: Penicillium *fungus — this fungus produces penicillin.*

Insulin production

Insulin is a hormone that's crucial for treating people with Type 1 diabetes. Insulin is made by genetically modified bacteria, which have had the gene for human insulin production inserted into their DNA. These bacteria are grown in an industrial fermenter on a massive scale and the insulin produced is collected and purified.

Bioremediation

Bioremediation is a posh name for the process of using organisms (usually microorganisms) to remove pollutants, like oil and pesticides, from contaminated sites. Most commonly, pollutant-removing bacteria that occur naturally at a site are provided with extra nutrients and enhanced growing conditions to allow them to multiply and thrive. These bacteria break down the pollutants into less harmful products, cleaning up the area.

> **Tip:** Bioremediation can also be carried out by introducing new bacteria to the environment that needs cleaning up, although this is less common.

In 1989 an oil tanker spilled around 40 million litres of crude oil into the sea near the port of Valdez on the southern coast of Alaska. Scientists found that microorganisms present in the area could naturally biodegrade (break down) the oil. They discovered that the growth rate of these microorganisms could be greatly increased with the use of fertiliser (a substance containing nutrients). Therefore, large amounts of fertiliser were added to the water to clean up the oil more quickly.

Pros and cons of using microorganisms in food production

Figure 4: *A selection of meat substitute products made from single-cell protein.*

Tip: An organic substrate is a carbon-containing substance that can be used as an energy source by an organism.

As you can see from the previous page, microorganisms play a key role in the production of lots of different foods. Some microorganisms can also be grown as a source of protein (called single-cell protein), which can act as a valuable food source for humans and other animals. Examples of microorganisms used to make single-cell protein include the fungus *Fusarium venenatum* (which is used to make the popular meat substitute Quorn™) and the bacteria *Methylophilus methylotrophus* (which is used to produce animal feed).

There are advantages and disadvantages of producing food for human consumption using microorganisms.

Advantages

- Microorganisms used to make single-cell protein can be grown using many different organic substrates, including waste materials such as molasses (a by-product of sugar processing). Production of single-cell protein could actually be used as a way of getting rid of waste products.
- Microorganisms can be grown quickly, easily and cheaply. Production costs are low because microorganisms have simple growth requirements, can be grown on waste products and less land is required in comparison to growing crops or rearing livestock.
- Microorganisms can be cultured anywhere if you have the right equipment. This means that a food source could be readily produced in places where growing crops and rearing livestock is difficult (e.g. very hot or cold climates). This could help tackle malnutrition in developing countries.
- Single-cell protein is also often considered a healthier alternative to animal protein.

Disadvantages

- Because the conditions needed to grow the desired microorganism are also ideal for other microorganisms, a lot of effort has to go into making sure that the food doesn't get contaminated with unwanted bacteria, which could be dangerous to humans or spoil the food.
- People may not like the idea of eating food that has been grown using waste products.
- Single-cell protein doesn't have the same texture or flavour as real meat.
- If single-cell protein is consumed in high quantities, health problems could be caused due to the high levels of uric acid released when the large amounts of amino acids are broken down.

Practice Questions — Application

Q1 Land that used to be the location of a large chemical factory was being redeveloped into a housing estate. Over the course of the use of the land as a factory site, the soil had become contaminated with several harmful chemical pollutants that posed a risk to humans and wildlife. Before the development could go ahead, the soil had to be decontaminated.

Suggest and explain a biotechnological method that could be used to help clean up the contaminants from the soil.

Q2 It is possible that single-cell protein could be used as a valuable food source in some developing countries, such as India, where the climate can be very hot and the population size is increasing very quickly.

a) Suggest why it may be advantageous to use single-cell protein as a food source in parts of India, rather than relying on food from crops and livestock.

b) Suggest two arguments against producing single-cell protein on a large scale so it can be used as a human food source in developing countries, such as India.

Tip: To answer Q2a, think about the strains that a hot climate and rapidly growing population could put on conventional food production.

Practice Questions — Fact Recall

Q1 What is biotechnology?

Q2 Give three reasons why biotechnology mostly uses microorganisms.

Q3 Explain how microorganisms are used in:
a) brewing,
b) baking,
c) cheese making,
d) yoghurt production,
e) penicillin production,
f) insulin production.

Learning Objectives:

- Understand the importance of manipulating the growing conditions in batch and continuous fermentation in order to maximise the yield of product required.

- Understand the standard growth curve of a microorganism in a closed culture and know how to estimate the number of individual organisms there will be in a culture using the formula $N = N_0 \times 2^n$.

- Know how to culture microorganisms effectively, using aseptic techniques (PAG7).

- Be able to carry out practical investigations into the factors affecting the growth of microorganisms (PAG7).

Specification Reference 6.2.1

Figure 2: *A vessel for the fermentation of yeast.*

Tip: Extremes of pH can denature (deactivate) enzymes.

4. Biotechnology — Culturing Microorganisms

If you want to use microorganisms for a particular industrial process, you have to grow them first. This topic tells you how.

Fermentation vessels

Biotechnology uses **cultures** of microorganisms. A culture is a population of one type of microorganism that's been grown under controlled conditions. Cultures are grown in large containers called fermentation vessels (see Figure 1) to either obtain lots of the microorganism (e.g. for production of single-celled protein — see page 240) or to collect lots of a useful product that the microorganism makes.

There are two main methods for culturing microorganisms — **batch fermentation** and **continuous fermentation**. Batch fermentation is where microorganisms are grown in individual batches in a fermentation vessel — when one culture ends it's removed and then a different batch of microorganisms is grown in the vessel. This is known as a **closed culture** — see next page. Continuous fermentation is where microorganisms are continually grown in a fermentation vessel without stopping. Nutrients are put in and waste products taken out at a constant rate.

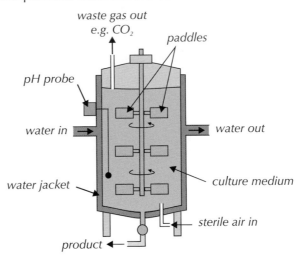

Figure 1: *A typical fermentation vessel.*

The conditions inside the fermentation vessels are kept at the optimum for growth — this maximises the yield of microorganisms and desirable products. The factors that need to be controlled in a fermentation vessel are explained below and on the next page.

pH

The pH is monitored by a pH probe and kept at the optimum level. This increases the product yield because enzymes can work efficiently, so the rate of reaction is kept as high as possible.

Temperature

The temperature is kept at the optimum level by a water jacket that surrounds the vessel. This increases the product yield because enzymes can work efficiently, so the rate of reaction is kept as high as possible.

Oxygen supply

The volume of oxygen is kept at the optimum level for respiration by pumping in sterile air when needed. This increases the product yield because microorganisms can always respire to provide the energy for growth.

Nutrient concentration

Microorganisms are kept in contact with fresh medium by paddles that circulate the medium around the vessel. This increases the product yield because microorganisms can always access the nutrients needed for growth.

Contamination

Vessels are sterilised between uses with superheated steam to kill any unwanted organisms and make sure the next culture is not contaminated. This increases the product yield because the microorganisms aren't competing with other organisms.

Tip: If you didn't have paddles stirring the medium, the nutrients would all sink to the bottom and the nutrient concentration wouldn't be the same throughout the vessel.

Closed cultures

A **closed culture** is when growth takes place in a vessel that's isolated from the external environment — extra nutrients aren't added and waste products aren't removed from the vessel during growth.

Tip: If a culture isn't isolated from the external environment it's called an <u>open culture</u>.

Growth curves

In a closed culture, such as in batch fermentation, a population of microorganisms follows a **standard growth curve**. This growth curve has four phases (see Figure 3).

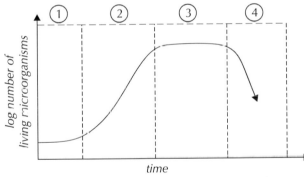

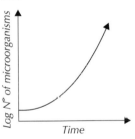

Tip: The growth curve for continuous fermentation looks like this:

There's no stationary or decline phase because it's an open culture — nutrients are constantly being added and waste is constantly being removed. So the microorganisms don't run out of food and waste can't build up to toxic levels.

Figure 3: *The standard growth curve of a population of microorganisms in a closed culture.*

Here's what's happening in each of the four phases:

1. **Lag phase** — the population size increases very slowly because the microorganisms have to make enzymes and other molecules before they can reproduce. This means the reproduction rate is low.

2. **Exponential (log) phase** — the population size increases quickly because the culture conditions are at their most favourable for reproduction (lots of food and little competition). The number of microorganisms doubles at regular intervals.

3. **Stationary phase** — the population size stays level because the death rate of the microorganisms equals their reproductive rate. Microorganisms die because there's not enough food and poisonous waste products build up.

4. **Decline phase** — the population size falls because the death rate is greater than the reproductive rate. This is because food is very scarce and waste products are at toxic levels.

Interpreting a standard growth curve can involve a bit of maths (see p. 244-245).

Exam Tip
Make sure you learn what each of the four phases are called, what the growth curve looks like during each phase and why the curve has the shape it does.

Estimating the number of cells in a culture

During the exponential growth phase, the number of cells in a culture of microorganisms doubles at regular intervals. You can work out how many cells will be present in a population (N) after a certain number of divisions using this formula:

N_0 is the initial number of cells $\quad N = N_0 \times 2^n \quad$ n is the number of divisions

Tip: The generation time is the time between divisions — the time taken for the cells to divide and reproduce.

Example — Maths Skills

For a particular species of bacteria, the cells divide approximately every 30 minutes during the exponential growth phase. There are 300 bacterial cells present at the start of the exponential growth phase. Estimate how many cells are present after 7 hours (assuming the culture remains in the exponential growth phase during this time).

- First work out how many divisions will have taken place. 7 hours is 420 minutes, so in 7 hours there will be $420 \div 30 = 14$ divisions.

- Then put the information into the formula:
$$\text{number of cells in population} = N_0 \times 2^n = 300 \times 2^{14}$$
$$= 4915200 \text{ cells} = \mathbf{4.9 \times 10^6 \text{ cells}}$$

Exam Tip
The number of cells in a culture of microorganisms can be very large, so it's not uncommon to see values in standard form. Before the exam make sure you've brushed up on your maths skills and are comfortable interpreting numbers in standard form.

Using logarithms in growth curves

Due to the rapid growth rate of microorganisms, the number of cells present after the exponential growth phase can vary massively from the number present at the beginning. This means that plotting the number of cells in a culture over time would be really difficult to do on a normal (linear) scale, because the y-axis would have to cover a really wide range of values.

Tip: The log explained here is actually $\log_{10}$ (log to the base of 10). You can get logs to the base of other numbers too, but $\log_{10}$ is most commonly used.

To get around this problem, logarithms ('logs') are used. The log of a number tells you how many times 10 has been multiplied by 10 to give you that number (see Figure 4).

Number	Power of 10	Log value
10	10^1	1
100	10^2	2
1000	10^3	3
10 000	10^4	4

Figure 4: Table showing how log values are derived.

Tip: Different calculators work differently so make sure you know how to calculate logs on yours.

You can calculate the log of a number using the log button on your calculator. All you do is press log, then the number you're using, then equals. Once the number of cells in a culture has been converted to logs, the growth curve is much easier to plot.

Example

A scientist recorded the number of cells present in a bacterial culture during its exponential growth phase. She converted the number of cells to log values to give a much narrower range of values, which are easier to plot on a graph (see Figure 5).

Tip: This is what the graph in the example on the right would look like if the actual number of cells were plotted, rather than their logs:

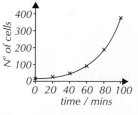

You can see it would be really hard to read values accurately from the y-axis because the scale is so small.

Time (mins)	Nº of cells	Log Nº of cells
0	12	1.08
20	25	1.40
40	46	1.66
60	97	1.99
80	189	2.28
100	388	2.59

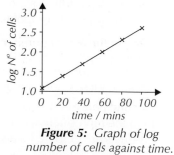

Figure 5: Graph of log number of cells against time.

Interpreting data values from a logarithmic scale

When you see microbial growth data presented on a logarithmic scale, the units on the y-axis may tell you the total number of cells rather than the log values. This makes it easier to work out how many cells are present at a given time, but you have to be careful because the smaller increments on the y-axis are not evenly spaced.

Example — Maths Skills

The graph below shows the growth of a bacterial culture over six hours. The graph is drawn with a logarithmic scale.
Estimate how many bacteria per cm³ were in the culture after four hours.

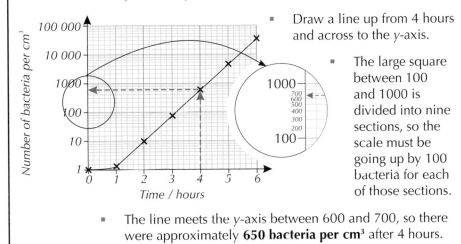

- Draw a line up from 4 hours and across to the y-axis.

- The large square between 100 and 1000 is divided into nine sections, so the scale must be going up by 100 bacteria for each of those sections.

- The line meets the y-axis between 600 and 700, so there were approximately **650 bacteria per cm³** after 4 hours.

Tip: If you work out the number of cells present at two time points on a growth curve, you can use them to work out the rate of growth during that time period. To do this you need to work out the gradient of the line (or of a tangent to the line if the line's curved) between your two time points. This is the formula to use:

$$\text{Gradient} = \frac{\text{Change in } y}{\text{Change in } x}$$

If only the log values are shown on the y-axis, it's still possible to work out how many cells are present at a given time by finding the **antilog**. To do this you need to use the 10^x button on your calculator. Simply press this, then enter the log value at your chosen time. When you press equals, you'll get the number of cells.

Tip: Sometimes, the antilog is referred to as the reverse log or inverse log.

Example — Maths Skills

The graph below shows part of a growth curve for a closed bacterial culture.

Estimate how many bacterial cells are present after 4 hours.

- You can see from the graph that at 4 hours, the log number of bacterial cells is 4.7.

- To get the actual number of bacterial cells, you need to calculate the antilog using your calculator:

  $10^{4.7} = \textbf{50118 cells}$
  present at 4 hours.

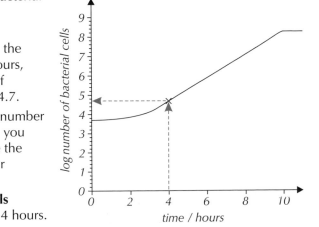

Tip: 10^x is usually found written above the log button on a calculator (it's a second function of log). But again, different calculators work differently so make sure you know how to use yours.

Tip: You should round estimations down to a whole number, because you can't get parts of cells.

Culturing microorganisms in the lab

Cultures of microorganisms can be grown in the lab. A common way to do this is on an agar plate — a sterile Petri dish containing agar jelly. Nutrients can be added to the agar to help improve the growing conditions. The microorganisms you use are likely to be provided in a liquid broth (a mixture of distilled water and nutrients). To culture the microorganisms, use a sterile implement like a wire inoculation loop to transfer some of the sample to the plate. A pipette could also be used to transfer the sample, which could then be gently spread across the whole surface of the agar using a glass or plastic spreader. The plates then need to be incubated to allow the microorganisms to grow.

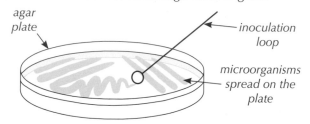

agar plate

inoculation loop

microorganisms spread on the plate

Figure 6: *An agar plate being used to culture microorganisms.*

Aseptic techniques

An important part of culturing microorganisms is using aseptic techniques. These are used to prevent contamination of cultures by unwanted microorganisms, which may affect the growth of the microorganism being cultured. Contaminated cultures in laboratory experiments give imprecise results and may be hazardous to health. Contamination on an industrial scale can be very costly because entire cultures may have to be thrown away. Below are some important aseptic techniques that you should follow when culturing microorganisms in the lab:

> **Examples** ─────────────────────
>
> - Regularly disinfect work surfaces to minimise contamination.
> - Work near a Bunsen flame. Hot air rises, so any microorganisms in the air should be drawn away from your culture.
> - Sterilise the instrument used to transfer cultures before and after each use, e.g. sterilise a wire inoculation loop by passing it through a hot Bunsen burner flame for 5 seconds. This will kill any microorganisms on the instrument. Pre-sterilised plastic instruments should only be used once and then safely discarded.
> - If you're using broth, briefly pass the neck of the broth container through a Bunsen burner flame just after it's opened and just before it's closed — this causes air to move out of the container, preventing unwanted organisms from falling in.
> - Minimise the time that the agar plate is open and put the lid on as soon as possible. This reduces the chance of airborne microorganisms contaminating the culture. You could even work in an inoculation cabinet (a chamber that has a flow of sterile air inside it).
> - Sterilise all glassware before and after use, e.g. in an autoclave (a machine which steams equipment at high pressure).
> - Wear a lab coat and, if needed, gloves. Tie long hair back to prevent it from falling into anything.

Tip: There are lots of risks associated with culturing microorganisms. Make sure you've carried out a full risk assessment and know all about using aseptic techniques before you start.

Tip: Microorganisms can also be cultured in a broth, as well as on agar plates.

Figure 7: *A scientist transferring a microorganism to a Petri dish.*

Tip: Your teacher may recommend other aseptic techniques you need to follow.

Figure 8: *An inoculation loop being sterilised in a Bunsen burner.*

Investigating factors that affect the growth of microorganisms

You can investigate the effects of different factors on the growth of microorganisms by growing them on agar plates under different conditions. The example below shows how you can investigate the effect of temperature on the growth of bacteria (although the same method can be used for other microorganisms, such as fungi).

Tip: Again, make sure you carry out a full risk assessment before you carry out this practical and follow aseptic techniques throughout the investigation.

Example

1. You should be supplied with a sample of bacteria (e.g. *E. coli*) in broth. Using a sterile pipette, add the same volume (e.g. 0.1 cm³) of your sample to each of six agar plates. Discard your pipette safely after use (e.g. if it's a glass pipette, put it into a beaker of disinfectant while you are working and then into an autoclave once you've finished).

Tip: You could also use another tool such as a sterile cotton swab to spread the broth on the plate — make sure you're aware of the aseptic techniques required for whatever tool you're using.

2. Spread the broth across the entire surface of the agar using a sterile plastic spreader (see Figure 9). Discard the spreader safely after use.

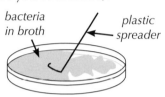

bacteria in broth   *plastic spreader*

Figure 9: *Bacteria being spread onto an agar plate.*

3. Put the lids on the agar plates and tape them shut.

4. Place three plates in a fridge at 4 °C and put three in an incubator at 25 °C. If you don't have access to an incubator, just leave the plates at room temperature, somewhere where the temperature is most likely to remain constant. The plates should be incubated upside down. This stops any condensation forming on the lid from dropping onto the agar.

Tip: Don't completely seal the Petri dish with tape before incubation — it will prevent oxygen from entering the dish, which may encourage the growth of anaerobic disease-causing bacteria. Don't open the dish after incubation.

5. Put another lidded agar plate in each of the two different temperature locations — these plates should be uncultured (i.e. you shouldn't have added any bacteria to them). These plates will act as negative controls.

6. Leave all the plates for the same amount of time (e.g. 24 hours) then observe the results.

Tip: A negative control is not expected to have any effect on the experiment — see page 3 for more.

7. If bacterial growth has occurred, you should see colonies of bacteria on the surface of the agar (see Figure 10).

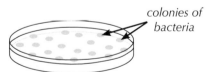

colonies of bacteria

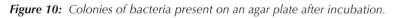

Figure 10: *Colonies of bacteria present on an agar plate after incubation.*

Tip: A colony is a large group of microorganisms, which usually originate from a single cell, living closely together on the agar. Colonies are visible to the naked eye.

8. Count the number of colonies that have formed on each plate and record your results in a table.

9. Work out the mean number of colonies formed at each temperature.

You might find that you have so many colonies that they overlap and you can't count them. If this happens, try making serial dilutions of your bacteria in broth and plate them on agar — this should give you a more manageable number of colonies because there will be fewer bacteria present in the solution to begin with.

Tip: Serial dilutions are a set of dilutions that decrease in concentration by the same factor each time.

The experiment on the previous page can be adapted to investigate the effects of different factors on the growth of microorganisms. For example, you could:

- investigate the effect of pH by adding buffers at different pH levels to the broth.
- investigate the effects of nutrient availability by using different preparations of agar, which contain different nutrients.

You could also investigate the growth of microorganisms directly in broth (without the need to plate the broth on agar) using a spectrophotometer. This is a machine that measures the turbidity (cloudiness) of the broth. Higher turbidity means that more cells are present and, therefore, more replication has taken place.

Practice Questions — Application

Q1 Turbidity is a measure of the cloudiness of a liquid. The more bacteria in a liquid, the cloudier it will be. A scientist grew two different species of bacteria in liquid broth to see which species grew more quickly at room temperature. She measured the turbidity of the samples over time to track the bacterial growth. The results are shown in the graph.

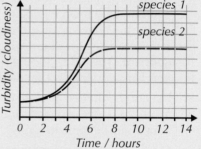

a) Suggest a suitable negative control for this experiment and explain why it should be used.

b) Describe two aseptic techniques that the scientist would need to carry out in the preparation of the broth.

c) Explain why it is important to use aseptic techniques when working with cultures of microorganisms in the lab.

d) Describe the differences between the growth curves of each species of bacteria and suggest an explanation for them.

Tip: Take a look back at page 243 if you need a reminder about the different phases on a microbial culture's growth curve.

Q2 A scientist was working with a species of bacteria that had been isolated from a highly acidic environment. He wanted to test the ability of the species to grow at higher pH levels. Suggest a suitable experiment that he could perform to measure the species' growth performance at pH 3, pH 5 and pH 7.

Practice Questions — Fact Recall

Q1 What is a culture?

Q2 State three things that are controlled in a fermentation vessel.

Q3 Explain what is meant by 'a closed culture'.

Q4 a) Name the four phases on the growth curve of a population of microorganisms in a closed culture.

b) Describe and explain what is happening during each phase.

5. Immobilised Enzymes

As you know from page 238, enzymes can be pretty important in biotechnology. Enzymes are often immobilised for use in industrial processes. These pages explain how and why immobilised enzymes are used.

Immobilising isolated enzymes

Isolated enzymes used in industry can become mixed in with the products of a reaction. The products then need to be separated from this mixture, which can be complicated and costly. This is avoided in large-scale production by using **immobilised enzymes** — enzymes that are attached to an insoluble material so they can't become mixed with the products. There are three main ways that enzymes are immobilised:

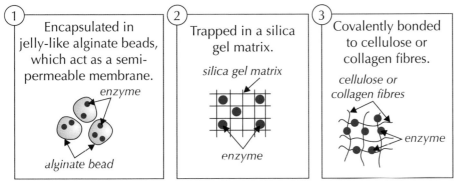

1. Encapsulated in jelly-like alginate beads, which act as a semi-permeable membrane.
   enzyme
   alginate bead

2. Trapped in a silica gel matrix.
   silica gel matrix
   enzyme

3. Covalently bonded to cellulose or collagen fibres.
   cellulose or collagen fibres
   enzyme

In industry, the substrate solution for a reaction is run through a column of immobilised enzymes (see Figure 1). The active sites of the enzymes are still available to catalyse the reaction but the solution flowing out of the column will only contain the desired product.

Here are some of the advantages and disadvantages of using immobilised enzymes in industry:

Advantages

- Columns of immobilised enzymes can be washed and reused — this reduces the cost of running a reaction on an industrial scale because you don't have to keep buying new enzymes.

- The product isn't mixed with the enzymes — no money or time is spent separating them out.

- Immobilised enzymes are more stable than free enzymes — they're less likely to denature (become inactive) in high temperatures or extremes of pH.

Disadvantages

- Extra equipment is required, which can be expensive to buy.

- Immobilised enzymes are more expensive to buy than free enzymes, so coupled with the equipment costs, they're not always economical for use in smaller-scale production.

- The immobilisation of the enzymes can sometimes lead to a reduction in the enzyme activity because they can't freely mix with their substrate.

substrate solution

column

immobilised enzymes in alginate beads

solution flowing out of column

Figure 1: *A column of immobilised enzymes.*

Learning Objectives:

- Understand the different methods of immobilising enzymes for use in biotechnology.

- Be able to evaluate the uses of immobilised enzymes in biotechnology — examples could include:

  - lactase for the hydrolysis of lactose to glucose and galactose,

  - penicillin acyclase for the formation of semi-synthetic penicillins (to which some penicillin-resistant organisms are not resistant),

  - glucoamylase for the conversion of dextrins to glucose,

  - glucose isomerase for the conversion of glucose to fructose,

  - aminoacyclase for production of pure samples of L-amino acids,

  - nitrilase for the conversion of acrylonitrile to acrylamide (for use in the plastics industry).

Specification Reference 6.2.1

Exam Tip
If you get asked about advantages and disadvantages of using immobilised enzymes in the exam, be specific — e.g. for an advantage, don't just say they're more economical than free enzymes, give the reasons why.

Uses of immobilised enzymes

Immobilised enzymes are used in a wide range of industrial processes.
Here are just a few examples of industrial processes that use them and the
particular enzyme that they make use of:

Conversion of lactose to glucose and galactose

Some people are unable to digest lactose (a sugar found in milk) because they
don't produce enough (or any) of the enzyme lactase. Lactase breaks lactose
down into glucose and galactose via a hydrolysis reaction. Industrially, fresh
milk can now be passed over immobilised lactase to produce lactose-free milk
for use in the production of lactose-free dairy products.

Production of semi-synthetic penicillins

Penicillin is a useful antibiotic, but some bacteria have become penicillin
resistant. Semi-synthetic penicillins can now be produced, which have the
same antibiotic properties as natural penicillin, but are effective against
penicillin-resistant organisms. Immobilised penicillin acylase enzyme is used
in their production.

Conversion of dextrins to glucose

Glucose and glucose syrup are used in massive amounts in industry, e.g.
they're used in the food industry to sweeten and thicken foods. Glucose
can be derived from starchy foods, such as corn and potatoes, with the help
of immobilised enzymes. Starch breaks down into dextrins (carbohydrate
products), which are then broken down into glucose by the immobilised
enzyme glucoamylase.

Conversion of glucose to fructose

Fructose is a sugar that's much sweeter than glucose. It's used as a sweetener
in food — using fructose rather than glucose means that less sugar is
needed to obtain the same level of sweetness in our foods. Immobilised
glucose isomerase is used to convert glucose to fructose on an industrial scale.

Production of pure samples of L-amino acids

Amino acids have two chemical forms (isomers) — L or D. Most amino acids
utilised by the body need to be in the L form. Scientists are able to chemically
synthesise amino acids, but end up with a mix of L and D forms. The enzyme
aminoacylase separates them. Immobilised aminoacylase is used for the
industrial production of pure samples of L-amino acids, which can be used
for many purposes in the production of animal and human food, as well as in
dietary supplements.

Conversion of acrylonitrile to acrylamide

Acrylamide is a chemical that is typically used in industry to produce
synthetic polymers (e.g. plastics), which have a wide range of uses. For
example, acrylamide is involved in the production of the polymer that's used
in disposable nappies to make them super-absorbent. In industry, immobilised
nitrilase is used to convert acrylonitrile (a man-made chemical) to acrylamide.

Practice Questions — Application

Q1 A scientist wants to remove all of the protein from a sample. He decides to use a protease enzyme, but since the enzyme is a protein itself it can't be left in the sample at the end. Suggest how the scientist could overcome this problem.

Q2 Biodiesel is an alternative fuel to diesel that can be produced from animal, vegetable or plant oils, such as rapeseed oil. Immobilised lipase enzymes are often used in its production.

a) Give two economical advantages of using immobilised lipase enzymes to produce large amounts of biodiesel, rather than free lipase.

b) Using immobilised lipase for small-scale biodiesel production does not have the same economic advantages as production on a large scale. Suggest why.

Figure 2: *A field of* Brassica napus. *Rapeseed oil is made from the seeds of this plant.*

Practice Questions — Fact Recall

Q1 Give the three main ways that enzymes can be immobilised.

Q2 How do columns of immobilised enzymes work to produce a desired product?

Q3 Give three examples of immobilised enzymes and the industrial processes they are each used in.

Section Summary

Make sure you know...

- That cloning is the process of producing genetically identical cells or organisms from the cells of an existing organism.

- That vegetative propagation is the natural production of plant clones from non-reproductive tissues.

- That plants produce natural clones via different methods of vegetative propagation (e.g. rhizomes, stolons/runners, suckers, tubers, bulbs) and that plant growers also use methods of vegetative propagation to produce clones (e.g. growing cuttings, grafting, layering).

- How to dissect plant material (e.g. the stem, roots or leaves) to produce cuttings, which can then be grown to produce plant clones.

- How plants can be artificially cloned using tissue culture and micropropagation (which is used to produce a large number of clones very quickly).

- The advantages and disadvantages of artificially cloning plants in agriculture and horticulture.

- How natural animal clones (e.g. twins) are produced — a fertilised egg splits in the very early stages of development and develops into multiple identical embryos, which leads to offspring that are clones.

- How artificial animal clones can be made by artificial embryo twinning and somatic cell nuclear transfer (SCNT).

- How artificial cloning of animals can be used, e.g. in agriculture and medicine.

- The arguments for and against the artificial cloning of animals.

- That biotechnology is the industrial use of living organisms to produce food, drugs and other products.

- That the organisms used in biotechnology are mostly microorganisms because their ideal growth conditions can be easily created, they have a short life-cycle so grow quickly under the right conditions, they can grow on inexpensive materials so are economical and they can be grown at any time of the year.

- The roles that microorganisms play in brewing, baking, cheese making, yoghurt production, penicillin production, insulin production and bioremediation.

- The advantages and disadvantages of using microorganisms to produce food for human consumption, e.g. foods made from single-cell protein.

- How microorganisms can be produced on an industrial scale for use in biotechnology using fermentation vessels.

- How growing conditions (i.e. pH, temperature, oxygen supply, nutrient concentration and contamination risk) in batch and continuous fermentation can be manipulated to maximise the yield of the desired product.

- What the standard growth curve for a population of microorganisms in a closed culture looks like, and what's happening during the lag, exponential (log), stationary and decline phases.

- How to estimate the number of individuals that will be present in a culture of microorganisms using the formula $N = N_0 \times 2^n$, where 'N_0' is the initial number of cells in the culture and 'n' is the number of divisions that there has been.

- How to culture microorganisms, and the aseptic techniques that need to be used when doing so.

- How to carry out an investigation into the effect of factors such as temperature, pH and nutrient availability on the growth of microorganisms.

- How enzymes can be immobilised for use in biotechnology.

- The advantages and disadvantages of using immobilised enzymes for industrial processes.

Exam-style Questions

1   A group of scientists are manufacturing insulin for use in the treatment of diabetes.

(a)   The researchers genetically modify bacteria to produce the human insulin protein and grow the cells by continuous fermentation in the fermentation vessel shown in **Fig. 1.1**.

(i)   Identify **three** features of the fermentation vessel in **Fig. 1.1** which help to increase the yield of protein produced. For each feature explain how it helps to increase the yield.

(3 marks)

(ii)   Explain why it's important that the air entering the fermentation vessel is sterile.

(2 marks)

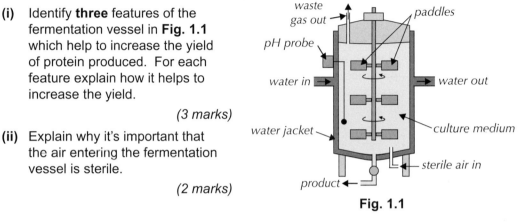

Fig. 1.1

(b)   The growth curve of the bacterial population is shown in **Fig. 1.2**. It has been plotted on a logarithmic scale.

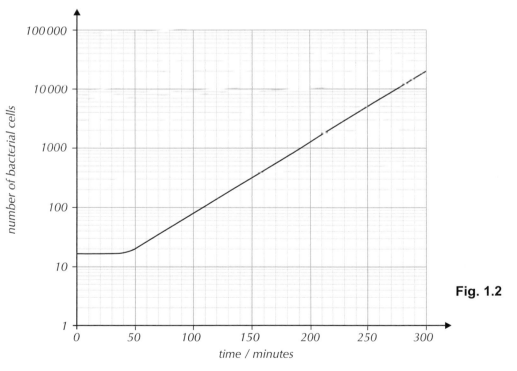

Fig. 1.2

(i)   Using **Fig. 1.2**, estimate the time between each cellular division of the bacteria during the exponential growth phase.

(1 mark)

(ii) Explain why there is no increase in the number of bacterial cells between 0 and 40 minutes.

(1 mark)

(iii) Sketch out the growth curve you would expect to see if the bacteria had been grown by **closed culture**.

(1 mark)

(iv) Explain the differences between the growth curve of a bacterial population in a closed culture and the growth curve in **Fig. 1.2**.

(4 marks)

(c) The scientists believe that, in the future, diabetes could be cured using cloning to produce embryonic stem cells from the patient's own cells. Describe how embryonic stem cells could be produced from a human body cell using somatic cell nuclear transfer.

(4 marks)

2 Plant cloning can occur naturally via vegetative propagation or can be carried out artificially with human intervention. Both produce genetically identical copies of the parent plant.

(a) Name and describe **two** natural methods of vegetative propagation used by plants to produce clones of themselves.

(2 marks)

(b) A gardener wants to take cuttings to produce a clone of his blueberry plant. Describe how he could produce a clone from a cutting from a stem of the plant.

(3 marks)

(c) A company decides to use tissue culture to produce clones of the gardener's blueberry plant after the normal growing season has ended.

(i) When performing tissue culture, explain why the cells that are removed from the original plant are usually taken from the stem and root tips.

(2 marks)

(ii) In addition to being able to produce plants out of season, give **two** further advantages of cloning plants.

(2 marks)

(d) When inspecting clones grown from the same culture, a scientist working for the company notices that one of the clones has a bacterial infection.

(i) Suggest why this could be major problem.

(1 mark)

(ii) An antibiotic against the bacteria causing the infection is produced by a fungus. The fungus can be cultured using batch fermentation or continuous fermentation. Explain **two** reasons why fungi are commonly used in the biotechnology industry.

(2 marks)

1. Ecosystems and Energy Flow

You need to know what an ecosystem is and how energy flows through it. You also need to learn a whole load of ecology-based definitions — so it's probably time to stop reading this introduction and get started...

What is an ecosystem?

An **ecosystem** is all the organisms living in a certain area and all the non-living conditions (factors) found there. It's a dynamic system — this means it's changing all the time. An ecosystem includes both **biotic** and **abiotic factors**:

- Biotic factors are the living features of an ecosystem, for example, the presence of predators or food.

- Abiotic factors are the non-living features of an ecosystem, such as the temperature, rainfall, shape of the land (topology) and soil nutrient availability. In an aquatic ecosystem these may also include the pH and salinity (salt content) of the water.

The place where an organism lives within an ecosystem is known as its **habitat** — for example, a rocky shore on a lake, or a field.

The impact of biotic and abiotic factors

Ecosystems cover different areas. They can be small, e.g. a pond, or large, e.g. an entire forest. Whatever size they are, ecosystems are influenced by biotic and abiotic factors. Here are some examples:

Example — Rock pools

- Biotic factors — Seaweed can be a food source for **consumers** such as limpets that graze on this **producer**. Intense competition for food (such as seaweed) can limit the number of organisms that are present in a small rock pool ecosystem.

- Abiotic factors — Rock pools are heavily influenced by the tides. At high tide they are completely submerged by the ocean so experience similar abiotic factors (e.g. pH, salinity, temperature, etc.) to the ocean ecosystem. However, at low tide they experience more extreme abiotic conditions (e.g. higher salinity and temperatures) — only some organisms can tolerate these conditions.

Example — Playing field

- Biotic factors — Producers include grass and other plants such as daisies, clover and dandelions. The large amount of these plants might attract a large number of organisms that use them as a food source (e.g. rabbits, caterpillars).

- Abiotic factors — Rainfall and sunlight affect the growth of the producers in the ecosystem. In a very wet year, the soil may become waterlogged, making it difficult for plants to grow. Poor plant growth may decrease the number of consumers the ecosystem is able to support.

Learning Objectives:

- Know that ecosystems are dynamic systems that range in size and are influenced by both biotic and abiotic factors.

- Be able to give named examples of biotic and abiotic factors for a variety of ecosystems of different sizes (e.g. a rock pool, a playing field and a large tree).

- Understand how biomass is transferred through ecosystems.

- Understand the efficiency of biomass transfers between trophic levels.

- Know how biomass transfers between trophic levels can be measured.

- Know how human activities can manipulate the transfer of biomass through ecosystems.

Specification Reference 6.3.1

Tip: A consumer is an organism that eats other organisms, e.g. animals and birds.

Tip: A producer is an organism that produces organic molecules using sunlight energy, e.g. all plants are producers.

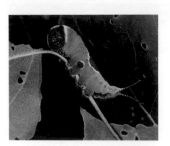

Figure 1: *A caterpillar eating the leaves on a tree is an example of a biotic factor.*

Example — Large tree

- Biotic factors — Insects, such as caterpillars, can use the leaves of a tree as a source of food. However, if they consume all the leaves on a tree (defoliation) they can slow tree growth and even lead to its death.

- Abiotic factors — Drought conditions (e.g. when there are prolonged periods of very low rainfall) can negatively impact the growth of a tree. In severe cases it can result in the whole tree (or parts of it) dying.

Energy transfer through ecosystems

The main route by which energy enters an ecosystem is photosynthesis (e.g. by plants, see page 110). (Some energy enters sea ecosystems when bacteria use chemicals from deep sea vents as an energy source.) During photosynthesis plants convert sunlight energy into a form that can be used by other organisms. Plants are called producers (see previous page). They store energy as **biomass**. Biomass is the mass of living material, e.g. the mass of plant material. After producers store sunlight energy as biomass, you can then think of the following energy transfers through ecosystems as biomass transfers.

Energy is transferred through the living organisms of an ecosystem when organisms eat other organisms. Producers are eaten by organisms called **primary consumers**. Primary consumers are then eaten by **secondary consumers** and secondary consumers are eaten by **tertiary consumers**. Primary consumers are mainly herbivores (plant-eaters). Secondary and tertiary consumers eat other animals, so they're known as carnivores (or carnivorous organisms).

Food chains and **food webs** show how energy is transferred through an ecosystem. Food chains show simple lines of energy transfer, and food webs show lots of food chains in an ecosystem and how they overlap — there's an example of each below. A **trophic level** is a stage in a food chain that's occupied by a particular group of organisms, e.g. producers are the first trophic level in a food chain.

Tip: Remember, the primary consumer is the first consumer in a food chain, the secondary consumer is the second consumer in the food chain, and the tertiary consumer is the third consumer.

Tip: The arrows in a food chain show you the direction of energy flow.

Example

The example below shows a food chain (red box) and a food web (blue box).

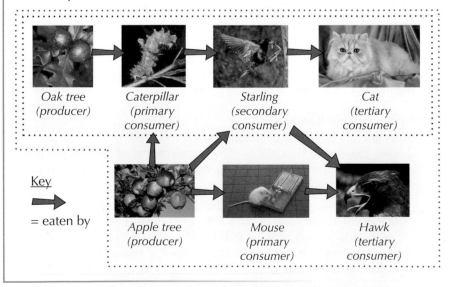

Energy locked up in the things that can't be eaten (e.g. bones, faeces) gets recycled back into the ecosystem by **decomposers** — organisms that break down dead or undigested organic material, e.g. bacteria and fungi.

Calculating energy transfer

Not all the energy (e.g. from sunlight or food) that's available to the organisms in a trophic level is transferred to the next trophic level — around 90% of the total available energy is lost in various ways. Some of the available energy (60%) is never taken in by the organisms in the first place. Reasons for this include:

- Plants can't use all the light energy that reaches their leaves, e.g. some is the wrong wavelength, some is reflected, and some passes straight through the leaves.

- Some sunlight can't be used because it hits parts of the plant that can't photosynthesise, e.g. the bark of a tree.

- Some parts of food, e.g. roots or bones, aren't eaten by organisms so the energy isn't taken in — they pass to decomposers.

- Some parts of food are indigestible so pass through organisms and come out as waste, e.g. faeces — this also passes to decomposers.

The rest of the available energy (40%) is taken in (absorbed) — this is called the **gross productivity**. But not all of this is available to the next trophic level either. 30% of the total energy available (75% of the gross productivity) is lost to the environment when organisms use energy produced from respiration for movement or body heat. This is called **respiratory loss**.

This means that only 10% of the total energy available (25% of the gross productivity) becomes biomass (e.g. it's stored or used for growth) — this is called the **net productivity**. Net productivity (or biomass) is the amount of energy that's available to the next trophic level. The flow of energy transfer continues at the next trophic level — the process starts again from the beginning (see Figure 3).

Tip: When light energy from the sun is 'lost', this doesn't mean it disappears — it's just converted into different forms of energy.

Tip: The photosynthetic pigments in plants only absorb the blue and red wavelengths of light in sunlight, see page 121.

Figure 2: Respiratory loss from a rabbit.

Tip: The net productivity of the first organism in a food chain (e.g. a plant) is called the net primary productivity. Factors that affect the rate of photosynthesis (e.g. light intensity, temperature, etc. — see pages 121-123) will affect the net primary productivity of food chains.

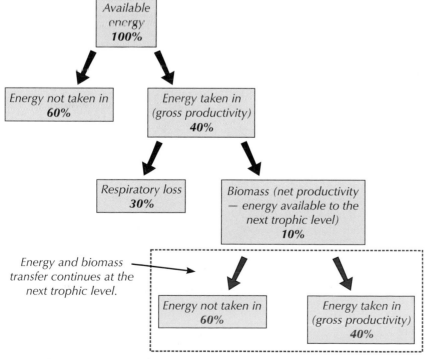

Figure 3: Diagram showing energy transfer in a typical food chain.

Tip: The percentages used are general figures — real values for a given ecosystem will vary.

Net productivity can be worked out with a simple calculation. Here's how it's calculated:

$$\text{net productivity} = \text{gross productivity} - \text{respiratory loss}$$

Example — Maths Skills

Tip: The unit $\text{kJm}^{-2}\text{yr}^{-1}$ just means kilojoules per square metre per year.

Rabbits feed on grass which contains $20\,000\ \text{kJm}^{-2}\text{yr}^{-1}$ of energy. However, they don't take in $12\,000\ \text{kJm}^{-2}\text{yr}^{-1}$ of the energy available to them. You can use this information to work out the rabbits' gross productivity.

$$\text{gross productivity} = \text{energy available} - \text{energy not taken in}$$
$$= 20\,000 - 12\,000$$
$$= \textbf{8000 kJm}^{-2}\textbf{yr}^{-1}$$

Tip: In this example, the rabbits take in $8000\ \text{kJm}^{-2}\text{yr}^{-1}$ of energy.

The rabbits lose $6000\ \text{kJm}^{-2}\text{yr}^{-1}$ using energy from respiration. You can use this to calculate the net productivity of the rabbits:

$$\text{net productivity} = \text{gross productivity} - \text{respiratory loss}$$
$$= 8000 - 6000$$
$$= \textbf{2000 kJm}^{-2}\textbf{yr}^{-1}$$

So $2000\ \text{kJm}^{-2}\text{yr}^{-1}$ is available to the next trophic level.

Efficiency of energy transfer

To find out how efficient the transfer of energy is between two trophic levels you need to work out the percentage efficiency of energy transfer. If you know the amount of energy available to a trophic level (net productivity of the previous trophic level) and the net productivity of that trophic level, you can work it out using this equation:

$$\frac{\text{\% efficiency of}}{\text{energy transfer}} = \frac{\text{net productivity of trophic level}}{\text{net productivity of previous trophic level}} \times 100$$

Example — Maths Skills

Tip: This just shows that 10% of the energy available in the grass is passed on to the rabbit.

Following on from the example above, the rabbits receive $20\,000\ \text{kJm}^{-2}\text{yr}^{-1}$ from the grass, and their net productivity is $2000\ \text{kJm}^{-2}\text{yr}^{-1}$. So the percentage efficiency of energy transfer is:

$$(2000 \div 20\,000) \times 100 = \textbf{10\%}$$

Exam Tip
Don't forget — the efficiency of energy transfer usually <u>increases</u> with increasing trophic level.

The efficiency of energy transfer is not the same throughout a food chain — as you move up a food chain, energy transfer generally becomes more efficient. Different amounts of energy are lost at different stages for different reasons, as shown in the table on the next page.

Even though the efficiency of energy transfer tends to increase as you move up the food chain, energy is still lost at each trophic level — so the more stages there are in a food chain, the more energy is lost overall. This energy loss limits the number of organisms that can exist in a particular ecosystem.

Stage of food chain	Efficiency of energy transfer	Reason
Sun to producer	Low, around 2-3%	Not all the light energy that plants receive can be absorbed (see page 257) and some energy that is absorbed is then lost during photosynthesis.
Producer to consumer	5-10%	Energy transfer is less efficient from producer to consumer (i.e. to herbivores) than from consumer to consumer (i.e. to carnivores). This is because plants contain a greater proportion of indigestible material (e.g. cellulose within plant cell walls) than animals (which contain a large proportion of relatively digestible meat).
Consumer to consumer	High, around 15-20%	

It might also be helpful to calculate how efficient organisms in one trophic level are at converting what they eat into energy for the next trophic level. You can work it out like this:

$$\frac{\text{energy transferred}}{\text{energy intake}} \times 100$$

Here, energy transferred means the net productivity of the trophic level.

Measuring the efficiency of energy transfer

To calculate the efficiency of energy transfer between trophic levels, you need to know the net productivity of each trophic level. This means measuring the amount of energy in each trophic level. To measure the energy of the organisms in one trophic level, first you calculate the amount of energy or biomass in a sample of the organisms.

You can measure the amount of energy in an organism by measuring its **dry mass** (its biomass). To do this, you need to dry the organism out — this is done by heating it up to 80 °C until all the water in it has evaporated. You then weigh the organism. Remember, energy is stored as biomass, so it indicates how much energy an organism contains.

Then you multiply the results from the sample to get an estimate of the energy in one trophic level.

Examples

- A field of grass measures 10 000 m². To find the amount of energy in the whole field you could find the amount of energy in a 1 m² sample of grass, then multiply this figure by 10 000.
- Twenty rabbits live in the field of grass. To find the amount of energy in the rabbit population, you could find the amount of energy in one rabbit, then multiply this figure by 20.

The difference in energy between the trophic levels is the amount of energy transferred.

Tip: Remember, energy that's used for growth and reproduction isn't lost — it becomes biomass in an organism.

Tip: The more digestible an organism's food, the more energy the organism can absorb from it. This means less is egested as waste (undigested) products.

Tip: An organism's mass before it has been dried is called its wet mass.

Tip: This method of measuring energy transfer may not be very ethical, so ecologists more commonly use existing data to estimate values.

Tip: A population is all the organisms of one species in a habitat.

There are problems with this method though. For example, the consumers (rabbits) might have taken in energy from sources other than the producer measured (grass). This means the difference between the two figures calculated wouldn't be an accurate estimate of the energy transferred between only those two organisms. For an accurate estimate you'd need to include all the individual organisms at each trophic level.

Controlling energy flow through ecosystems

Farmers try to reduce the amount of energy lost from food chains in order to increase productivity. They use farming methods that make the transfer of energy between trophic levels more efficient:

Herbicides

Herbicides kill weeds that compete with agricultural crops for energy. Reducing competition means crops receive more energy, so they grow faster and become larger, increasing productivity.

Fungicides

Fungicides kill fungal infections that damage agricultural crops. The crops use more energy for growth and less for fighting infection, so they grow faster and become larger, increasing productivity.

Insecticides

Insecticides kill insect pests that eat and damage crops. Killing insect pests means less biomass is lost from crops, so they grow to be larger, which means productivity is greater.

Natural predators

Natural predators introduced to the ecosystem eat the pest species, e.g. ladybirds eat greenfly. This means the crops lose less energy and biomass, increasing productivity.

Fertilisers

Fertilisers are chemicals that provide crops with minerals needed for growth, e.g. nitrates. Crops use up minerals in the soil as they grow, so their growth is limited when there aren't enough minerals. Adding fertiliser replaces the lost minerals, so more energy from the ecosystem can be used to grow, increasing the efficiency of energy conversion.

Rearing livestock intensively

Rearing livestock intensively involves controlling the conditions they live in and when they're slaughtered, so more of their energy is used for growth and less is used for other activities — the efficiency of energy conversion is increased so more biomass is produced and productivity is increased.

> **Examples**
> - Animals may be kept in warm, indoor pens where their movement is restricted. Less energy is wasted keeping warm and moving around.
> - Animals may be given feed that's higher in energy than their natural food. This increases the energy input, so more energy is available for growth.
> - Animals may be slaughtered before they reach adulthood. Young animals use a greater amount of their energy for growth, so this means more energy is transferred to their biomass.

Tip: All these methods try to increase (or prevent the loss) of an organism's biomass, which increases the amount of energy available to the next trophic level.

Tip: Restricting an animal's movement means they respire less, which lowers their respiratory loss.

Figure 4: *Battery farmed hens are an example of intensively reared livestock.*

The benefits of these methods are that more food can be produced in a shorter space of time, often at lower cost. However, enhancing productivity by intensive rearing raises ethical issues. For example, some people think the conditions intensively reared animals are kept in cause the animals pain, distress or restricts their natural behaviour, so it shouldn't be done.

Practice Questions — Application

Q1 In a food chain mussels have a gross productivity of 22 861 $kJm^{-2}yr^{-1}$ and a respiratory loss of 17 000 $kJm^{-2}yr^{-1}$.
a) Calculate the net productivity of the mussels.

The mussels provide food for crayfish which have a net productivity of 627 $kJm^{-2}yr^{-1}$.
b) Calculate the efficiency of energy transfer between the mussels and the crayfish.

Q2 The diagram below shows the net productivity in a food chain. Use the diagram to answer the following questions.

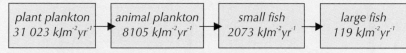

| plant plankton 31 023 $kJm^{-2}yr^{-1}$ | animal plankton 8105 $kJm^{-2}yr^{-1}$ | small fish 2073 $kJm^{-2}yr^{-1}$ | large fish 119 $kJm^{-2}yr^{-1}$ |

a) The total amount of energy taken in by the small fish is 8072 $kJm^{-2}yr^{-1}$. Calculate how much energy the small fish lose through respiration.

b) The respiratory loss of the large fish is 450 $kJm^{-2}yr^{-1}$. Calculate the gross productivity of the large fish. Give your answer in standard form in $kJkm^{-2}yr^{-1}$.

c) Give one reason why the gross productivity of the large fish is less than the net productivity of the small fish.

d) Calculate the percentage efficiency of energy transfer between each stage of the food chain.

Exam Tip
You might have to do calculations like these in the exam, so make sure you know the equations for net productivity and the efficiency of energy transfer. Look back to page 258 for a reminder.

Exam Tip
If you're asked to do a calculation, always check the question to see if it specifies what units you should give your answer in.

Practice Questions — Fact Recall

Q1 Describe what is meant by the biotic factors in an ecosystem.

Q2 Give an example of an abiotic factor that might affect:
a) a rock pool,
b) a playing field,
c) a large tree.

Q3 Define the term: a) producer,   b) consumer.

Q4 What is the main route by which energy enters an ecosystem?

Q5 What name is given to the amount of energy taken in by an organism?

Q6 Is energy transfer more efficient to herbivores or to carnivores? Explain your answer.

Q7 Give one method that can be used to measure the amount of energy in a sample of organic material.

Q8 Give two examples of farming methods that increase the transfer of energy through an ecosystem. Explain how each of the methods work.

Learning Objectives:

- Understand the role of recycling within ecosystems.

- Know the importance of the carbon cycle, including the role of organisms (photosynthesis, decomposition and respiration) and physical and chemical effects in the cycling of carbon within ecosystems.

- Know the role of decomposers and roles of microorganisms in recycling nitrogen within ecosystems, including *Rhizobium*, *Azotobacter*, *Nitrosomonas* and *Nitrobacter*.

Specification Reference 6.3.1

2. Recycling in Ecosystems

Photosynthesis is the main way that energy enters an ecosystem — it's how energy from sunlight is used to make carbon compounds, and so it's where the carbon cycle begins...

The carbon cycle

All organisms need carbon to make essential compounds, e.g. plants use CO_2 (carbon dioxide) in photosynthesis to make glucose. The carbon cycle is how carbon moves through living organisms and the non-living environment. The cycle includes processes that involve organisms (photosynthesis, respiration, and decomposition) and also chemical and physical processes such as combustion and weathering:

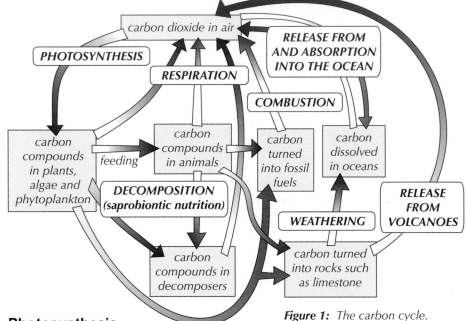

Figure 1: *The carbon cycle.*

Photosynthesis

Carbon (in the form of CO_2 from air and water) is absorbed by plants when they carry out photosynthesis — it becomes carbon compounds in plant tissues. Carbon is passed on to primary consumers when they eat the plants. It's passed on to secondary and tertiary consumers when they eat other consumers.

Decomposition

All living organisms die and are broken down by microorganisms called **decomposers**, e.g. bacteria and fungi. Decomposers secrete enzymes which break down the carbon compounds (e.g. starch) in dead organic material. The decomposers then absorb the products of digestion (e.g. maltose) for use in respiration. Feeding on dead organic matter is called **saprobiontic nutrition** (see Figure 2).

Respiration

Carbon is returned to the air (and water) as all living organisms (including the decomposers) carry out respiration, which produces CO_2.

Combustion

If dead organic matter ends up in places where there aren't any decomposers, e.g. deep oceans or bogs, its carbon compounds can be turned into fossil fuels over millions of years (by heat and pressure). The carbon in fossil fuels (e.g. oil and coal) is released when they're burnt — this is called combustion.

Tip: CO_2 diffuses into the air spaces within a leaf (via stomata), and then into the plant cells — they don't absorb carbon compounds through their roots.

Figure 2: *Fungi (white areas) have begun decomposing these slices of bread.*

Tip: Microorganisms that carry out saprobiontic nutrition are called saprobionts.

Release from volcanoes

As well as coal, other types of rock can be formed from dead organic matter deposited on the sea floor. For example, rocks such as limestone and chalk are mainly composed of calcium carbonate ($CaCO_3$). This comes from marine organisms like crabs, mussels, sea urchins and coral that utilise this compound in their development, e.g. to form shells.

One way carbon can be returned to the atmosphere from these rocks is by them being drawn down deep into the Earth's crust by the movement of tectonic plates. There they undergo chemical changes and release carbon dioxide, which is returned to the atmosphere by volcanoes.

Weathering

The rocks can also eventually become land, which is then weathered (broken down by exposure to the atmosphere). This can happen chemically by rainwater (which is naturally slightly acidic due to the CO_2 dissolved in it) and physically, e.g. by plant roots, animals, etc. Chemical weathering causes mineral ions and bicarbonate ions (HCO_3^-) to be released from the rock into solution and enter groundwater, from where they are transported into rivers and the oceans. There they combine to form carbon-containing compounds such as $CaCO_3$.

Release from and absorption into the ocean

CO_2 can also dissolve directly into the oceans from the atmosphere and be transported in the ocean by deep underwater currents (a physical process). CO_2 can remain in these slow-moving currents for hundreds of years before returning to the surface and being released back into the atmosphere.

The nitrogen cycle

Plants and animals need nitrogen to make proteins and nucleic acids (DNA and RNA) for growth. The atmosphere's made up of about 78% nitrogen, but plants and animals can't use it in that form — they need bacteria to convert it into nitrogen compounds first. The nitrogen cycle shows how nitrogen is converted into a usable form and then passed on between different living organisms and the non-living environment. The nitrogen cycle includes food chains (nitrogen is passed on when organisms are eaten), and four different processes that involve bacteria — nitrogen fixation, ammonification, nitrification and denitrification:

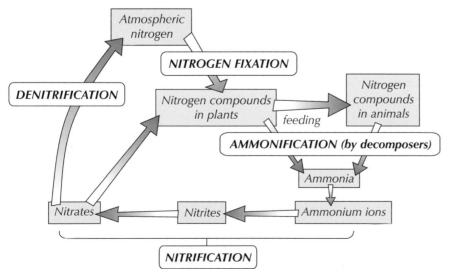

Figure 4: The four main processes in the nitrogen cycle.

Figure 3: Weathering has formed these ridges and clefts on this limestone pavement.

Tip: The carbon and nitrogen cycles show that carbon and nitrogen are recycled and can be reused by organisms. This recycling within the environment helps maintain balance in ecosystems.

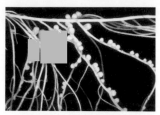

Figure 5: Pink nodules of Rhizobium *on plant roots.*

Tip: A mutualistic relationship is where two organisms are dependent on one another, with both of them benefitting.

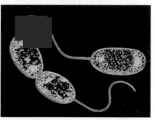

Figure 6: Nitrobacter *bacteria.*

Nitrogen fixation

Nitrogen fixation is when nitrogen gas in the atmosphere is converted to ammonia by bacteria such as *Rhizobium* and *Azotobacter*. The ammonia can then be used by plants. *Rhizobium* are found inside root nodules (growths on the roots — see Figure 5) of leguminous plants (e.g. peas, beans and clover). They form a **mutualistic relationship** with the plants — they provide the plant with nitrogen compounds and the plant provides them with carbohydrates. *Azotobacter* are found living in the soil. They don't form mutualistic relationships with plants.

Ammonification

Ammonification is when nitrogen compounds from dead organisms are turned into ammonia by decomposers, which goes on to form ammonium ions. Animal waste (urine and faeces) also contains nitrogen compounds. These are also turned into ammonia by decomposers and go on to form ammonium ions.

Nitrification

Nitrification is when ammonium ions in the soil are changed into nitrogen compounds that can then be used by plants (nitrates). First nitrifying bacteria called *Nitrosomonas* change ammonium ions into nitrites. Then other nitrifying bacteria called *Nitrobacter* change nitrites into nitrates.

Denitrification

Denitrification is when nitrates in the soil are converted into nitrogen gas by denitrifying bacteria — they use nitrates in the soil to carry out respiration and produce nitrogen gas. This happens under anaerobic conditions (where there's no oxygen), e.g. in waterlogged soils.

Other ways for nitrogen to enter an ecosystem

Not all of the usable nitrogen in an ecosystem has come from nitrogen fixation by bacteria. Other ways that nitrogen gets into an ecosystem is by lightning (which also fixes atmospheric nitrogen) or by artificial fertilisers (they're produced from atmospheric nitrogen on an industrial scale in the Haber process).

Practice Questions — Fact Recall

Q1 Describe how organisms contribute to the movement of carbon through the carbon cycle.

Q2 Explain where the carbon released during combustion comes from.

Q3 Describe the role of weathering in the carbon cycle.

Q4 Describe how carbon is absorbed into the oceans.

Q5 Give one reason why plants and animals need nitrogen.

Q6 Copy and complete the table below about processes in the nitrogen cycle.

Name of process	Bacteria responsible
Nitrogen fixation	
Ammonification	
Nitrification	
Denitrification	

Q7 Describe the process of ammonification.

Q8 Name the process by which nitrates in the soil are converted into nitrogen gas by bacteria.

3. Succession

The types of organisms found in an environment change over time — and the environment itself changes too. This is due to a process called succession.

What is succession?

Succession is the process by which an ecosystem (see page 255) changes over time. Succession happens in a series of stages. At each stage, the species in an area slowly change the environmental conditions (for example, by making the soil more fertile), making those conditions more suitable for other species. This means that the **biotic conditions** change as the **abiotic conditions** change, causing one community of organisms to be succeeded (replaced) by another. There are two main types of succession — primary succession (see below) and secondary succession (see page 267).

Primary succession

Primary succession happens on land that's been newly formed or exposed, e.g. where a volcano has erupted to form a new rock surface, or where sea level has dropped exposing a new area of land. There's no soil or organic material to start with, e.g. just bare rock.

Pioneer stage of succession

Primary succession starts when species colonise a new land surface. Seeds and spores are blown in by the wind and begin to grow. The first species to colonise the area are called **pioneer species**. The abiotic conditions are hostile (harsh) and only pioneer species can grow because they're specialised to cope with the harsh conditions.

--- Examples ---

Hostile abiotic conditions

- There is limited water available because there's no soil to retain water.

- There are few minerals or nutrients because there's no soil.

- There may be high light intensity, exposure to wind and rain, and fluctuating temperatures because the area is directly exposed to the Sun and the elements.

Pioneer species

- Marram grass can grow on sand dunes near the sea because it has deep roots to get water and can tolerate the salty environment (see Figure 1).

- Lichens are organisms usually made up of a fungus and an alga. They're able to survive in rocky conditions because the fungus secretes acids which erode the rock, releasing minerals.

- Shrubs of the *Calligonum* genus are pioneer species that can grow in areas that experience periodic drought.

The pioneer species change the abiotic conditions — they die and microorganisms decompose the dead organic material (humus). This forms a basic soil. This makes conditions less hostile, e.g. the basic soil helps to retain water, which means new organisms can move in and grow. The new organisms then die and are decomposed, adding more organic material, making the soil deeper and richer in minerals such as nitrates. Nitrogen-fixing bacteria turn nitrogen from the atmosphere into ammonia, which can then be used by plants (see page 264). This means larger plants like shrubs can start to grow in the deeper soil, which retains even more water and contains more nutrients.

Learning Objective:

- Understand the process of primary succession in the development of an ecosystem, including succession from pioneer species to a climax community and deflected succession.

  Specification Reference 6.3.1

Tip: Remember, biotic conditions (factors) are the living features of an ecosystem, e.g. the plant and animal communities. Abiotic conditions (factors) are the non-living features, such as light, CO_2 and water availability.

Figure 1: *Marram grass is able to grow in hostile conditions on sand dunes.*

Tip: The pioneer species help to stabilise an environment — they make it possible for other species to grow there.

Later stages of succession

At each stage, different plants and animals that are better adapted for the improved conditions move in, out-compete the plants and animals that are already there, and become the dominant species in the ecosystem. The dominant species are the ones which cause the most change to the abiotic environment, making it more suitable for other species.

As succession goes on, the ecosystem becomes more complex. New species move in alongside existing species, which means the species diversity increases. Plants create more habitats for animals, the abiotic conditions become less hostile and the amount of biomass increases.

Eventually these changes result in a **climax community** — the ecosystem is supporting the largest and most complex community of plants and animals it can. It won't change much more — it's in a steady state.

Tip: You learnt about species diversity in Year 1 — it's the number of different species and the abundance of each species in an area.

Tip: A community is all the populations of different species found in a habitat.

Figure 2: *Lichens (orange and white) have adaptations that allow them to live on bare rock.*

Tip: Primary succession also happens on sand dunes, salt marshes and even in lakes.

--- **Example — primary succession** ---

1. Bare rock lacks soil, is exposed to strong winds and has periods of drought. Lichens (the pioneer species) are able to survive because they can grow in cracks to avoid the wind, break down rock to release minerals and are adapted to survive periods of drought.

bare rock   *lichen*

2. The lichens die and are decomposed helping to form a thin soil, which thickens as more organic material is formed. This means other species such as mosses can grow.

thin soil   *moss*

3. Larger plants that need more water can move in as the soil deepens, e.g. grasses and small flowering plants. The soil continues to deepen as the larger plants die and are decomposed.

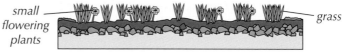

small flowering plants   *grass*

4. Shrubs, ferns and small trees begin to grow, out-competing the grasses and smaller plants to become the dominant species. Diversity increases.

shrubs   *small trees (rowan and alder)*   *ferns*

5. Finally, the soil is deep and rich enough in nutrients to support large trees. These become the dominant species, and the climax community is formed.

large trees (oak, birch and ash)   *deep soil*

Secondary succession

Secondary succession happens on land that's been cleared of all the plants, but where the soil remains, e.g. after a forest fire or where a forest has been cut down by humans. The established community of species is usually destroyed, but without too much disturbance to the soil. It can occur during any stage (including the climax community) after the pioneer stage.

The process of secondary succession is similar to primary succession, but because there's already a soil layer, secondary succession starts at a later stage — and the pioneer species are larger plants, e.g. shrubs.

Figure 3: Secondary succession following a forest fire.

Climatic climax communities

Which species make up the climax community depends on what the climate's like in an ecosystem. The climax community for a particular climate is called its **climatic climax**.

Examples

- In a temperate climate, e.g. the UK, there's plenty of available water, mild temperatures and not much change between the seasons. The climatic climax will contain large trees because they can grow in these conditions once deep soils have developed (see Figure 4).

- In a polar climate there's not much available water, temperatures are low and there are massive changes between the seasons. Large trees won't ever be able to grow in these conditions, so the climatic climax contains only herbs or shrubs, but it's still the climax community (see Figure 5).

Figure 4: The climax community in many parts of Britain is deciduous woodland.

Practice Questions — Application

A team analysed data on ecological changes in part of a national park. Their results are shown in the graph below.

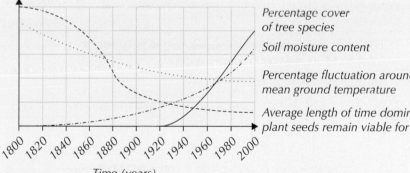

Percentage cover of tree species

Soil moisture content

Percentage fluctuation around mean ground temperature

Average length of time dominant plant seeds remain viable for

Time (years)

Q1 What type of succession is shown on the graph? Explain your answer.

Q2 Describe the characteristics of the dominant plant community between 1800 and 1860.

Q3 Describe and suggest an explanation for the change shown in the average length of time dominant plant seeds remain viable for.

Q4 During what time period would you expect to see a high percentage of plants whose seeds require high light intensity for germination? Explain your answer.

Q5 Describe and suggest an explanation for the change in the soil moisture content shown on the graph.

Figure 5: The climax community in most of Greenland is arctic tundra.

Tip: 'Remains viable for' means how long the plant seeds are capable of germinating (sprouting).

Preventing and deflecting succession

Human activities can prevent succession, stopping the normal climax community from developing. When succession is stopped artificially like this, the climax community is called a **plagioclimax**.

Figure 6: *Succession is prevented at a nature reserve in Dorset, creating a plagioclimax.*

Example

The management of a nature reserve in Dorset prevents the growth of large trees on areas of the land. This keeps the land as heathland and is done to protect some of the small reptiles that inhabit the area — if large trees were allowed to grow, other species of animals would move into the area which would out-compete the reptiles. The nature reserve is a plagioclimax.

Deflected succession is when succession is prevented by human activity, but the plagioclimax that develops is one that's different to any of the natural stages of the ecosystem — the path of succession has been deflected from its natural course.

Example

A regularly mown grassy field won't develop woody plants, even if the climate of the ecosystem could support them. The growing points of the woody plants are cut off by the lawnmower, so larger plants can't establish themselves — only the grasses can survive being mowed, so the climax community is a grassy field. A grassy field isn't a natural stage — there should also be things like small flowering plants, so succession has been deflected.

Tip: Grazing and burning have the same effect as mowing.

Exam Tip
You need to be able to use the correct ecological terms (like primary succession and climax community) in your exam.

Practice Questions — Fact Recall

Q1 What is succession?

Q2 Which type of succession happens in areas with no soil?

Q3 What name is given to the first species to colonise an area in primary succession?

Q4 What is a climax community?

Q5 Suggest an event that could cause secondary succession.

Q6 What is a climatic climax community?

Q7 What is a plagioclimax?

4. Investigating Ecosystems

You need to be able to investigate populations of organisms. There are loads of ways of doing this. Whichever method you use, you need to make sure your samples are random...

Abundance and distribution

Investigating populations of organisms involves looking at the abundance and distribution of species in a particular area.

 PRACTICAL ACTIVITY GROUP 3

Abundance

Abundance is the number of individuals of one species in a particular area. The abundance of motile organisms and plants can be estimated by simply counting the number of individuals in samples taken. **Percentage cover** can also be used to measure the abundance of plants — this is how much of the area you're investigating is covered by a species (see next page).

Distribution

Distribution is where a particular species is within the area you're investigating.

Sampling

Most of the time it would be too time-consuming to measure the number of individuals and the distribution of every species in the entire area you're investigating, so instead you take samples:

1. Choose an area to sample — a small area within the area being investigated.

2. Samples should be random to avoid bias, e.g. by picking random sample sites (see below).

3. Use an appropriate technique to take a sample of the population (see next two pages).

4. Repeat the process, taking as many samples as possible in the time you have available. This gives a more precise estimate for the whole area.

5. The number of individuals for the whole area can then be estimated by taking an average of the data collected in each sample and multiplying it by the size of the whole area. The percentage cover for the whole area can be estimated by taking the average of all the samples.

Random sampling

If you were investigating populations in a field, you could pick random sample sites by dividing the field into a grid and using a random number generator and a random letter generator to select coordinates. This will give you coordinates at random, e.g. B7, E5, etc. (see Figure 1). Then you just take your samples from these coordinates.

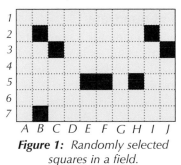

Figure 1: *Randomly selected squares in a field.*

Methods for investigating populations

There are lots of different methods for studying populations of organisms, but you need to choose the most suitable one to use — this depends on the type of organism and its habitat.

Quadrats and **transects** can be used for studying non-motile (sessile) organisms, e.g. plants and corals, or slow-moving organisms like limpets.

Learning Objectives:

- Know how sampling and recording methods can be used to determine the distribution and abundance of organisms in a variety of ecosystems.

- Know how the distribution and abundance of organisms in an ecosystem can be measured (PAG3).

Specification Reference 6.3.1

Tip: You'll have learnt more about random sampling in Module 4.

Tip: When you are recording species it's important to identify them correctly. An identification key (a tool that allows you to identify species by their features) can help you do this.

Tip: Using tables of random numbers is another way of generating random numbers.

Tip: Remember, you need to be aware of any safety issues before carrying out an investigation.

On the other hand, if you're studying more motile animals, like birds and insects, nets and traps are more appropriate.

Frame quadrats

A frame quadrat is a square frame divided into a grid of 100 smaller squares by strings attached across the frame — see Figure 2.

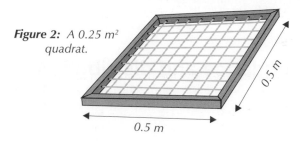

Figure 2: A 0.25 m² quadrat.

0.5 m

0.5 m

Quadrats are placed on the ground at different points within the area you're investigating. This can be done by selecting random coordinates (see previous page). The number of individuals of each species is recorded in each quadrat.

The percentage cover of a species can also be measured by counting how much of the quadrat is covered by the species — you count a square if it's more than half-covered (see Figure 4). Percentage cover is a quick way to investigate populations and you don't have to count all the individual plants.

Figure 3: Quadrats can be used to measure the abundance of plant species in a field.

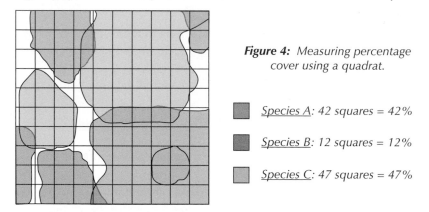

Figure 4: Measuring percentage cover using a quadrat.

Species A: 42 squares = 42%

Species B: 12 squares = 12%

Species C: 47 squares = 47%

Frame quadrats are useful for quickly investigating areas with plant species that fit within a small quadrat — most frame quadrats are 1 m by 1 m. Areas with larger plants and trees need very large quadrats. Large quadrats aren't always in a frame — they can be marked out with a tape measure.

Point quadrats

A point quadrat is a horizontal bar on two legs with a series of holes at set intervals along its length (see Figure 5). Point quadrats are placed on the ground at random points within the area you're investigating. Pins are dropped through the holes in the frame and every plant that each pin touches is recorded. If a pin touches several overlapping plants, all of them are recorded. The number of individuals of each species is recorded in each quadrat.

wood frame   pins   hole to place pin

Figure 5: A point quadrat.

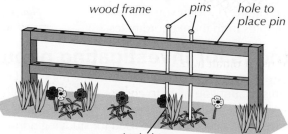

multiple hits

The percentage cover of a species can also be measured by calculating the number of times a pin has touched a species as a percentage of the total number of pins dropped. Point quadrats are especially useful in areas where there's lots of dense vegetation close to the ground.

Transects

You can use lines called transects to help find out how plants are distributed across an area, e.g. how the distribution of a plant species changes from a hedge towards the middle of a field. There are three types of transect:

- **Line transects** — a tape measure is placed along the transect and the species that touch the tape measure are recorded.

- **Belt transects** — data is collected along the transect using frame quadrats placed next to each other.

- **Interrupted transects** — instead of investigating the whole transect of either a line or a belt, you can take measurements at intervals. E.g. by placing point quadrats at right angles to the direction of the transect at set intervals along its length, such as every 2 m.

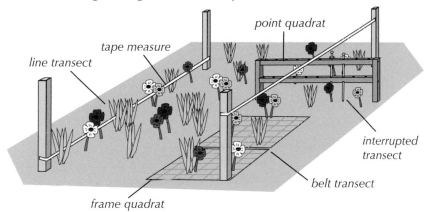

Figure 6: A line transect, a belt transect and an interrupted transect.

Capturing motile organisms

If you're investigating motile organisms, you'll need to use equipment to capture them. The best method of capturing organisms will depend on what you're studying.

Examples

For aquatic animals you'd use a net. Large nets suspended between tall poles can be used for capturing birds and bats.

For flying insects (e.g. bees) you'd use a sweepnet (a net on a pole).

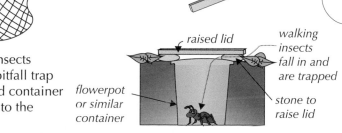

For ground insects you'd use a pitfall trap (a steep-sided container that's sunk into the ground).

Tip: Transects can be used in many different ecosystems, not just fields. For example, along a beach or in a woodland.

Tip: Line transects are quick to carry out but a belt transect will give more data (as it covers a wider area). An interrupted belt transect is a good compromise between the two — it's quicker than a belt transect and gives more information than a line transect.

Tip: You could encounter lots of different risks working outdoors. Remember, you need to do a risk assessment before carrying out any investigations.

Practice Questions — Application

Q1 A student is investigating the abundance of daisies in a field.

    a) She decides to use a frame quadrat to measure the percentage cover of daisies in the field. Describe how she could do this.

    b) Describe how the student could take random samples using a frame quadrat.

Q2 A scientist has been investigating the effect of salt spray from a road adjacent to an inland field. Her results are shown below.

Tip: A kite diagram shows the distribution and abundance of organisms along a transect. The thickness of the kite shape shows the abundance — the thicker the kite shape, the more organisms there are.

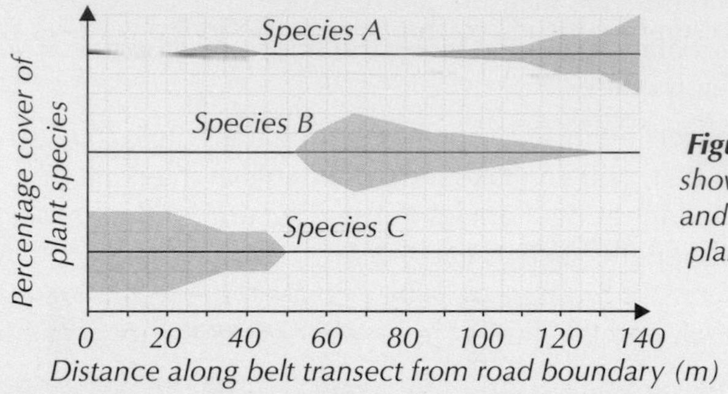

Figure 7: *Kite diagram showing the distribution and abundance of three plant species in a field.*

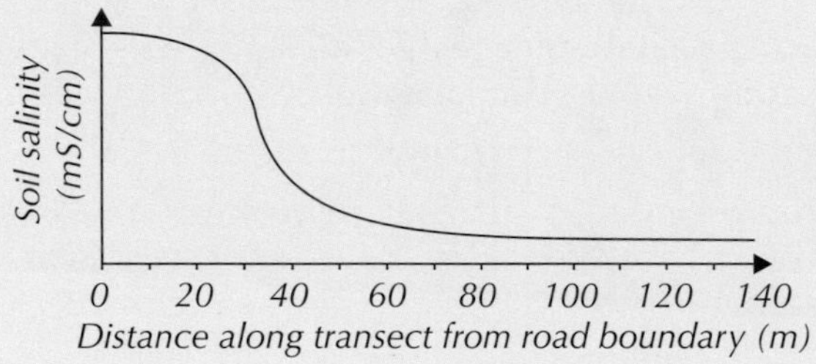

Figure 8: *Graph showing the change in soil salinity in a field.*

    a) Describe the data shown in the kite diagram and the graph.

    b) One of the plant species is normally found in coastal areas. Which species is this likely to be, A, B or C? Explain your answer.

    c) The scientist is unable to prove that salt spray from the road is responsible for the absence of species B between 0 and 20 m from the road using the data shown above. Explain why.

Practice Questions — Fact Recall

Q1 What is meant by the terms:

    a) abundance?

    b) distribution?

Q2 a) Why would an ecologist investigating the abundance of a species in an area take samples?

    b) Why is it important that these samples are taken at random?

Q3 Describe how a point quadrat would be used to investigate the abundance of a plant species in a field.

Q4 Explain the difference between a line transect and a belt transect.

Q5 Describe what you would use a pitfall trap for.

Section Summary

Make sure you know:

- That an ecosystem is all the organisms living in a certain area and all the non-living conditions (factors) found there, and that it's a dynamic system — it's changing all the time.

- That biotic factors (e.g. the presence of predators and food) are all the living features of an ecosystem and that abiotic factors (e.g. temperature, soil) are all the non-living features of an ecosystem.

- The biotic and abiotic factors that affect ecosystems of different sizes, for example a rock pool, a playing field and a large tree.

- That biomass (stored energy) is transferred in an ecosystem through food chains and food webs from producers to primary consumers, then to secondary consumers and tertiary consumers by feeding.

- That not all of the energy that's available to the organisms in a trophic level is transferred to the next trophic level and that you can work out the total amount of energy that can be passed from one trophic level to the next using the equation: net productivity = gross productivity – respiratory loss.

- How to work out percentage efficiency of biomass transfer using the equation:
  (net productivity of trophic level ÷ net productivity of previous trophic level) × 100

- That the efficiency of biomass transfer increases as you move up the food chain but that energy is still lost at each level, and this limits the number of organisms that can exist in a particular environment.

- That you can measure the amount of energy in an organism by measuring its dry mass (biomass) and that you can use this to measure biomass transfers between trophic levels.

- That farming activities such as using herbicides, fungicides, insecticides, natural predators, fertilisers and intensively rearing livestock can increase the efficiency of energy transfer through an ecosystem.

- That the carbon cycle is important because all organisms need carbon to make essential compounds.

- That organisms play an important role in the carbon cycle — carbon in the air becomes carbon compounds in plants by photosynthesis, these carbon compounds are passed on through the food chain by feeding and are broken down by microorganisms during decomposition, and carbon is released back into the atmosphere by respiration.

- That physical and chemical processes also have a role in the carbon cycle and that they eventually return carbon to the atmosphere through combustion, weathering and via volcanoes.

- The four main processes of the nitrogen cycle and the microorganisms involved: nitrogen fixation (*Rhizobium*, *Azotobacter*), ammonification, nitrification (*Nitrosomonas*, *Nitrobacter*) and denitrification.

- That succession is the process by which an ecosystem changes over time, and how this happens.

- That succession begins with a pioneer species and ends with a climax community.

- That at each stage in succession, species change the abiotic conditions, so that the environment becomes more suitable for other species, increasing species diversity.

- That human activities can artificially stop succession from occurring, or can deflect succession from its natural course, leading to the formation of a plagioclimax.

- How samples of populations can be taken and recorded to investigate the distribution and abundance of organisms in different ecosystems.

- How the abundance and distribution of organisms can be measured using different methods such as frame quadrats, point quadrats, line transects, belt transects and interrupted transects.

1   **Fig. 1.1** below shows the carbon cycle.

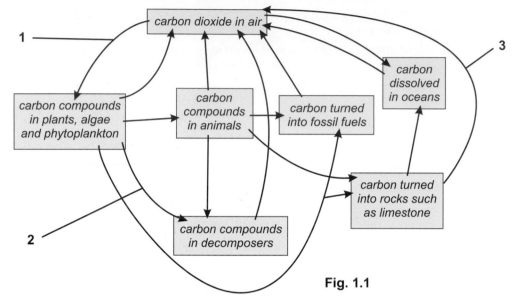

Fig. 1.1

Which of the following numbered processes is the result of action by organisms?

A   Only 1

B   Only 1 and 2

C   Only 2 and 3

D   1, 2 and 3

(1 mark)

2   The process of primary succession leads to the development of ecosystems.
Which of the following statements about primary succession is/are correct?

1   Primary succession starts on land where there is no soil or organic material.

2   Pioneer species make the abiotic conditions in an ecosystem less hostile.

3   The climax community is the largest and most complex community an ecosystem
can support.

A   Only 1

B   Only 1 and 2

C   Only 2 and 3

D   1, 2 and 3

(1 mark)

3   A team of scientists are investigating the distribution of marsh marigolds across a field that is directly next to a stream.

(a) (i) Suggest and describe a method the scientists could use to investigate the distribution of marsh marigolds.

(2 marks)

    (ii) The team decide they want to record the percentage cover of marsh marigolds. Describe how they could measure the percentage cover **and** give **two** advantages of measuring species abundance this way.

(3 marks)

(b)   Abiotic factors were investigated at the same places as the data on marsh marigolds was recorded. Explain what is meant by the term 'abiotic factors'.

(1 mark)

(c)   Sheep frequently graze in the field that the scientists are investigating. Explain how this may result in deflected succession.

(2 marks)

4   **Fig. 4.1** shows the net productivity of some organisms in a food web. All the figures are in $kJm^{-2}yr^{-1}$.

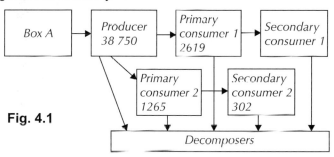

Fig. 4.1

(a)   What source of energy is represented by Box A?

(1 mark)

(b)   476 $kJm^{-2}yr^{-1}$ of biomass energy is lost from primary consumer 1 to the decomposers. The respiratory loss of secondary consumer 1 is 1571 $kJm^{-2}yr^{-1}$. Calculate the net productivity of secondary consumer 1.

(2 marks)

(c)   Give **two** reasons why the energy absorbed by secondary consumer 2 will not equal 1265 $kJm^{-2}yr^{-1}$.

(2 marks)

(d)   Calculate the difference in the percentage efficiency of energy transfer between the producer and primary consumer 1, and the producer and primary consumer 2.

(3 marks)

(e)   Nitrogen is passed on in a food web when organisms eat each other. Describe how nitrogen compounds in organisms are recycled back to atmospheric nitrogen.

In your answer, you should describe the specific roles of named microorganisms.

(4 marks)

1. Variation in Population Size

The size of a population changes all the time for lots of different reasons. But to understand why a population grows and shrinks, first you need to know exactly what a population is...

Learning Objectives:

- Know the factors that determine the size of a population.
- Understand the significance of limiting factors in determining the carrying capacity of a given environment and the impact of these factors on final population size.
- Understand how populations interact, including interspecific and intraspecific competition.
- Understand predator-prey relationships, including their effects on both prey and predator populations.

Specification Reference 6.3.2

Populations

A **population** is all the organisms of one species in a habitat.

Examples

- All the foxes in a wood form a population.
- All the people in a town form a population.

Population size is the total number of organisms of one species in a habitat. This number changes over time because of the effect of various factors.

Abiotic factors and population size

The population size of any species varies because of abiotic factors, e.g. the amount of light, water or space available, the temperature of their surroundings or the chemical composition of their surroundings. When abiotic factors are ideal for a species, organisms can grow fast and reproduce successfully.

Example

When the temperature of a mammal's surroundings is the ideal temperature for metabolic reactions to take place, they don't have to use up as much energy maintaining their body temperature. This means more energy can be used for growth and reproduction, so their population size will increase.

When abiotic factors aren't ideal for a species, organisms can't grow as fast or reproduce as successfully.

Example

When the temperature of a mammal's surroundings is significantly lower or higher than their optimum body temperature, they have to use a lot of energy to maintain the right body temperature. This means less energy will be available for growth and reproduction, so their population size will decrease.

Tip: Remember — abiotic factors are the non-living features of the ecosystem.

Biotic factors and population size

Population size can also vary because of biotic factors. These factors include interspecific competition, intraspecific competition and predation.

Tip: Remember — biotic factors are the living features of the ecosystem.

1. Interspecific competition

Interspecific competition is when organisms of different species compete with each other for the same resources. This can mean that the resources available to both populations are reduced, e.g. if they share the same source of food, there will be less available to both of them. This means both populations will be limited by a lower amount of food. They'll have less energy for growth and reproduction, so the population sizes will be lower for both species.

Interspecific competition can also affect the distribution of species. If two species are competing but one is better adapted to its surroundings than the other, the less well adapted species is likely to be out-competed — it won't be able to exist alongside the better adapted species.

Tip: Don't think it's only animals that compete with each other — plants compete with each other for things like minerals and light.

― Example ―――――――――――――――――――

Grey squirrels were introduced to the UK. They now compete with the native red squirrels for the same food sources and habitats. As they share the same source of food, there is less available to both of them. So in areas where both red and grey squirrels live, both populations are smaller than they would be if there was only one species there.

Since the introduction of the grey squirrel to the UK, the native red squirrel has disappeared from large areas. The grey squirrel has a better chance of survival because it's larger and can store more fat over winter. It can also eat a wider range of food than the red squirrel.

2. Intraspecific competition

Intraspecific competition is when organisms of the same species compete with each other for the same resources. It can cause a cyclical change in population size, where the population grows, shrinks, grows again and so on (see Figure 1). This is because the population of a species increases when resources are plentiful. As the population increases, there'll be more organisms competing for the same amount of space and food. Eventually, resources such as food and space become limiting — there isn't enough for all the organisms. The population then begins to decline. A smaller population then means that there's less competition for space and food, which is better for growth and reproduction — so the population starts to grow again. The maximum stable population size of a species that an ecosystem can support is called the **carrying capacity**.

Tip: Don't get inter- and intra specific competition mixed up. If you're struggling, just remember   inter means different species, whereas intra means the same species.

― Example ―――――――――――――――――――

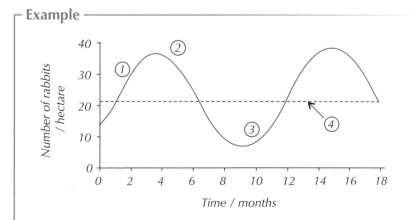

Tip: The stages of this graph are described on the next page.

Figure 1: Size of a rabbit population over time.

1. There were lots of resources available so the population of rabbits grew.

2. The population grew so large that the resources became limiting. As there weren't enough resources, the rabbit population fell.

3. A smaller population of rabbits meant there was less competition, so the population of rabbits began to grow again.

4. The carrying capacity of the ecosystem was about 22 rabbits per hectare.

3. Predation

Predation is where an organism (the predator) kills and eats another organism (the prey), e.g. lions kill and eat (predate on) buffalo. The population sizes of predators and prey are interlinked — as the population of one changes, it causes the other population to change through **negative feedback** (see Figure 3). Negative feedback is when a system reacts to a change in a way that pushes it back towards a stable state.

In a predator-prey system, as the prey population increases, there's more food for predators, so the predator population grows. As the predator population increases, more prey is eaten so the prey population then begins to fall — this is a negative feedback effect that restores the prey population to a more stable size. This means there's less food for the predators, so their population decreases (another negative feedback effect), and so on.

Figure 2: Predation of snowshoe hares by lynxes causes the populations of both species to fluctuate over time.

┌─ **Example** ─────────────

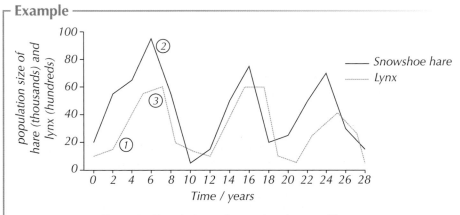

Figure 3: Populations of snowshoe hare and lynx.

1. In the graph above, the lynx population grew after the snowshoe hare population increased. This is because there was more food available for the lynx.

2. Greater numbers of lynx ate lots of snowshoe hares, so the population of hares fell. This is an example of negative feedback — the increase in the size of the lynx population pushed the snowshoe hare population back down.

3. Reduced snowshoe hare numbers meant there was less food for the lynx, so the population of lynx fell (again, a negative feedback effect).

Predator-prey relationships are usually more complicated than this though because there are other factors involved, like availability of food for the prey. E.g. it's thought that the population of snowshoe hare initially begins to decline because there's too many of them for the amount of food available. This is then accelerated by predation from the lynx.

Limiting factors

Limiting factors stop the population size of a species increasing — they determine the carrying capacity of an ecosystem. Limiting factors can be abiotic or biotic.

Example — an abiotic limiting factor

The amount of shelter in an ecosystem limits the population size of a species as there's only enough shelter for a certain number of individuals.

Example — a biotic limiting factor

Interspecific competition limits the population size of a species because the amount of resources available to a species is reduced.

Tip: Disease is another example of a biotic limiting factor of population growth — it could even make a population extinct.

Practice Questions — Application

A team investigated changes in the size of a population of owls and a population of mice over twenty years. They also monitored changes in temperature. Their results are shown on the graph below.

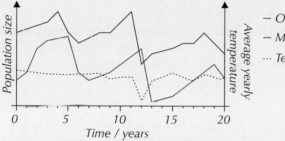

— Owl population
— Mouse population
··· Temperature

Q1 Give one factor affecting the population of owls which is biotic.

Q2 Describe how the fall in temperature between years 11 and 12 affected the mouse population size, and suggest a reason for the change in population size.

Q3 Explain how variation in the mouse population size over the twenty year period could have caused changes in the owl population size.

Tip: In the exam, if you're given a graph with two *y*-axes like the one on the left, make sure you read the key carefully so you know which line relates to which axis.

Tip: With 'suggest' questions, like in Q2 on the left, you probably won't have learned the exact answer — you need to use the information you're given and apply your own knowledge to answer the question.

Practice Questions — Fact Recall

Q1 What is a population?

Q2 a) What is interspecific competition?

b) Explain how interspecific competition may affect:
i) the population sizes of two species competing.
ii) the distribution of two species competing, if one species is better adapted to its surroundings.

c) Describe an example of interspecific competition.

Q3 a) What is intraspecific competition?

b) Explain why intraspecific competition causes a cyclical change in population size.

Q4 What is meant by the term 'carrying capacity'?

Q5 Explain how an increase in prey population will affect predator population.

Q6 What term is used to describe something that stops the population size of a species from growing?

- Understand the economic, social and ethical reasons for conservation of biological resources.

- Know the difference between conservation and preservation.

- Understand how the management of an ecosystem can provide resources in a sustainable way, including timber production and fishing.

- Understand how environmental resources can be managed and the effects of human activities on the environment.

- Understand how ecosystems can be managed to balance the conflict between conservation/preservation and human needs, for example in the Maasai Mara region of Kenya, the Terai region in Nepal, and with regards to peat bogs.

Specification Reference 6.3.2

Tip: Benefits people obtain from ecosystems are sometimes called 'ecosystem services'. These include things like the pollination of crop plants by wild insects as well as resources that can be harvested like wood and food. In recent years scientists and policy-makers have become more aware of ecosystem services, which has led to their increasing consideration in research and policy.

2. Conservation of Ecosystems

Ecosystems provide us with natural resources that we use in everyday life, such as food, fuel and drugs. It's important that we protect ecosystems so that species living in the ecosystems aren't destroyed and that these resources won't run out.

What is conservation?

Conservation is the protection and management of ecosystems so that the natural resources in them can be used without them running out. E.g. using rainforests for timber without any species becoming extinct and without any habitats being destroyed. This means the natural resources will still be available for future generations.

Conservation is a dynamic process — conservation methods need to be adapted to the constant changes (caused naturally and by humans) that occur within ecosystems. It involves the management of ecosystems — controlling how resources are used and replaced.

Conservation can also involve reclamation — restoring ecosystems that have been damaged or destroyed so they can be used again, e.g. restoring forests that have been cut down so they can be used again.

Conservation is important for many reasons:

Economic reasons

Ecosystems provide resources for lots of things that humans need, e.g. rainforests contain species that provide things like drugs, clothes and food. These resources are economically important because they're traded on a local and global scale. If the ecosystems aren't conserved, the resources that we use now will be lost, so there will be less trade in the future.

Social reasons

Many ecosystems bring joy to lots of people because they're attractive to look at and people use them for activities, e.g. birdwatching and walking. The species and habitats in the ecosystems may be lost if they aren't conserved, so future generations won't be able to use and enjoy them.

Ethical reasons

Some people think we should conserve ecosystems simply because it's the 'right' thing to do — for example most people think organisms have a right to exist, so they shouldn't become extinct as a result of human activity. Some people think we have a moral responsibility to conserve ecosystems for future generations, so they can enjoy and use them.

Ecological reasons

Conserving species and habitats can help to prevent climate change. E.g. when trees are burnt, CO_2 is released into the atmosphere, which contributes to global warming. If the trees are conserved, this doesn't happen. Conserving species and habitats also helps to prevent the disruption of food chains. Disruption of food chains can have knock-on effects on other organisms, e.g. some species of bear feed on salmon, which feed on herring — if the number of herring decreases it can affect both the salmon and the bear populations.

Preservation

Preservation is different from conservation — it's the protection of ecosystems so they're kept exactly as they are. Nothing is removed from a preserved ecosystem and they're only used for activities that don't damage them.

> **Example**
>
> Antarctica is a preserved ecosystem because it's protected from exploitation by humans — it's only used for limited tourism and scientific research, not mining or other industrial activities.

Figure 1: Antarctica is a preserved ecosystem.

Tip: Preservation has been the traditional way of protecting the natural environment. A greater understanding of the importance of balancing the needs of local populations with environmental considerations has made conservation more widely used.

Managing ecosystems in a sustainable way

Ecosystems can be managed to provide resources in a way that's sustainable — this means enough resources are taken to meet the needs of people today, but without reducing the ability of people in the future to meet their own needs.

Temperate woodland

Temperate woodland can be managed in a sustainable way — for every tree that's cut down for timber, a new one is planted in its place. The woodland should never become depleted. Cutting down trees and planting new ones needs to be done carefully to be successful:

- Trees are cleared in strips or patches — woodland grows back more quickly in smaller areas between bits of existing woodland than it does in larger, open areas.

- The cleared strips or patches aren't too large or exposed — lots of soil erosion can occur on large areas of bare ground. If the soil is eroded, newly planted trees won't be able to grow.

- Timber is sometimes harvested by coppicing — cutting down trees in a way that lets them grow back. This means new trees don't need to be planted.

- Native tree species tend to be planted in preference to non-native species. This is better for biodiversity because native species have long-established interactions with other native species (e.g. plants, fungi, animals), so their presence should help species thrive in an area. Also some species might not adapt to the presence of non-native tree species.

- Planted trees are attached to posts to provide support, and are grown in plastic tubes to stop them being eaten by grazing animals — this makes it more likely the trees will survive to become mature adults.

- Trees aren't planted too close together — this means the trees aren't competing with each other for space or resources, so they're more likely to survive.

Managing fishing

Overfishing has led to a decline in fish stocks in many parts of the world. This may lead to some species of fish disappearing altogether in some areas, and has the potential to severely disrupt ocean food chains.

Fish are an important part of many people's diets and fishing provides employment for many people, so we need to maintain fish stocks at a level where the fish continue to breed. This is sustainable food production — having enough food without using resources faster than they renew. There are a few different ways of managing fish stocks, including using fishing quotas and making regulations on mesh sizes (see next page).

Tip: Temperate woodland is found between the tropics and the polar circles (so the UK has temperate woodland).

Figure 2: The plastic around this young tree was fitted to protect it while it grows.

Tip: As the population of the Earth increases, it becomes more important to manage resources sustainably to ensure they're available for future generations.

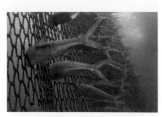

Figure 3: The fish in this picture are all 'unwanted' — they've been caught accidentally in a net intended to catch a different species.

Tip:
Managing conflicts between the environment and humans is difficult. For example, the best solution for fish stocks might be to completely ban fishing for a time, but this may not be acceptable to people who depend on fishing for their food and livelihoods. Policy-makers need to weigh up the ethical arguments relating to humans and the environment, as well as the scientific evidence, when making conservation decisions.

Figure 4: The greater one-horned rhinoceros is found in the Terai Arc. Conservation efforts in the area have rescued it from the brink of extinction.

Fishing quotas

Fishing quotas are limits to the amount of certain fish species that fishermen are allowed to catch. Fishing quotas are supposed to help to conserve fish species by reducing the numbers that are caught and killed, so the populations aren't reduced too much and the species aren't at risk from becoming extinct.

To set fishing quotas, scientists study different species and decide how big their populations need to be for them to maintain their numbers. Then they decide how many it's safe for fishermen to take without reducing the population too much. International agreements are then made (e.g. the Common Fisheries Policy in the EU) that state the amount of fish each country can take, and where they're allowed to take them from.

There are problems with fishing quotas though — e.g. fish of the wrong species or size are still caught, but they end up being thrown back into the sea, often dead or dying, because the restrictions don't allow the fishermen to bring them ashore. However, new rules for the Common Fisheries Policy are banning the discarding of fish like this and the whole catch will have to be brought ashore to be counted against the quota.

Mesh sizes

Governments can set limits for the mesh size of the fishing net, which vary depending on what's being fished. This reduces the number of 'unwanted' and discarded fish that are accidently caught, e.g. shrimp caught along with cod, as the 'unwanted' species can escape through the holes in larger meshes. It also means that younger fish will slip through the net, allowing them to reach breeding age.

However, it can be difficult to determine exactly how big the mesh size should be in areas where several different fish species are fished for at the same time. And two nets, each of which meets regulations, could be used one inside the other so that their meshes overlap — effectively reducing the reported mesh size.

Managing ecosystems and human needs

The goals of conservation and preservation are often in conflict with human needs. Ecosystems can be managed to reduce these conflicts.

Example — the Terai Arc

The Terai Arc is an area of forest and grasslands on the border between Nepal and India. A variety of plants and animals are found there, including endangered species like the Bengal tiger and Asian elephant. Nearly 7 million people also live in this area and many of them depend on the forest's resources to survive.

Areas of the forest are also being destroyed to make way for more housing and other development — this destruction of habitat brings humans and animals into closer contact and increases conflict between the two. For example, elephants can eat and trample crop fields and tigers can kill livestock. This increases the likelihood of these animals being shot and killed.

Conservation charity the WWF has worked with local people to help balance their needs with conserving the forest and its wildlife. For example, the charity has provided people with things like solar cookers and biogas generators, so they don't need to use wood from the forest as fuel. Farmers are encouraged to plant mint hedges around their crops to keep animals (which don't like the taste of mint) away.

Example — the Maasai Mara

The Maasai Mara is a national reserve in Kenya. It's a large area of grassland (savannah), which is home to huge populations of wildebeest and zebra, as well as lions and cheetahs. The Maasai Mara is named after the Maasai people who live in the area.

The Maasai people traditionally earn a living by raising livestock, such as cattle. This can bring them into conflict with conservationists — e.g. overgrazing by livestock can destroy grassland for wildlife.

Conservation trusts are working with the Maasai people to help them make money from their land through conservation and ecotourism projects rather than farming, and to farm in a sustainable way. So, the economic needs of the Maasai people are met, while still allowing the area to be conserved.

Tip: Solutions like this, where alternative forms of income are developed, represent a sustainable long-term solution to conflicts between conservation and human needs, as they don't require indefinite funding from charities.

Example — UK Peat Bogs

Lots of upland parts of the UK are home to peat bogs — areas of wet peat. These peat bogs store water and carbon dioxide, and are home to lots of different plants and animals, such as *Sphagnum* moss — these mosses actually help the peat bog form by retaining water.

Farmers use the peat bogs to graze sheep and deer. However, this can lead to conflict with conservationists because overgrazing causes loss of moss species, soil compaction (which increases water runoff down sheep paths, taking sediment with it) and general peat bog erosion.

Recent government-funded programmes, like the Environmental Stewardship Scheme, have given farmers money to use the peat bogs in a sustainable way, e.g. to carry out measures to reduce water runoff, to lower the number of livestock that use the peat bogs, and to remove livestock over winter.

Tip: Ecotourism can be a useful way to make conservation economically viable, but it needs to be managed carefully to make sure that tourists don't damage the ecosystem they've come to visit.

Tip: Peat bogs are really useful to humans. By holding water in the landscape they can help to reduce flooding, and by storing CO_2 they may be useful in combatting climate change.

Practice Questions — Fact Recall

Q1 Outline an economic reason for conserving an ecosystem.

Q2 Give one reason why ecosystems might be conserved for social reasons.

Q3 Describe and explain two practices used when managing a woodland for sustainable timber production.

Q4 How can restrictions on fishing net mesh sizes help to make fishing sustainable?

Q5 Describe how human and environmental needs come into conflict in the Terai Arc.

Q6 Describe one way in which conflicts between human and environmental needs have been reduced in the Maasai Mara.

Tip: Native plants and animals are those which naturally occur on the islands.

Figure 1: The existence of the Galapagos land iguanas is under threat because of non-native animals introduced to the islands.

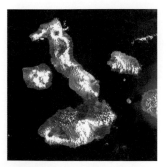

Figure 2: Satellite picture of the western Galapagos Islands.

3. Human Impact on Ecosystems

The animal and plant populations in important, but fragile, ecosystems have been affected by human activity in many places. We often need to conserve or preserve these ecosystems to try to reduce or counteract these effects.

The Galapagos Islands

Human activities have had a negative effect on the Galapagos Islands, a small group of islands in the Pacific Ocean about 1000 km off the coast of South America. Many species of animals and plants have evolved there that don't live anywhere else, e.g. the Galapagos giant tortoise and the Galapagos sea lion.

Effects of human activities on the Galapagos Islands

- Explorers and sailors that visited the Galapagos Islands in the 19th century directly affected the populations of some animals by eating them.

  > **Example**
  > A type of giant tortoise found on Floreana Island was hunted to extinction for food.

- Non-native animals introduced to the islands eat some native species. This has caused a decrease in the populations of native species.

  > **Examples**
  > Non-native dogs, cats and black rats eat young giant tortoises and Galapagos land iguanas. Pigs also destroy the nests of the iguanas and eat their eggs. Goats have eaten much of the plant life on some of the islands.

- Non-native plants have also been introduced to the islands. These compete with native plant species, causing their populations to decrease.

  > **Example**
  > Quinine trees are taller than some native plants — they block out light to the native plants, which then struggle to survive.

- Fishing has caused a decrease in the populations of some of the sea life around the Galapagos Islands.

  > **Examples**
  > - The populations of sea cucumbers and hammerhead sharks have been reduced because of overfishing.
  > - Galapagos green turtle numbers have also been reduced by overfishing and they're also killed accidentally when they're caught in fishing nets. They're now an endangered species.

- A recent increase in tourism (from 41 000 tourists in 1991 to over 210 000 in 2014) has led to an increase in development on the islands. The population on the islands has also increased due to the increased opportunities from tourism. This could lead to further development and so more damage to the ecosystems.

Controlling the impact of humans on the Galapagos Islands

Eradication programmes have removed wild goats from some of the smaller islands and wild dogs from the largest island. Quinine trees are kept in check using chemical herbicides and by uprooting young trees. A marine protected area has been established around the islands, which sets limits and controls on fishing.

When people visit the Galapagos National Park they are expected to follow a list of rules, which includes not bringing any live plants or animals onto the islands, or moving them between the islands. People are also only allowed to visit the Galapagos National Park in the company of a licensed guide.

> **Tip:** Balancing the interests of tourists and the needs of the environment is tricky. Although tourists can cause damage to sensitive ecosystems, they can provide money to fund conservation projects.

Antarctica

Antarctica is the world's southernmost continent. It has a unique icy landscape with plants and animals that have adapted to its harsh conditions. For at least 200 years it has attracted visitors, e.g. research scientists and tourists. The waters around Antarctica support high levels of primary productivity during the Antarctic summer, and are home to penguins and numerous other seabirds, whales, seals and many species of fish.

> **Tip:** Primary production is the conversion of the Sun's energy to chemical energy via photosynthesis. Photosynthetic algae grow well around Antarctica in the Antarctic summer, as days are long and the water is nutrient-rich.

Effects of human activities on Antarctica

Historically, hunting of various animals around Antarctica was a large industry. During the twentieth century, whaling in the waters surrounding Antarctica was intense, leading to a huge decrease in whale numbers. As a result of this hunting, the Antarctic blue whale is critically endangered, and the populations of other species of whale have been severely depleted. Seal hunting in the nineteenth century drove the Antarctic fur seal to the brink of extinction. The seas around Antarctica are still exploited by fishing vessels.

Human activities can also lead to problems with pollution. In the past, visitors to Antarctica have dumped sewage into the sea and left behind rubbish. Shipping accidents have led to oil spills, which severely affect wildlife.

Controlling the impact of humans on Antarctica

The continent of Antarctica is internationally protected by the Antarctic Treaty, and is now treated as a nature reserve. Commercial whaling was banned completely in the ocean surrounding Antarctica in 1994, and seal hunting has been banned for longer. Populations of the Antarctic fur seal have now recovered, but the populations of many species of whale are still considered to be dangerously low. Fishing still occurs, but within limits set with the help of scientists.

Figure 3: *Antarctic fur seal*

To reduce the impacts of pollution, all waste apart from food waste and sewage must be taken away by ship for disposal in other countries. Many research stations now treat their sewage before releasing it, to reduce its effects on the environment. Ships that use thick oil as a fuel are now banned from Antarctic waters, as heavy oil spills are likely to cause more damage and be harder to clean up than spills of lighter fuels. To prevent damage by tourists, tourist restrictions have been introduced — e.g. tourists are only allowed on land at certain locations for a few hours.

> **Tip:** Antarctica is also threatened by global warming — changes in sea temperature could affect algae and fish populations, and the populations of animals that feed on them. Melting sea ice may negatively affect some of the species of penguin that breed in these areas.

The Lake District and Snowdonia National Parks

The Lake District and Snowdonia are beautiful national parks — both are areas of hills and lakes, with the Lake District in North West England and Snowdonia in Wales. Both also attract millions of visitors per year.

Effects of human activities on the Lake District and Snowdonia

Many of the visitors to the Lake District go walking on the region's footpaths. This leads to the erosion of the footpaths and the loss of soil from hillsides. Soil that ends up in waterways and lakes can disturb the pH of the water, causing knock-on effects for wildlife. As the paths become harder to walk on, people can start to trample and destroy the sensitive vegetation either side of the paths. It's a similar story in Snowdonia — a lot of rain falls in the Snowdonia hills, which leads to the erosion of the paths. Walkers often trample the surrounding vegetation as they try to walk around the floods.

The Lake District also has problems with water pollution in some areas. Phosphates in fertilisers used on farms, in detergents used for cleaning clothes and dishes and in water released by local sewage works have accumulated in some of the lakes. These act as fertilisers for algal growth, and can contribute to algal blooms, which deoxygenate the water and can kill fish.

Figure 4: Windermere in the Lake District is very popular with tourists, including walkers and cyclists.

Controlling human impact on the Lake District and Snowdonia

To counteract footpath erosion in the Lake District, conservation charities and the Lake District National Park Authority attempt to carry out regular repair and maintenance work on the paths and encourage the regrowth of damaged vegetation. Walkers are also educated about the importance of sticking to the paths and not taking short cuts, as these increase erosion. In Snowdonia, volunteers have dug drains next to the paths to prevent them from flooding.

The pollution problem in the Lake District has been tackled by improving sewage treatment in the area, supplying grants to local farmers to improve farming practices and encouraging local businesses and residents to only use detergents that are phosphate-free.

Practice Questions — Fact Recall

Q1 Describe two of the ways in which human activity has had a negative impact on the environment of the Galapagos Islands.

Q2 What actions have been taken to reduce the negative effects of human activity in Antarctica?

Q3 Outline one environmental effect of human activity in the Lake District.

Section Summary

Make sure you know:

- That the size of a population varies because of the effect of abiotic factors (such as the temperature of the surroundings) and biotic factors (which include interspecific competition, intraspecific competition and predation).

- That interspecific competition is when individuals of different species compete with each other for the same resources.

- That intraspecific competition is when individuals of the same species compete with each other for the same resources.

- That the carrying capacity of an ecosystem is the maximum stable population size of a species that it can support.

- That population sizes of predators and prey are interlinked and have negative feedback effects on each other — as the prey population increases, there's more food for predators, so the predator population grows. As the predator population increases, more prey is eaten, so the prey population then begins to fall. This means there's less food available for predators, causing the predator population to decrease and allowing the prey population to increase once more.

- That limiting factors (e.g. amount of shelter) stop the population size of a species increasing.

- That conservation is the protection and management of ecosystems.

- How conservation is important for economic, social, ethical and ecological reasons.

- That preservation is the protection of ecosystems so that they're kept exactly as they are.

- That ecosystems (such as temperate woodland and oceans) can be managed in a sustainable way to make sure there are enough resources to meet the needs of people today and in the future.

- That human activities affect the environment, and that environmental resources can be managed to limit these effects.

- That ecosystems can be managed to balance the conflict between conservation and preservation and human needs, as in the Maasai Mara, the Terai Arc and peat bogs in the UK.

- That human activities have had an effect on environmentally sensitive ecosystems, such as the Galapagos Islands, Antarctica, Snowdonia National Park and the Lake District, and some of the ways that these effects can be controlled.

1 Coral reefs are environmentally sensitive ecosystems that are popular with tourists. **Fig. 1.1** shows the annual number of tourists visiting a particular area of coral reef between 2009 and 2015.

What was the percentage increase in visitor numbers between 2009 and 2015?

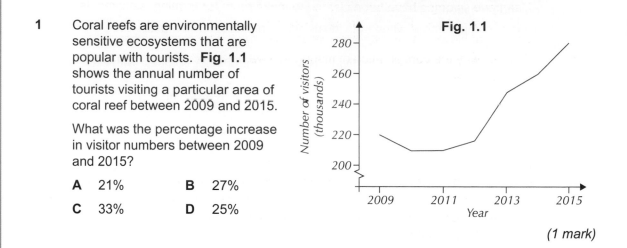

Fig. 1.1

A	21%	B	27%
C	33%	D	25%

(1 mark)

2 An investigation has been conducted on two species of grasshopper, species A and species B, in an area of grassy fields. **Fig. 2.1** shows changes in the population sizes of species A and B in the area under investigation.

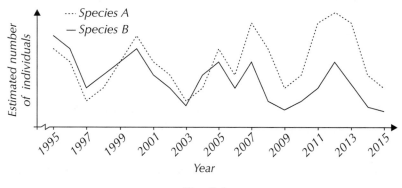

Fig. 2.1

(a) Describe **and** explain the trend shown by **Fig. 2.1**, with reference to the type of competition it shows.

(3 marks)

(b) The amount of food available prevents the population size of each grasshopper species from increasing further.

What term is used to describe the amount of food available in this case?

(1 mark)

(c) In a second area, species A is present but species B is not. The population of species A in this area remains roughly stable, with some smaller fluctuations.

State the name given to this stable population size.

(1 mark)

3   Mangrove swamps are found in coastal areas in the tropics and sub-tropics. These swamps provide a unique habitat for many species of plant and fish. They also absorb wave energy, protecting the coastline behind them from storms.

Mangrove swamps have been cleared to make room for farming, settlements and tourist resorts. In some areas, wood is harvested from mangrove swamps at unsustainable levels. Mangrove swamps are globally threatened ecosystems.

(a)   Suggest why the conservation of mangrove swamps is considered important by some people.

(2 marks)

A conservation charity is investigating methods for protecting a mangrove swamp in a Less Economically Developed Country in East Asia, where the swamp is threatened by overexploitation from the local population for charcoal making. Possible methods of protecting the swamp suggested by the charity include:

- Creating a nature reserve around the mangrove swamp and restricting access to the swamp to everyone except for conservation workers and scientists.
- Paying local people to only take wood from the mangrove swamp at sustainable levels.
- Promoting ecotourism in the area, based around the mangrove swamp.

(b)* Compare these options, giving the advantages and disadvantages of each.

(9 marks)

(c)   Ecosystems can be protected through conservation or preservation.

   (i) Explain the difference between conservation and preservation.

(1 mark)

  (ii) State which of the methods outlined above represents a preservation method.

(1 mark)

4   Many areas of woodland around the world are part of conservation projects.

(a)   Outline **one** ethical reason for the conservation of woodland.

(1 mark)

(b)   Ecosystems such as woodland can be managed in a sustainable way. Briefly describe what this means.

(1 mark)

(c)   Complete the table below to give **two** different methods used to manage timber production in temperate woodland in a sustainable way **and** explain how each method works.

Method	Explanation

(4 marks)

* The quality of your response will be assessed in this question.

Exam Help

1. The Exams

You'll take three exams as part of OCR A A-level Biology. Everything you need to know about them is summarised below.

It seems obvious, but if you know exactly what will be covered in each of the exams, how much time you'll have to do them and how they'll be structured, you can be better prepared. So let's take a look at the ins and outs of the exams you'll be facing for A-level Biology...

Tip: All this exam info is only relevant if you're taking the OCR A A-level in Biology. If you're taking the OCR A AS-level, you'll be sitting a completely different set of papers, which are structured in a different way. There are two AS-level papers that both test Modules 1 to 4.

How are the exams structured?

OCR A A-Level Biology is examined in three papers. Papers 1 and 2 are each worth 37% of the total marks and Paper 3 is worth 26% of the total marks.

	Paper	Total marks	Time	Modules assessed
1	Biological Processes	100	2 hours 15 minutes	1, 2, 3 & 5
2	Biological Diversity	100	2 hours 15 minutes	1, 2, 4 & 6
3	Unified Biology	70	1 hour 30 minutes	1 to 6

Exam Tip
All three A-level papers test you on practical skills.

- This book covers Modules 5-6 — the material from Year 2 of your course. However, as you can see from the table, all three papers cover theory from both years of your course — this means you need to make sure you revise your Year 1 modules (1-4) as well as your Year 2 modules (5-6) for these exams. The papers will contain some synoptic questions, which connect and test different areas of Biology from Years 1 and 2.

Exam Tip
Synoptic means it tests you on different areas of Biology.

- The 'Biological Processes' and 'Biological Diversity' papers are both split into two sections — A and B. Section A of each paper contains 15 multiple choice questions and is worth 15 marks in total. Each multiple choice question will have four possible answers (A-D) but only one will be correct. Section B of these papers contains short answer questions and extended response questions. Section B is worth 85 marks in total.

- The 'Unified Biology' paper includes both short answer questions and extended response questions, but no multiple choice questions.

Exam Tip
Even though you're taking an A-level in Biology, you'll still need to do some maths in the exams — but it'll be set in a biological context.

- Short answer questions may involve problem solving, calculations or a practical context (see next page). There's more about extended response questions below...

Extended response questions

In each of your three papers there will be one or more extended response questions. These questions are worth 6 or 9 marks and will require a long answer. They often want you to use a source (such as some text or a diagram, table or graph) to help you answer the question. Extended response questions are shown with an asterisk (*) next to their number.

You'll be awarded marks for the quality of your extended response as well as the content of your answer, so your answer needs to:

- Be legible (the same goes for all your written answers).
- Have a clear and logical structure.
- Show good reasoning — i.e. show that you have thought about and understood the question, and can justify your answer.
- Include information that's relevant to the question.

You can gain practice at extended response questions by doing the exam questions marked with an asterisk in this book.

Tip: To help you to structure your answer logically, you could briefly jot down the main points you want to include in your answer before you start writing.

Solving problems in a practical context

In the exams, you'll get plenty of questions set in a 'practical context'. As well as answering questions about the methods used or the conclusions drawn, you'll need to be able to apply your scientific knowledge to solve problems set in these contexts.

Exam Tip
Make sure you read all the information you're given at the start of an exam question carefully, and pay attention to what's being shown in any figures that are included too.

┌─ Example ─────────────────────

1   A scientist is investigating the effect on plant growth of adding additional CO_2 to the air in a greenhouse. The results are shown in **Fig. 1.1**.

Fig. 1.1

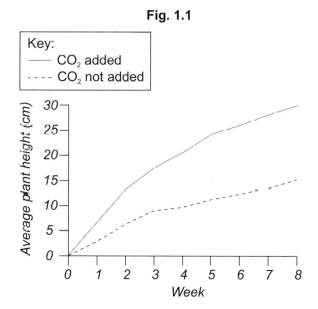

Key:
— CO_2 added
---- CO_2 not added

Exam Tip
Make sure you learn the language that goes with experiments too, e.g. precision, accuracy, validity — see your notes from Module 1 of your Year 1 course for more.

(a)   Explain the difference in the two curves shown on the graph.

(3 marks)

You should remember from Module 5 that plants use carbon dioxide to produce glucose by photosynthesis (see page 110). The more carbon dioxide plants have, the more glucose they can produce (until something other than CO_2 becomes a limiting factor) meaning they can also respire more. This gives them more ATP for DNA replication, cell division and protein synthesis, leading to increased plant growth.

Exam Tip
Questions like this can look a bit scary, but you just have to apply what you already know about Biology to a real-life example. There are plenty of questions like this for you to have a go at in this book.

2. Command Words

Command words are just the bits of a question that tell you what to do.

You'll find answering exam questions much easier if you understand exactly what they mean, so here's a brief summary table of the most common command words:

Command word:	What to do:
Give / Name / State	Give a brief one or two word answer, or a short sentence.
Identify	Pick out information or say what something is.
Describe	Write about what something's like, e.g. describe the structure of fish gills.
Explain	Give reasons for something.
Suggest	Use your scientific knowledge to work out what the answer might be.
Compare	Give the similarities and differences between two things.
Outline	Write about the main points of a topic.
Calculate	Work out the solution to a mathematical problem.
Discuss	Write about a topic, considering different issues or ideas.

Some questions will also ask you to answer 'using the information/data provided' (e.g. a graph, table or passage of text) or 'with reference to figure X' — if so, you must refer to the information, data or figure you've been given or you won't get the marks. Some questions may also ask you to answer 'using your calculation' — it's the same here, you need to use your answer to a particular calculation, otherwise you won't get the marks.

Not all of the questions will have command words, e.g. the multiple choice questions — instead they may just ask a which / what / how type of question.

3. Time Management

Time management is really important in your exams — it's no good writing a perfect answer to a 3 mark question if it takes you an hour.

For each paper you get just over a minute per mark. This means if you get stuck on a short question it's sometimes worth moving onto another one and then coming back to it if you have time. However, bear in mind that you might want to spend a bit longer on the extended response questions, in which case you'll have to spend less time on the multiple choice and short answer questions.

If you've got any time left once you've finished the paper, hold off on celebrating and have a look back through the questions. You can use the time to go back to any questions you've skipped, check your answers to calculation questions and to make sure you haven't accidentally missed any questions out.

Exam Tip
When you're reading exam questions, underline the command words. That way you'll know exactly what type of answer to give.

Exam Tip
If you're answering a longer 'compare' question make a mental list of the similarities and differences or pros and cons first, so you know what you want your answer to include before you start writing.

Exam Tip
Make sure you take a calculator and ruler into all your exams to help you with the calculation questions. A pencil and a spare pen may come in handy as well.

Exam Tip
If the question is only worth 1 mark, don't waste time writing more than you need to. Questions with more marks require longer answers.

Answers

Module 5

Section 1 — Communication and Homeostasis

1. Communication Basics

Page 14 — Fact Recall Questions
Q1 To increase their chances of survival.
Q2 E.g. to make sure that the activities of different organs are coordinated to keep the organism working effectively.
Q3 The way in which cells communicate with other cells.

2. The Nervous System

Page 18 — Application Questions
Q1 threshold level
Q2 a) B, because its generator potential reaches -60mV/the threshold level.
   b) Approximately -87.5 mV (accept any value between -87 mV and -88 mV)
   Make sure you always read the axes carefully — especially on graphs to do with potential differences across cell membranes, because they nearly always involve negative numbers.

Page 18 — Fact Recall Questions
Q1 a) To transmit nerve impulses from receptors to the CNS.
   b) To transmit nerve impulses from the CNS to effectors.
   c) To transmit nerve impulses between sensory neurones and motor neurones.
Q2 A — dendrite, B — cell body, C — axon, D — axon terminal
Q3 E.g. any two from: the dendrites in a sensory neurone are further away from the cell body than they are in a motor neurone. / The axon in a sensory neurone is shorter than the axon in a motor neurone. / A sensory neurone has one long dendron whereas a motor neurone doesn't have a dendron. / Dendrites connect directly to the cell body in a motor neurone but not in a sensory neurone.
   The questions asks for two structural differences, so you need to concentrate on the structure — not the function — of the different types of neurone.
Q4 Receptor cells detect a stimulus. Sensory neurones transmit electrical impulses from the receptors to the CNS. The CNS processes the information, decides what to do with it and sends impulses along motor neurones to effectors, which respond.
Q5 Because they convert the energy of a stimulus into electrical energy. / Because they convert one form of energy into another.
Q6 When a stimulus is detected, the cell membrane is excited and becomes more permeable, allowing more ions to move in and out of the cell. This alters the potential difference across the cell membrane and therefore produces a generator potential.

Q7 A bigger stimulus excites the membrane more, causing a bigger movement of ions and a bigger change in potential difference, so a bigger generator potential is produced.
Q8 When a Pacinian corpuscle is stimulated, the lamellae are deformed and press on the sensory nerve ending. This causes deformation of stretch-mediated sodium channels in the sensory neurone's cell membrane. The sodium ion channels open and sodium ions diffuse into the cell, creating a generator potential. If the generator potential reaches the threshold, it triggers an action potential.

3. The Nervous Impulse

Page 23 — Application Questions
Q1 A — The neurone is stimulated.
   B — Depolarisation / Voltage-gated sodium ion channels are open and lots of sodium ions are diffusing into the neurone.
Q2 −40 mV
Q3 −60 mV
   Remember to always include units in your answer when they're given on the graph.
Q4 a) At a potential difference of +40 mV the sodium ion channels close and the potassium ion channels open. The membrane is more permeable to potassium so potassium ions diffuse out of the neurone down the potassium ion concentration gradient. This starts to get the membrane back to its resting potential. At the bottom of the curve the potassium ion channels are slow to close so there's a slight 'overshoot' where too many potassium ions diffuse out of the neurone. The potential difference (−70 mV) is more negative than the resting potential (−60 mV). The sodium-potassium pump then returns the membrane to its resting potential (−60 mV).
   b) refractory period
Q5 The action potential would have the same potential difference values as the graph shown because once the threshold is reached, an action potential will always fire with the same change in voltage, no matter how big the stimulus is. However, there may be another action potential shown on the graph because a bigger stimulus will cause action potentials to fire more frequently.

Page 23 — Fact Recall Questions
Q1 Sodium-potassium pumps and potassium ion channels.
   Sodium ion channels are involved when a stimulus excites the neurone cells membrane but they're not involved in maintaining the resting membrane potential.
Q2 Sodium ions diffuse into the neurone down the sodium ion electrochemical gradient. This makes the inside of the neurone less negative and so decreases the potential difference across the membrane.
Q3 a) More sodium ions diffuse into the neurone because sodium ion channels open.
   b) positive feedback
Q4 a) The ion channels are recovering and can't be made to open.
   b) It makes action potentials discrete/separate impulses. It makes action potentials unidirectional.

Q5 During an action potential, some of the sodium ions that enter the neurone diffuse sideways. This causes sodium ion channels in the next region of the neurone to open and sodium ions diffuse into that part. This causes a wave of depolarisation.

Q6 A myelinated neurone has a myelin sheath. The myelin sheath is made of a type of cell called a Schwann cell which is wrapped around the axon (and/or dendron). Between the Schwann cells are tiny patches of bare membrane called the nodes of Ranvier. Sodium ion channels are concentrated at the nodes of Ranvier.

Q7 In a myelinated neurone depolarisation/action potentials only happen at the nodes of Ranvier. However in a non-myelinated neurone, depolarisation/action potentials occur as a wave along the whole length of the axon membrane. Conduction along a myelinated neurone is faster than along a non-myelinated neurone.

Q8 Axon diameter and temperature.

4. Synapses

Page 26 — Application Question

Q1 Carbachol mimics the action of ACh so the presence of carbachol will activate even more cholinergic receptors. This will make more action potentials fire in the postsynaptic neurone, so more saliva will be produced.

Page 27 — Fact Recall Questions

Q1 a) The action potential stimulates voltage-gated calcium ion channels in the presynaptic neurone to open, so calcium ions diffuse into the synaptic knob.

b) The influx of calcium ions into the synaptic knob causes the synaptic vesicles to fuse with the presynaptic membrane. The vesicles release ACh into the synaptic cleft. ACh diffuses across the synaptic cleft and binds to specific cholinergic receptors on the postsynaptic membrane. This causes sodium ion channels in the postsynaptic neurone to open. If the threshold is reached, the influx of sodium ions into the postsynaptic neurone causes an action potential on the postsynaptic membrane.

Q2 a) Information from one neurone can be dispersed to different areas of the body (as one neurone connects to many neurones).

b) Information from many neurones can be amplified (as many neurones connect to one neurone).

Q3 a) Where two or more presynaptic neurones converge and release their neurotransmitters at the same time onto the same postsynaptic neurone, the small amount of neurotransmitter released from each of these neurones can be enough altogether to reach the threshold in the postsynaptic neurone. This makes an action potential more likely.

b) Where two or more nerve impulses arrive in quick succession from the same presynaptic neurone, more neurotransmitter is released into the synaptic cleft. This makes an action potential more likely.

1 a) i) Action potentials have a refractory period *(1 mark)*. During this period the ion channels are recovering and can't be made to open *(1 mark)*. This means that no more sodium ions can diffuse into the neurone to trigger another action potential *(1 mark)*.

ii) There are 5 action potentials in 20 ms. 500 ms ÷ 20 ms = 25. So 5 × 25 = **125 action potentials**. *(2 marks for correct answer, otherwise 1 mark for correct working.)*

b) i) *5-6 marks:*
The answer correctly identifies the stages of the action potential at each time and explains fully what is happening during those stages, including the movement of specific ions across the membrane. The answer has a clear and logical structure. The information given is relevant and detailed.
3-4 marks:
The answer correctly identifies the stages of the action potential at each time and explains briefly what is happening during those stages.
The answer has some structure. Most of the information given is relevant and there is some detail involved.
1-2 marks:
The answer includes a basic explanation of at least one stage of an action potential. The answer has no clear structure. The information given is basic and lacking in detail. It may not all be relevant.
0 marks:
No relevant information is given.
Here are some points your answer may include:
Time 1 shows repolarisation because the sodium ion channels are closed and the potassium ion channels are open. The membrane is more permeable to potassium so potassium ions diffuse out of the neurone down their concentration gradient.
Time 2 shows hyperpolarisation/the refractory period because both the sodium and potassium ion channels are closed. There is no movement of sodium or potassium through their ion channels (by facilitated diffusion).

If a question tells you to 'use evidence' from a source (like a diagram, graph, table, etc.) this means you need to include figures or descriptions from the source. So in this case, you need to say which ion channels are open and closed in the diagram.

ii) Sodium-potassium pumps use active transport *(1 mark)* to move three sodium ions out of the cell *(1 mark)* for every two potassium ions moved in *(1 mark)*.

iii) The potassium ion channel is slow to close so too many potassium ions diffuse out of the neurone *(1 mark)*. The potential difference is more negative than the neurone cell membrane's resting potential, so the pump returns the membrane to its resting potential *(1 mark)*.

c) Sodium ions won't be able to diffuse into the neurone through voltage-gated sodium ion channels *(1 mark)*. This means that the neurone won't be depolarised so there will be no action potentials/no nervous impulses *(1 mark)*.

2 a) i) Schwann cell *(1 mark)*
   ii)

	Structure	Function
B	axon	Carries nerve impulses from the cell body to effector cells / axon terminal.
C	dendrites	Carry nerve impulses from the central nervous system to the cell body.

(1 mark for each correct answer)

The diagram shows a <u>motor neurone</u>, so dendrites carry information <u>from the CNS</u>.

b) i) To transmit nerve impulses from receptors to the central nervous system *(1 mark)*.
   ii) To transmit nerve impulses between sensory neurones and motor neurones *(1 mark)*.

c) Conduction of nervous impulses in non-myelinated neurones is slower than in myelinated neurones *(1 mark)*. If the myelin is damaged then the nerve impulse may be conducted much more slowly or not at all, resulting in muscle weakness or paralysis *(1 mark)*.

3 a) The action potential arrives in the synaptic knob of the motor neurone and stimulates voltage-gated calcium ion channels to open *(1 mark)*. Calcium ions diffuse into the synaptic knob *(1 mark)* and cause the synaptic vesicles to fuse with the presynaptic membrane *(1 mark)*. The vesicles release acetylcholine (ACh) into the synaptic cleft by exocytosis *(1 mark)*.

b) i) (temporal) summation *(1 mark)*
   ii) More neurotransmitter/ACh will be released into the synaptic cleft *(1 mark)*. This means more neurotransmitter/ACh will bind to receptors on the postsynaptic membrane/muscle cell *(1 mark)*. This causes more sodium ion channels to open *(1 mark)* and a greater influx of sodium ions *(1 mark)*, which makes the muscle cell more likely to reach threshold and fire an action potential *(1 mark)*.

c) Tubocurarine prevents ACh from binding to the cholinergic receptors *(1 mark)*. This means sodium ion channels on the muscle cell do not open *(1 mark)* so there's no influx of sodium ions into the muscle cell *(1 mark)*. No action potentials can be fired so the muscles cannot be stimulated to contract/move *(1 mark)*.

5. The Hormonal System and Glands

Pages 32-33 — Application Questions
Q1

Molecule / Structure	Name
Hormone	Oxytocin
Target cells	Myoepithelial cells
Target tissue	Epithelial tissue
Endocrine gland	Posterior pituitary gland

Q2 E.g. because oxytocin has to travel in the blood to the target cells, which may take several minutes.

Page 33 — Fact Recall Questions
Q1 A group of cells that is specialised to secrete hormones.
Q2 A change in concentration of a specific substance/another hormone, electrical impulses.
Q3 Each hormone will only bind to specific receptors for that hormone, found on the membranes of target cells.
Q4 a) cyclic AMP/cAMP
   b) It activates a cascade of enzyme reactions to make more glucose available to the cell by catalysing the breakdown of glycogen into glucose.
   c) adrenaline
Q5 a) The outer part is called the cortex and the inner part is called the medulla.
   b) The medulla secretes catecholamine hormones, such as adrenaline and noradrenaline. These act to make more energy available in the short-term by increasing heart and breathing rate, causing cells to break down glycogen into glucose and constricting some blood vessels so that blood is diverted to the brain and muscles.
Q6 a) islet of Langerhans
   b) i) glucagon
      ii) insulin

6. Homeostasis Basics

Page 36 — Application Questions
Q1 A is an example of negative feedback because increasing respiration rate will increase the rate at which carbon dioxide is removed from the body. This will increase the pH of the blood back to the normal level. B is an example of positive feedback because more oestrogen being released will increase the levels of LH further and amplify the change.
Q2 a) i) At point A low concentrations of calcium in the blood are detected. This stimulates the secretion of PTH, which travels in the blood to effectors. At point B effectors are responding by increasing the concentration of calcium in the blood.
      ii) At point C high concentrations of calcium in the blood are detected. This stimulates the secretion of calcitonin which travels in the blood to effectors. At point D effectors are responding by decreasing the concentration of calcium in the blood.
   b) The concentration of calcium in the blood may fall very low. This is because less PTH will be released to bring the levels back up to normal.

Page 36 — Fact Recall Questions
Q1 The maintenance of a constant internal environment.
Q2 So that metabolic reactions can occur at an optimum rate. Low temperatures make metabolic reactions slower, but if the temperature gets too high the reaction essentially stops.

Q3 A — receptors detect change, B — communication via hormonal or nervous system, C — effectors respond.

Q4 A positive feedback mechanism amplifies a change from the normal level, whereas a negative feedback mechanism restores the level to normal.

7. Control of Body Temperature

Pages 37-38 — Application Questions

Q1 a) The external temperature was low/it was cold because the snake is an ectotherm and appears dark/is not radiating any heat/is cold.

b) The mouse because it's warmer than the snake, meaning it has more energy available (from metabolic reactions) for activity.

Q2 a) The internal temperature of the chuckwalla increases as the external temperature increases. This suggests that the chuckwalla is an ectotherm as its internal temperature depends on the external temperature. The internal temperature of the hoatzin stays roughly the same as the external temperature increases. This suggests that the hoatzin is an endotherm as it can control its internal body temperature by homeostasis.

b) The chuckwalla because its internal temperature varied the most, meaning its metabolic reactions would have been most disrupted.

Remember, metabolic reactions are controlled by enzymes and enzyme activity is greatest at an optimum temperature. Any variation from the optimum temperature will reduce enzyme activity and therefore slow down metabolic reactions.

Page 40 — Application Questions

Q1 The hot water in the bath heats up the temperature of the skin. Thermoreceptors in the skin detect body temperature is too high and send impulses to the hypothalamus. The hypothalamus then sends impulses to the arterioles near the surface of the skin causing them to dilate. More blood then flows through the capillaries in the surface layers of the dermis so more heat is lost by radiation and the body temperature is lowered. The increased blood flow in the capillaries might make the skin appear pink.

Q2 A cold external environment. When internal body temperature falls the body's responses include shivering and increased release of adrenaline and thyroxine. These mechanisms increase the rate of metabolism, which means more glucose is used. Blood glucose concentration will fall, so feelings of hunger will occur more quickly than they would do in a hot environment.

Q3 In hot weather the internal body temperature rises. Normally one of the ways the body responds to this is by vasodilation to increase heat loss. However, cocaine causes the opposite effect — vasoconstriction. This will reduce heat loss so the internal temperature will remain high. Also, an increase in muscular activity will increase respiration, so more heat will be produced. This will increase the internal body temperature further and make the person at risk of hyperthermia.

Page 40 — Fact Recall Questions

Q1 a) By changing behaviour.

b) Internally by homeostasis as well as by changing behaviour.

Q2 Ectotherms have a variable metabolic rate and endotherms have a constantly high metabolic rate.

Q3 When the body's too hot sweat glands secrete more sweat. The water in sweat evaporates from the surface of the skin and takes heat from the body so the skin is cooled. When the body's too cold sweat glands secrete much less sweat, reducing the amount of heat lost.

In this question you need to write about how sweat glands help the body lose heat <u>and</u> how they help it to conserve heat.

Q4 Muscles in the body contract in spasms when it's cold. This makes the body shiver and more heat is produced from increased respiration. The hormones adrenaline and thyroxine are released, which increases metabolism, so more heat is produced.

Q5 They constrict.

Q6 The hypothalamus.

Q7 Thermoreceptors in the skin/peripheral temperature receptors detect external/skin temperature and send impulses via sensory neurones to the brain/hypothalamus.

Q8 When thermoreceptors detect body temperature is too low, they send impulses to the hypothalamus, which sends impulses to effectors. Effectors respond to decrease heat loss from the body and increase heat production so body temperature returns to normal.

8. Control of Blood Glucose Concentration

Page 42 — Application Questions

Q1 It will increase blood glucose concentration.

Remember, glycogenolysis is the process of breaking down glycogen into glucose. So when this process is activated, blood glucose concentration increases.

Q2 Carbohydrates are broken down into glucose, so their blood glucose concentration will increase. When the pancreas detects the blood glucose concentration is too high, the β cells will secrete insulin and the α cells will stop secreting glucagon. Insulin will then bind to receptors on liver and muscle cells (the effectors). These cells will respond by taking up more glucose, activating glycogenesis and by respiring more glucose. Blood glucose concentration will then return to normal.

Q3 Glycogenolysis and gluconeogenesis both increase blood glucose concentration. If these processes don't work properly then when blood glucose concentration falls (i.e. if the person doesn't eat regularly) the body will be unable to raise the blood glucose concentration back to normal, so the person will suffer from hypoglycaemia.

Page 45 — Application Questions

Q1 The person with Type 2 diabetes doesn't produce as much insulin as the person without diabetes. / The body's cells don't respond properly to the insulin that's produced. Insulin lowers blood glucose concentration when it's too high, so if there's not enough insulin/the body can't respond to insulin properly, this process will be much slower.

Q2 A person with Type 1 diabetes wouldn't produce any insulin. This means that blood glucose concentration would remain high for much longer than for the person with Type 2 diabetes.

Q3 22.5 minutes. This is because this is the time when the blood glucose concentration is at its upper limit / 110 mg per 100 cm^3.

You're told the normal range for blood glucose concentration in the introduction to the question — make sure you always read questions thoroughly in the exam.

Q4 Insulin is a hormone, so it takes time to travel in the blood to receptor cells.

Q5 When blood glucose concentration falls below 82 mg per 100 cm^3 the pancreas is stimulated to secrete glucagon and stop secreting insulin. Glucagon binds to specific receptors on liver cells. The liver cells respond to increase blood glucose concentration — glycogenolysis is activated, gluconeogenesis is activated and the cells respire less glucose.

Page 46 — Fact Recall Questions

Q1 It increases the permeability of liver and muscle cell membranes to glucose, activates enzymes that convert glucose into glycogen/activates glycogenesis and increases the rate of respiration of glucose in those cells.

Q2 glycogenesis

Q3 Gluconeogenesis — fatty acids or amino acids are converted to glucose. Glycogenolysis — glycogen is converted to glucose.

Q4 a) The potassium ion channels are open and the calcium ion channels are closed.
b) The potassium ion channels close and the calcium ion channels open.

Q5 a) It is an auto-immune disease, in which the body attacks and destroys the β cells in the islets of Langerhans.
b) For most people with Type 1 diabetes insulin therapy involves having regular insulin injections throughout the day. For some people it involves using an insulin pump — a machine that continuously delivers insulin into the body via a tube inserted beneath the skin.
c) Type 1 diabetes can be treated by having islet cell transplantation. This involves receiving healthy islet cells from a donor so the person's pancreas can produce some insulin (although they usually still need some additional insulin therapy).

Q6 Type 2 diabetes is initially managed through lifestyle changes, such as eating a healthy, balanced diet, getting regular exercise and losing weight if needed. If blood glucose concentration can't be controlled through lifestyle changes alone, then medication may be prescribed. In some people with Type 2 diabetes, these types of medication are not enough to control blood glucose concentration so insulin therapy is used in addition or instead.

Q7 Any three from: e.g. producing insulin using GM bacteria is cheaper than extracting it from animal pancreases. / Larger quantities of insulin can be produced using GM bacteria. / GM bacteria make human insulin, which is more effective than animal insulin and less likely to trigger an allergic response or be rejected by the immune system. / Some people prefer insulin from GM bacteria for ethical or religious reasons.

Q8 Stem cells could be grown into β cells which would then be implanted into the pancreas of a person with Type 1 diabetes. This means the person would be able to make insulin as normal.

Exam-style Questions — pages 49-50

1 B *(1 mark)*
Eating a healthy balanced diet will reduce the amount of insulin that a person with Type 1 diabetes needs to inject but, as they cannot produce insulin, it won't control the diabetes by itself.

2 a) adrenal medulla *(1 mark)*
b) Adrenaline binds to specific receptors in the cell membrane *(1 mark)*, which activates an enzyme/adenylyl cyclase in the cell membrane *(1 mark)*. The activated enzyme/adenylyl cyclase catalyses the production of cyclic AMP/cAMP from ATP *(1 mark)*, which triggers a cascade.
c) i) glycogenolysis *(1 mark)*
ii) glucagon *(1 mark)*

3 a) A mechanism that restores a level back to normal in a system *(1 mark)*.
b) i) β cell *(1 mark)*
ii) The person will have had a high blood glucose concentration, which caused more glucose to enter the β cell by facilitated diffusion *(1 mark)*, which increased the respiration rate and caused more ATP to be made *(1 mark)*. The rise in ATP triggered the potassium ion channels to close *(1 mark)*.
iii) The build up of potassium ions inside the cell depolarises the cell membrane *(1 mark)*. This triggers the calcium ion channels in the cell membrane to open *(1 mark)*. Calcium ions diffuse into the cell *(1 mark)*, which causes the vesicles to move to and fuse with the cell membrane and release insulin by exocytosis *(1 mark)*.
c) Glycogenesis is the process of forming glycogen from glucose *(1 mark)*.

4 a) As the temperature increases the activity level of Organism A increases, and as the temperature decreases the activity level of Organism A decreases / there is a positive correlation between the activity level of Organism A and temperature *(1 mark)*. The activity level of Organism B changes randomly as the temperature changes / there is no correlation between the activity level of Organism B and temperature *(1 mark)*.
b) i) Organism A because an ectotherm is more active in warmer external temperatures than it is in colder temperatures *(1 mark)*.
ii) Squirrels are endotherms so they can control their body temperature internally by homeostasis *(1 mark)*. This means their internal temperature is much less affected by external temperature compared to tortoises, so they can survive in a wider range of external temperatures *(1 mark)*.
c) i) Point X was relatively cold, so thermoreceptors/peripheral temperature receptors in the squirrel's skin will have detected the low temperature *(1 mark)*. The thermoreceptors/peripheral temperature receptors will have sent impulses to the hypothalamus *(1 mark)* which will have sent impulses to erector pili muscles/effectors to make the hairs stand up *(1 mark)* to trap more air and so prevent heat loss *(1 mark)*.
ii) Any two from: e.g. more sweat may be secreted from the squirrel's sweat glands *(1 mark)*. When the sweat evaporates it will take heat from the body so the skin is cooled *(1 mark)*. / The squirrel's erector pili muscles may relax so its hairs lie flat *(1 mark)*. This means less air is trapped, so the skin is less insulated and heat can be lost more easily *(1 mark)*. / Vasodilation may occur near the surface of the squirrel's skin *(1 mark)*. This means more heat is lost from the skin by radiation so the temperature of the skin is lowered *(1 mark)*. *(Maximum of 4 marks available.)*

Section 2 — Excretion

1. The Liver and Excretion

Page 55 — Application Questions
Q1 a) The level of argininosuccinate in the blood would be low. This is because argininosuccinate would still be used up in the cycle but there would be a lack of AS to convert citrulline to more argininosuccinate.

    b) The level of citrulline would be high. This is because citrulline would still be made in the cycle but it would not be converted to argininosuccinate, so it would build up in the blood.

Q2 The proteins that we eat are made up of amino acids, which contain nitrogenous substances. Via deamination, these nitrogenous substances enter the ornithine cycle in the form of ammonia. If a person suffering from AS deficiency eats a low protein diet then fewer excess amino acids will be produced by digestion, so less ammonia will enter the ornithine cycle.

Page 55 — Fact Recall Questions
Q1 The removal of the waste products of metabolism from the body.

Q2 e.g. carbon dioxide, nitrogenous waste

Q3 Excretion helps to keep the levels of certain substances in the blood roughly constant by removing the waste products of metabolism.

Q4 The duodenum and the ileum / the small intestine.

Q5 the hepatic vein

Q6 The capillaries that connect the hepatic artery and the hepatic portal vein to the central vein in the liver.

Q7 X — central vein, Y — sinusoids

Q8 First, the nitrogen-containing amino groups ($-NH_2$) are removed from any excess amino acids, forming ammonia (NH_3) and organic acids. This process is called deamination. Ammonia is then combined with CO_2 in the ornithine cycle to create urea (and water).

Q9 It is the process in which harmful substances, such as excess hormones/alcohol/drugs/excess insulin, are broken down by the liver into less harmful substances so they can be excreted.

Q10 The liver converts excess glucose to glycogen via glycogenesis and stores it as granules in its cells.

2. The Kidneys and Excretion

Page 60 — Application Questions
Q1 A — Bowman's capsule

    B — loop of Henle

    C — distal convoluted tubule/DCT

    D — ureter

Q2 a) X — basement membrane

       Y — epithelium / podocyte

    b) E.g. the structure of the barrier normally prevents larger molecules such as proteins from entering the tubules. If its structure is affected, large molecules such as proteins may be able to pass into the tubules and eventually end up in the urine, producing proteinuria.

Page 60 — Fact Recall Questions
Q1 a) afferent arteriole

    b) Bowman's capsule

    c) Because vessel A/the afferent arteriole is larger in diameter than vessel B/the efferent arteriole, the blood in the glomerulus is under high pressure. The high pressure forces liquid and small molecules in the blood out of the capillary and into the Bowman's capsule (ultrafiltration).

If you're struggling to remember the difference between the afferent and efferent arterioles, think a̲fferent comes first, because it's first alphabetically.

Q2 Any three from: e.g. glucose / amino acids / vitamins / salts / urea / water.

Q3 X — renal capsule, Y — renal pyramid / medulla, Z — renal calyx / renal pelvis

Q4 a) The wall of the artery will be thicker than the wall of the vein. The ureter is likely to have the most adipose (fatty) tissue round it.

    b) You would expect to see the cone-shaped renal pyramids, which would probably appear stripy.

3. The Kidneys and Water Potential

Page 63 — Application Questions
Q1 a) The runner is dehydrated because he has sweated a lot and not replaced any of the fluids he has lost. This has caused his blood water content/potential to drop.

    b) The low water potential of the runner's blood is detected by osmoreceptors in his hypothalamus.

    c) ADH molecules bind to receptors on the plasma membranes of cells of the runner's distal convoluted tubule/DCT and collecting duct. When this happens, protein channels called aquaporins are inserted into the plasma membrane. These channels allow water to pass through via osmosis, so make the walls of the DCT and collecting duct more permeable to water. This allows water to be reabsorbed from these tubules into the medulla and into the blood by osmosis, therefore conserving water in the runner's body.

    d) The presence of sodium (Na^+) and chloride (Cl^-) ions in the sports drink increases the concentration of Na^+ and Cl^- in the runner's filtrate. These ions are used to lower the water potential of the medulla in the loop of Henle in order to create a water potential gradient to drive the reabsorption of water back into the blood by osmosis.

Make sure you understand water potential. If you don't, it makes understanding the regulation of water content by the kidneys pretty tricky. Remember, high water potential means a high concentration of water molecules and low water potential means a low concentration of water molecules. Water moves from a region of higher water potential to a region of lower water potential — from where there are more water molecules to where there are fewer.

Q2 a) Normally if a person has consumed too much fluid, the osmoreceptors in the hypothalamus detect that the water content of the blood, and so its water potential, has risen. This causes the posterior pituitary gland to release less ADH into the blood. Less ADH means that the DCT and collecting duct are less permeable, so less water is reabsorbed into the blood by osmosis. This causes a large amount of dilute urine to be produced and so more water is lost.

b) If the body can't suppress ADH production, the DCT and collecting duct will continue to be made permeable, so water is reabsorbed into the blood by osmosis. This means that the excess water is not excreted and therefore accumulates, potentially affecting the balance of fluid in cells.

Page 63 — Fact Recall Questions
Q1 the ascending limb
Q2 A longer ascending limb allows more ions to be actively pumped out into the medulla, which creates a really low water potential in the medulla. This means more water moves out of the nephron and collecting duct into the capillaries, giving very concentrated urine.

4. Kidney Failure

Page 66 — Application Questions
Q1 a) In order to maintain a steep concentration gradient between the two fluids. This increases the rate of diffusion of waste products and excess water and ions across the membrane out of the blood and into the dialysis fluid.
    b) E.g. the patient will have to undergo a major operation, which is risky. / The patient's immune system may reject the transplant.
Q2 a) If there is 0 mg of glucose in the urine, all the glucose filtered out of the blood must be reabsorbed. So:
    $5200 \times 0.9 = 4680$ mg hour^{-1}
    $4680 \div 60 = $ **78 mg min^{-1}**
    b) e.g. kidney failure / kidney infection / high blood pressure

Page 66 — Fact Recall Questions
Q1 It can be detected by measuring the glomerular filtration rate (GFR)/rate at which blood is filtered from the glomerulus into the Bowman's capsule.
Q2 Kidney infections can cause inflammation of the kidneys. This can damage the cells and create problems with reabsorption.
Q3 Any two from: e.g. waste products that the kidneys would normally remove begin to build up in the blood. / Fluid starts to accumulate in the tissues. / The balance of electrolytes (ions) in the body becomes unbalanced. / Long-term kidney failure can cause anaemia.
Q4 During haemodialysis, blood is passed through a dialysis machine. Blood flows on one side of a partially permeable membrane and dialysis fluid flows on the other side. The blood and dialysis fluid flow in opposite directions, which creates a concentration gradient. This means that waste products, excess water and electrolytes diffuse out of the blood into the dialysis fluid, restoring the balance of electrolytes in the blood.
Q5 Any two from: e.g. there's a risk of infection around the tube. / The patient has to have dialysis everyday, which can be inconvenient. / It can be an expensive treatment option.

5. Detecting Chemicals

Page 68 — Application Questions
Q1 Test strips use antibodies which are specific to different molecules/drugs and so only bind to a particular type of molecule/drug.
Q2 a) Codeine may have a similar structure to opiates or the breakdown products of opiates and so would bind to the same antibodies.
    b) The urine sample could be analysed using gas chromatography/mass spectrometry / GC/MS. This would determine whether the molecule producing the positive result was codeine or an illegal opiate.

Page 68 — Fact Recall Questions
Q1 human chorionic gonadotropin (hCG)
Q2 white / it won't change colour
    Remember, the test strip will only change colour in a positive pregnancy test (when hCG is present).
Q3 a) gas chromatography/mass spectrometry / GC/MS
    b) In gas chromatography the urine sample is vaporised and passed through a column containing a polymer. Different substances move through the column at different speeds, so substances in the urine sample separate out. The mass spectrometer converts them into ions, then separates the ions depending on their mass and charge. The results are analysed by a computer and the substances are identified by comparing them to the results of known substances.

Exam-style Questions — pages 70-71
1   D **(1 mark)**
    The urine of pregnant women contains the hormone human chorionic gonadotropin (hCG). This binds to monoclonal antibodies on the application area of the test stick, which are attached to coloured beads. As the urine moves up the stick, the hCG binds to more monoclonal antibodies that are fixed in position on the test strip. This concentrates the coloured beads in this area, so the strip changes colour.
2   a) Microvilli **(1 mark)**. The epithelium of the wall of the PCT has microvilli to provide a large surface area **(1 mark)** for the selective reabsorption of useful materials from the filtrate into the blood **(1 mark)**.
    b) i) glomerulus **(1 mark)**
       ii) E and F **(1 mark)**
       iii) The longer the loop of Henle, the more water that can be reabsorbed from the filtrate **(1 mark)**. When there's a longer ascending limb, more ions are actively pumped out into the medulla **(1 mark)**, which creates a really low water potential in the medulla **(1 mark)**. This means more water moves out of the nephron and collecting duct into the capillaries, giving very concentrated urine **(1 mark)**.
3   a) i)

Substance	TF/P ratio of 1.0
glucose	✓
serum albumin (protein)	X
sodium ions (Na⁺)	✓
urea	✓
red blood cells	X

    (2 marks for 3 correct answers, 1 mark for 2 correct)
    Don't let the numbers throw you in this question. All you're really being asked is which substances can cross the filtration barrier and which can't.

ii) The protein serum albumin is too large to pass through the filtration barrier into the tubular fluid, so it stays in the blood *(1 mark)*.

iii) E.g. high blood pressure can damage the capillaries in the glomeruli *(1 mark)*. This means larger molecules like proteins may be able to get through the capillary walls and into the tubular fluid *(1 mark)*. This could cause the concentration of proteins like serum albumin to be the same in the plasma as in the tubular fluid, producing a TF/P ratio of 1.0 *(1 mark)*.

b) i) $100 - 98.2 = 1.8\%$ of the filtrate is not reabsorbed so must be urine *(1 mark)*

1.8% of $1200 = \dfrac{1.8}{100} \times 1200$

$= 21.6 \text{ cm}^3 \text{ hour}^{-1}$ *(1 mark)*

$21.6 \times 24 = \textbf{518.4 cm}^3 \textbf{day}^{-1}$ *(1 mark)*

ii) The reabsorption of Na^+ from the kidney tubule back into the capillaries lowers the water potential of the medulla *(1 mark)*. This drives the reabsorption of water from the kidney tubule via osmosis *(1 mark)*. If the amount of sodium reabsorbed is decreased then the amount of water reabsorbed will also decrease *(1 mark)*. This means more water will be removed from the body in the urine, lowering the water content of the blood *(1 mark)*. This in turn will reduce blood volume, and therefore blood pressure *(1 mark)*.

c) i) hepatic vein *(1 mark)*

Remember, blood leaves the liver via the hepatic vein.

ii) In the ornithine cycle, ammonia produced from the deamination of amino acids *(1 mark)* is combined with carbon dioxide, which produces urea (and water) *(1 mark)*.

iii) E.g. weight loss *(1 mark)* / vomiting *(1 mark)*

Section 3 — Animal Responses

1. The Nervous System

Page 73-74 — Application Questions

Q1 a) cerebrum / (left) cerebral hemisphere
b) cerebellum
c) i) E.g. vision / hearing / learning / thinking
ii) E.g. controls breathing rate / controls heart rate
iii) E.g. maintains body temperature at a normal level / produces hormones that control the pituitary gland / involved in regulation of blood water potential

Q2 The cerebellum plays an important role in muscle coordination and coordination of balance. If the cerebellum is abnormally developed it could lead to problems with balance and coordination. This could make tasks such as throwing and catching difficult and make people more likely to fall over.

Page 75 — Application Question

Q1 a) The response is automatic and happens quickly.
b) Receptors in the hand/skin detect the heat stimulus and send a nerve impulse along a sensory neurone to a relay neurone in the CNS. The nerve impulse is then passed to a motor neurone, which carries the impulse to muscle cells (effectors) in the arm. The muscle cells contract to pull the hand away from the source of heat.

Page 75 — Fact Recall Questions

Q1 The brain and the spinal cord.
Q2 To control unconscious activities of the body.
Q3 Pituitary gland. It releases hormones and stimulates other glands to release their hormones.
Q4 At the base of the brain / top of the spinal cord.
Q5 A reflex action is where the body responds to a stimulus without making a conscious decision to respond.
Q6 Sensory nerve endings in the cornea detect the touch stimulus. A nerve impulse is sent along the sensory neurone to a relay neurone in the CNS. The impulse is then passed from the relay neurone to motor neurones. The motor neurones send impulses to the effectors, the (orbicularis oculi) muscles that move your eyelids. These muscles contract causing your eyelids to close quickly.

2. 'Fight or Flight' Response and Heart Rate

Page 78 — Application Questions

Q1 The chemoreceptors in a person with anaemia will detect low oxygen levels in the blood. The chemoreceptors will send impulses along sensory neurones to the cardiovascular centre, which will send impulses along sympathetic neurones. These neurones will secrete noradrenaline, which will bind to receptors on the sinoatrial node/SAN and cause the heart rate to increase.

Q2 a) The 'fight or flight' response. This response prepares the body for action in reaction to a threat.
b) The sympathetic nervous system.
c)

Response	Increased or decreased?
strength of contraction of heart muscle	increased
depth of breathing	increased
blood supply to the gut	decreased
blood supply to the skeletal muscles	increased
blood glucose level	increased
blood supply to the skin	decreased

Page 81 — Application Question

Q1 a) The chest strap of the heart rate monitor contains electrodes/sensors, which detect the electrical activity of the heart as it beats. The information picked up by the electrodes/sensors is transmitted wirelessly to a monitor worn on the wrist, which displays the data as a heart rate in beats per minute.

b) Null hypothesis: there is no significant difference between the mean heart rate of the people who were given caffeine and those who were not.
Find the mean for each data set:
Mean of data set 1 (caffeine) = $(71 + 90 + 82 + 76 + 88 + 85 + 66) \div 7 = \textbf{79.7}$
Mean of data set 2 (no caffeine) = $(58 + 72 + 65 + 67 + 60 + 74 + 78) \div 7 = \textbf{67.7}$
Find the standard deviation for each data set:

Data set 1	x	$(x - \bar{x})^2$
	71	75.7
	90	106.1
	82	5.3
	76	13.7
	88	68.9
	85	28.1
	66	187.7
	Total	**485.5**

Standard deviation for data set 1 = $\sqrt{(485.5 \div 6)} = \sqrt{(80.9)}$ = **9.0**

Data set 2	x	$(x - \bar{x})^2$
	58	94.1
	72	18.5
	65	7.3
	67	0.5
	60	59.3
	74	39.7
	78	106.1
	Total	**325.5**

Standard deviation for data set 2 = $\sqrt{(325.5 \div 6)} = \sqrt{(54.3)}$ = **7.4**
Use the formula for Student's t-test to calculate t.

$$t = \frac{79.7 - 67.7}{\sqrt{(9.0^2 / 7) + (7.4^2 / 7)}} = \frac{12}{4.4} = \textbf{2.7}$$

Remember you can ignore the sign for your t value — if you've used the data set after exposure to caffeine as data set 1 you won't get a negative value here anyway.
Degrees of freedom = $(7 + 7) - 2 = \textbf{12}$
The critical value at P = 0.05 is 2.179. The t value (2.7) is greater than 2.179. So the null hypothesis is rejected and the difference in heart rate between the people who were given caffeine and those who was not is concluded to be significant.
You are asked to use a 95% confidence limit — this means using a P value of 0.05 (or 5%).

Page 81 — Fact Recall Questions
Q1 hypothalamus
Q2 a) baroreceptor/pressure receptor
   b) aorta and carotid arteries
Q3 They cause the heart rate to slow down/decrease.
Q4 E.g. you could record the heart rate of a group of people under normal controlled conditions using pulse measurements or an electronic heart rate monitor. You could then record their heart rate shortly after a loud noise using the same method. You could determine if any change in heart rate was significant by using a statistical test.

3. Muscle Contraction
Page 84 — Application Questions
Q1 a) B
   b) C
   c) A and C
   d) B
Q2 Option 1. The A-band has stayed the same length, the I-band is shorter and the H-zone is shorter.
   Remember, the A-band is the length of the myosin filament and this doesn't get shorter during contraction. During contraction more of the actin filament slides over the myosin filament so the sections with only actin (the I-bands) get shorter and the sections with only myosin (the H-zones) get shorter too.

Page 86-87 — Application Questions
Q1 The influx of calcium ions triggers muscle contraction, so more calcium ions in the sarcoplasm would increase the strength of contraction of cardiac/heart muscle, which would help to pump more blood around the body of patients with heart failure.
Q2 a) i) X. The Ca^{2+} concentration is low, suggesting that the muscle is at rest. Muscle fibres are longest when they are relaxed.
      ii) Y. There is an influx of Ca^{2+} ions into the sarcoplasm following an action potential, and the Ca^{2+} ions bind to troponin.
      iii) Y. The Ca^{2+} ion concentration is high and Ca^{2+} ions activate ATPase.
   b) The Ca^{2+} ions are moved by active transport from the sarcoplasm back into sarcoplasmic reticulum, where they're stored.
   c) An action potential from a motor neurone stimulates a muscle cell and depolarises the sarcolemma. Depolarisation spreads down the T-tubules to the sarcoplasmic reticulum, causing the sarcoplasmic reticulum to release stored Ca^{2+} ions into the sarcoplasm.

Page 89 — Fact Recall Questions
Q1 a) They help to spread electrical impulses throughout the sarcoplasm so they reach all parts of the muscle fibre.
   b) It stores and releases calcium ions that are needed for muscle contraction.
   c) They provide the ATP that's needed for muscle contraction.
Q2 An A-band contains myosin filaments and some overlapping actin filaments. Under an electron microscope it appears as a dark band.
Q3 Myosin and actin filaments slide over one another to make the sarcomeres contract (the myofilaments themselves don't contract).
Q4 Troponin and tropomyosin.
Q5 Calcium ions in the sarcoplasm bind to troponin in the myofibrils, causing troponin to change shape. This pulls the attached tropomyosin out of the actin-myosin binding site on the actin filament. This exposes the binding site, which allows the myosin head to bind and form an actin-myosin cross bridge.
Q6 ATP is broken down by ATPase to provide the energy needed to move the myosin head from side to side, which pulls the actin filament along in a rowing action. ATP also provides the energy needed to break the myosin-actin cross bridge, so the myosin head detaches from the actin filament after it's moved.

Q7 a) Advantage: e.g. the ATP-CP system generates ATP very quickly / it can be used during short bursts of vigorous exercise / it's anaerobic/doesn't need oxygen / it's alactic/ doesn't form any lactate.

Disadvantage: e.g. CP runs out after only a few seconds.

b) Aerobic respiration and anaerobic respiration.

Q8

	Skeletal	Involuntary	Cardiac
Number of nuclei	many	one	one
Length	e.g. can be many centimetres	~ 0.2 mm	~ 0.1 mm
Shape of muscle fibres	e.g. long, straight shape	spindle-shaped (with pointed ends)	cylinder shaped / branched
Are cross-striations visible under a light microscope?	yes	no	yes (a few)

Q9 To pump blood around the body.

4. Nerve Impulses and Muscle Contraction

Page 92 — Application Questions

Q1 They might have weaker muscle responses than normal. If receptors are destroyed at neuromuscular junctions then there will be fewer receptors for acetylcholine/ACh to bind to, so there will be less chance of depolarisation being triggered in the postsynaptic cell. This means fewer muscle cells will be stimulated.

Q2 Galantamine would stop acetylcholinesterase/AChE breaking down acetylcholine/ACh, so there would be more ACh in the synaptic cleft and it would be there for longer. This means more nicotinic cholinergic receptors would be stimulated.

Q3 a) The athlete is relaxing/resting the muscle in his forearm.

b) The maximum amplitude of the electrical activity recorded during time period A is lower than it is during time period B. This could be because, e.g. the person is picking up a heavier weight during time period B. The amplitude of the trace increases because more motor units are required to lift the heavier weight.

c) The trace would continue to increase in amplitude because the brain would be trying to activate more motor units to generate the force needed to hold the weight up.

Page 92 — Fact Recall Questions

Q1 A synapse between a motor neurone and a muscle cell.

Q2 acetylcholine/ACh

Q3 It is broken down by the enzyme acetylcholinesterase (AChE), which is released from clefts on the postsynaptic membrane.

Q4 They may prevent the action potential from being passed on to the muscle, so the muscle won't contract. If they affect the muscles involved in breathing, e.g. the diaphragm and intercostal muscles, ventilation can't take place and the organism can't respire aerobically.

Q5 Two electrodes (sensors) are placed on the skin near the muscle to be monitored and a third electrode is placed on an inactive point on the body to act as a control. The electrodes are connected to an amplifier and a computer. When the muscle contracts, the electrodes detect the electrical activity caused by nervous impulses arriving at neuromuscular junctions in the muscle. Information from the electrodes is transferred to the computer where it is displayed on a screen.

Exam-style Questions — Pages 94-95

1 A *(1 mark)*

2 a) Medulla oblongata *(1 mark)*. Controls breathing and heart rate *(1 mark)*.

b) i) Y *(1 mark)*

Structure Y is the cerebellum.

ii) The somatic nervous system because this is the part of the nervous system that is responsible for conscious activities *(1 mark)*.

iii) In a reflex action the pathway of communication goes through the spinal cord/unconscious parts of the brain so doesn't involve the cerebellum *(1 mark)*.

iv) Acetylcholine is released at neuromuscular junctions and binds to nicotinic cholinergic receptors on the motor end plate/postsynaptic membrane *(1 mark)*, which triggers depolarisation in the muscle cell *(1 mark)*. If nicotinic cholinergic receptors are being blocked by trihexyphenidyl, less depolarisation of the muscle cells will occur and the muscle won't be able to contract *(1 mark)*.

3 a) i) The adrenal glands / adrenal medulla *(1 mark)*.

ii) E.g. it causes the cardiac muscle to contract more frequently *(1 mark)* and with more force *(1 mark)*.

iii) E.g. muscles in the arterioles supplying the skin and gut constrict, and muscles in the arterioles supplying the heart, lungs and skeletal muscles dilate *(1 mark)*. This means that blood is diverted from the skin and gut to the heart, lungs and skeletal muscles *(1 mark)*. This increases blood flow to skeletal muscles (e.g. in the legs), making them ready for action *(1 mark)*.

b) Cardiac muscle is composed of branched *(1 mark)*, cylinder-shaped muscle fibres *(1 mark)* that are connected by intercalated discs *(1 mark)*. The muscle fibres are uninucleate *(1 mark)*. *(Maximum of 2 marks available.)*

4 a) A — H-zone *(1 mark)*, B — I-band *(1 mark)*, C — A-band *(1 mark)*

b) A/the H-zone and B/the I-band will appear longer *(1 mark)* and C/the A-band will stay the same length *(1 mark)*.

c) i) Myosin filaments have globular heads that are hinged *(1 mark)*. Each myosin head has a binding site for actin *(1 mark)* and a binding site for ATP *(1 mark)*.

ii) **5-6 marks:**
The answer explains fully how energy released from ATP enables the movement of the myosin filament and is required for the breaking of the actin-myosin cross bridge.
The answer has a clear and logical structure.
The information given is relevant and detailed.
3-4 marks:
The answer explains briefly how energy released from ATP enables the movement of the myosin filament and is required for the breaking of the actin-myosin cross bridge.
The answer has some structure. Most of the information given is relevant and there is some detail involved.
1-2 marks:
The answer includes a basic explanation as to either how energy released from ATP enables the movement of the myosin filament or how it is required for the breaking of the actin-myosin cross bridge.
The answer has no clear structure. The information given is basic and lacking in detail. It may not all be relevant.
0 marks:
No relevant information is given.
Here are some points your answer may include:
The myosin head binds to the actin filament and forms an actin-myosin cross bridge. Energy released from ATP moves the myosin head to the side, which pulls the actin filament along in a rowing action/ power stroke. ATP also provides the energy to break the actin-myosin cross bridge so the myosin head detaches from the actin filament after it's moved. The myosin head then returns to it's starting position and reattaches to a different binding site further along the actin filament. As the cycle is repeated, the myosin head pulls the actin filament along, causing the muscle to contract.

d) i) ATP is made by phosphorylating ADP *(1 mark)* with a phosphate group taken from creatine phosphate *(1 mark)*.
Remember, the ATP-creatine phosphate (CP) system is used during short bursts of vigorous exercise.
ii) ATP is generated very quickly *(1 mark)*. / No oxygen is needed / the process is anaerobic *(1 mark)*. / The process is alactic / no lactate is formed *(1 mark)*.

e) Any three from: e.g. a skeletal muscle fibre/muscle fibre in the biceps is multinucleate whereas an involuntary muscle fibre/muscle fibre in a blood vessel is uninucleate *(1 mark)*. / A skeletal muscle fibre/muscle fibre in the biceps is much longer than an involuntary muscle fibre/ muscle fibre in a blood vessel *(1 mark)*. / A skeletal muscle fibre/muscle fibre in the biceps has a long, straight shape whereas an involuntary muscle fibre/ muscle fibre in a blood vessel is spindle-shaped with pointed ends *(1 mark)*. / A skeletal muscle fibre/muscle fibre in the biceps has cross-striations visible under a microscope whereas involuntary muscle/muscle in a blood vessel doesn't *(1 mark)*. *(Maximum of 3 marks available.)*
Always read exam questions carefully — this one asks for three structural differences, so you won't get marks for comparing the functions.

Section 4 — Plant Responses and Hormones

1. Plant Responses

Pages 100-101 — Application Questions
Q1 a) The auxin will have diffused straight down from the sponge into the left-hand side of the shoot. This will have stimulated the cells on this side to elongate, so the shoot grew towards the right.
b) Equal amounts of auxin will have diffused down both sides, making all the cells elongate at the same rate.
c) The shoots in experiment B were exposed to a light source. This will have caused the auxin to diffuse into the shoot and accumulate on the shaded side (left-hand side) regardless of where the sponge was placed. All the shoots grew towards the right because most auxin accumulated on the left, stimulating cell elongation there.
d) Sponge D was a negative control (a sponge soaked in water rather than auxin), included to show that it was the auxin having an effect and nothing else.
e) The sponges were soaked in glucose so that the shoots would have energy to grow in the dark, as no photosynthesis can take place.
Sponges from experiment B were also soaked in glucose, even though they were in the light, so were able to photosynthesise. This is done in order to keep the set-up of both experiments as similar as possible.
Q2 a) positive
The shoot is bending <u>towards</u> the stimulus.
b) Y because this is where cell elongation is taking place, causing the shoot to bend towards the opposite side.

Page 101 — Fact Recall Questions
Q1 Anything harmful that's natural, but non-living.
Q2 E.g. producing toxic chemicals (e.g. tannins and alkaloids) to act as chemical defences / releasing pheromones to signal to other organisms / folding up in response to being touched.
Q3 Growth away from a (directional) stimulus.
Q4 phototropism
Q5 The growing regions of the plant / shoot and root tips.
Q6 inhibit growth
Q7 E.g. indoleacetic acid/IAA
Q8 a) by active transport and diffusion
b) via the phloem
Q9 a) Auxins move to the more shaded parts of the shoot. This means the cells on the shaded part of the shoot grow faster than the cells most exposed to light. This pattern of growth causes the shoot to bend towards the light.
b) Auxins move to the underside of roots. This means the growth of cells on the underside of the root is inhibited so they don't grow as quickly as the cells on the upper side. This pattern of growth causes the root to grow downwards in the same direction as gravity.

2. The Effects of Plant Hormones

Page 106 — Application Questions
Q1 To minimise the differences between plants at the start of the experiment. The more variables the student controls, the more valid her results will be. Choosing plants of a similar age, height, mass, etc., makes it less likely that any differences observed between the three experimental conditions will result from differences between the plants.

Q2 The plants watered with a 100 mg dm⁻³ gibberellin solution. Gibberellins are growth hormones that stimulate the stems of plants to grow by stem elongation, so the higher the concentration of gibberellin, the taller the plant will grow. *This is only true up to a point though — as the concentration of gibberellin gets higher, the effect it has on the plant changes and it doesn't stimulate the plant to grow any further.*

Q3 a) Total growth = 26 cm – 8 cm = 18 cm
6 weeks = 6 × 7 days = 42 days
Average growth rate = 18 ÷ 42 = **0.43 cm day⁻¹**
b) Total growth = 18 cm
Percentage increase = (18 ÷ 8) × 100 = 2.25 × 100 = **225%**
To calculate percentage increase, divide the total growth by the initial plant height and then multiply your answer by 100.

Page 106 — Fact Recall Questions

Q1 It saves the plants' energy and prevents side shoots from the same plant competing with the shoot tip for light. This allows a plant in an area where there are many other plants to grow tall very fast, past smaller plants, to reach the sunlight (instead of wasting energy growing side shoots).

Q2 Gibberellins stimulate seed germination by triggering the breakdown of starch into glucose in the seed. The plant embryo in the seed can then use the glucose to begin respiring and release the energy it needs to grow.

Q3 a) Losing their leaves helps plants to conserve water, which is lost from the leaves.
Remember, in winter it might be difficult for plants to absorb water from the soil because the soil water may be frozen.
b) Auxins inhibit leaf loss.
c) Ethene stimulates the cells in the abscission layer to expand, breaking the cells walls and causing the leaf to fall off.

Q4 a) guard cells
b) abscisic acid/ABA

Q5 Ethene stimulates enzymes that break down cell walls, break down chlorophyll and convert starch into sugars. This makes the fruit ripen.

Exam-style Questions — pages 108-109

1 B *(1 mark)*
2 a) phototropism *(1 mark)*
b) The seedling should have been from a Goosegrass plant and potted in soil from the same source *(1 mark)*. There should have been no lamp/light from any direction present *(1 mark)*.
c) E.g. to make sure that only the variable being tested (light intensity) was changing *(1 mark)*. / To keep all variables other than light intensity the same *(1 mark)*.
d) Seedling A will be bent to the right because it will have grown towards the light *(1 mark)*. Seedling B will have grown straight up because the rotation of the seedling means that the light is not continuously coming from one direction *(1 mark)*. Seedling C will be bent towards the right but may have a kink in, so that it is not a smooth bend because it will have grown to the right for five days, then to the left for five days and to the right again for the last five days, as the position of the light source was changed during the experiment *(1 mark)*.
e) IAA/auxins moved to the more shaded parts of the plant/shoots *(1 mark)*. This meant the shaded parts of the shoot grew faster/elongated more than the parts exposed to light *(1 mark)*. This uneven growth led to the shoots bending towards the light *(1 mark)*.

3 a) lateral buds *(1 mark)*
b) i) Removing bud 1 from the plant means that the plant would no longer produce auxins *(1 mark)*. Auxins cause apical dominance, inhibiting the growth of side shoots from lateral buds, so removing bud 1 would allow side shoots to develop from lateral buds/buds 2-5 by cell division and cell elongation *(1 mark)*.
ii) Applying a source of auxin (the gel) to where the tip had been removed would result in the inhibition of side shoot development, so side shoots would not develop from lateral buds/buds 2-5 *(1 mark)*.
iii) E.g. as a source of rooting hormones / a substance for promoting root growth in a plant stem cutting *(1 mark)*.
c) E.g. ethene stimulates ripening, so exposing the plants to ethene gas would help to speed up the ripening of the fruits/tomatoes and help to ensure that they all ripen at roughly the same time/uniformly for harvesting *(1 mark)*.
4 a) pheromones *(1 mark)*
b) E.g. tannins have a bitter taste *(1 mark)*. / In some herbivores, such as cattle, they can bind to proteins in the gut, making the plant hard to digest *(1 mark)*.
c) E.g. boosting the levels of defensive chemicals that crop plants produce might enable their defences against herbivory to be more effective, resulting in less tissue damage *(1 mark)*.

Section 5 — Photosynthesis

1. Storing and Releasing Energy

Page 112 — Application Question

Q1 a) 07:30 and 16:30
Anything between 07:20 and 07:40 would be acceptable for the first compensation point. Anything between 16:20 and 16:40 would be OK for the second one.
b) The rate of photosynthesis depends partly on the intensity of light. 07:30 is shortly after the Sun has risen. The light intensity has increased to a level where the rate of photosynthesis has increased to match the rate of respiration. 16:30 is shortly before the Sun completely sets. The light intensity has decreased to a level where the rate of photosynthesis has decreased to match the rate of respiration.

Page 112 — Fact Recall Questions

Q1 Any three from, e.g. photosynthesis / active transport / DNA replication / cell division.
Q2 Carbon dioxide and water are products of respiration and are also raw materials used in photosynthesis. Photosynthesis produces oxygen and glucose, which are raw materials used in respiration.
Q3 ATP is the immediate source of energy in a cell.
Q4 A molecule of ATP is made from adenine, a ribose sugar and three phosphate groups.
If you're asked to describe the structure of ATP in the exam, make sure you're specific and put that it's a 'ribose sugar'. If you just put 'sugar' you won't get the mark.
Q5 a) ADP and P$_i$
b) hydrolysis

2. Photosynthesis and the Light-dependent Reaction

Page 117 — Application Questions

Q1 a) proton/hydrogen ion/H^+

b) Because this forms a proton gradient across the membrane. Protons move down their concentration gradient, into the stroma, via an enzyme called ATP synthase. The energy from this movement combines ADP and inorganic phosphate (P_i) to form ATP.

Q2 PSII / photosystem II

Q3 D

Q4 ATP

Cyclic photophosphorylation doesn't produce any reduced NADP or O_2 — just ATP.

Page 117 — Fact Recall Questions

Q1 A – circular DNA

B – outer membrane of envelope

C – inner membrane of envelope

D – stroma

E – granum

F – thylakoid

G – thylakoid membrane

H – lamella

I – starch grain

Q2 a) Coloured substances that absorb the light energy needed for photosynthesis.

b) chlorophyll a

Q3 Accessory pigments that surround the reaction centres. They transfer light energy to the reaction centres to boost the energy available for electron excitement to take place.

Q4 Photosystem I and photosystem II / PSI and PSII

Q5 hydrogen

Q6 the thylakoid membranes

Q7 ATP and reduced NADP

In the exam, always read the question very carefully. For example, this question didn't ask for all the products of the light-dependent reaction — it specifically asked for the products that are needed for the light-independent reaction. So if you put oxygen it would be wrong because it's not needed for the light-independent reaction.

Q8 The process of adding phosphate to a molecule using light

Q9 A chain of proteins through which excited electrons flow.

Q10 a) protons, electrons and oxygen

b) To replace excited electrons in PSII.

Q11 a) Photosystems: photosystem I/PSI and photosystem II/PSII
Products: ATP, reduced NADP and oxygen

b) Photosystem: photosystem I/PSI

Product: ATP

3. Light-independent Reaction

Page 120 — Application Questions

Q1 X = ribulose bisphosphate (RuBP)

Y = glycerate 3-phosphate (GP)

Z = triose phosphate (TP)

Q2 A = ribulose bisphosphate carboxylase (RuBisCO)

B = reduced NADP

Q3

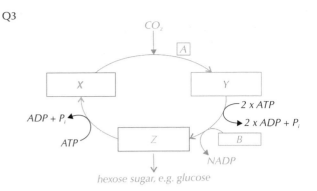

Page 120 — Fact Recall Questions

Q1 It is combined with ribulose bisphosphate to form glycerate 3-phosphate.

Q2 a)

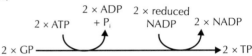

(GP is glycerate 3-phosphate and TP is triose phosphate)

b) reduction

Although the conversion of GP to TP is a reduction reaction, ATP and reduced NADP are both oxidised.

Q3 In the Calvin cycle ATP is needed for the reduction of glycerate 3-phosphate (GP) to triose phosphate (TP). It's also needed for the regeneration of ribulose bisphosphate (RuBP) from triose phosphate.

Q4 five

Q5 a) six

Six turns of the Calvin cycle produces 12 molecules of triose phosphate (TP). Ten of these molecules (5 out of every 6) are used to make ribulose bisphosphate (RuBP) and two are used to make one hexose sugar.

b) 18

Six turns of cycle × 3 ATP molecules per turn = 18 ATP

c) 12

Six turns of cycle × 2 reduced NADP molecules per turn = 12 reduced NADP

Q6 a) Two triose phosphate molecules are joined together to produce a hexose sugar. Large carbohydrates are then made by joining the hexose sugars together.

b) Lipids are made from glycerol and fatty acids. Glycerol is synthesised from triose phosphate, while fatty acids are made from glycerate 3-phosphate.

c) Some amino acids are made from glycerate 3-phosphate.

4. Limiting Factors in Photosynthesis

Page 125 — Application Questions

Q1 a) Outside plants week 2 height = 12 cm
(accept 11-14 cm).
Outside plants week 5 height = 30 cm
Difference in plant height = 30 – 12 = 18 cm
% difference in plant height =
(difference ÷ original) × 100 = (18 ÷ 12) × 100 = **150%**
Greenhouse plants week 2 height = 28 cm
(accept 26-29 cm).
Greenhouse plants week 5 height = 45 cm
(accept 44-46 cm).
Difference in plant height = 45 – 28 = 17 cm
% difference in plant height = (17 ÷ 28) × 100 = **60.7%**

b) E.g. the farmer may have increased the carbon dioxide concentration in the greenhouse by burning a small amount of propane in a carbon dioxide generator. / The farmer may have used lamps to provide light at night. / The farmer may have made use of heaters and cooling systems in order to keep a constant optimum temperature.

Q2 a) When plants don't have enough water, their stomata close to preserve what water they do have. This can lead to a decrease in the rate of photosynthesis because less CO_2 is able to enter the leaves, so CO_2 becomes a limiting factor.

b) Unlike electric heaters, the paraffin heaters would produce CO_2, which would increase the atmospheric CO_2 concentration of the greenhouse. The loss of this source of CO_2 could result in the atmospheric CO_2 concentration decreasing to a level where it becomes a limiting factor to photosynthesis.

Q3 a) Plant B. This is because plant A has been under a green light, which is reflected by the plant, reducing the rate of photosynthesis. However, plant B has been under blue light, which is absorbed by photosynthetic pigments, increasing the rate of photosynthesis. This means plant B will have made more glucose and so had more energy for growth.

b) E.g. even though the plant is getting enough light and water, it is exposed to high temperatures of around 40 °C. At these temperatures its stomata may close to avoid losing too much water. This means less carbon dioxide can enter the leaf, so photosynthesis will slow right down. In turn, the plant will produce much less glucose, which means it'll have much less energy to carry out all its life processes and may die.

Page 125 — Fact Recall Questions

Q1 A low light intensity will slow down the light-dependent reaction, so that less ATP and reduced NADP are produced. This means there will be less ATP and reduced NADP entering the Calvin cycle, which means the Calvin cycle will slow down.

Q2 a) The concentration of RuBP will decrease.
The level of RuBP decreases at low light intensities because the light-dependent reaction is slower, so less ATP and reduced NADP are produced and the conversion of GP to TP and RuBP is slower.

b) The concentration of RuBP will decrease.
The level of RuBP decreases at low temperatures because the enzymes in the Calvin cycle work more slowly.

c) The concentration of RuBP will increase.
The level of RuBP increases at low CO_2 concentrations because there is less CO_2 and so less RuBP will be combined with CO_2 to produce GP.

5. Photosynthesis Experiments

Page 127 — Application Question

Q1 a) R_f value = $\dfrac{\text{distance moved by the solute}}{\text{distance moved by the solvent}}$
= 7.90 cm ÷ 9.00 cm = **0.878** (3 s.f.)

b) Using paper chromatography means a different stationary phase and solvent would have been used, which would have affected the R_f values. An R_f value for a pigment is obtained under specific conditions.

Page 128 — Fact Recall Question

Q1 A test tube containing the pondweed and water is connected to a capillary tube full of water, which is connected to a syringe. A source of white light is placed at a specific distance from the pondweed. The pondweed is left to photosynthesise for a set amount of time. At the end of the experiment, the syringe is used to draw the gas bubble in the tube up alongside a ruler and the length of the gas bubble (proportional to the volume of O_2) is measured. The experiment is repeated and the average length of gas bubble is calculated. The whole experiment is then repeated with the light source placed at different distances from the pondweed.

Exam-style Questions — pages 130-131

1 a) i) A – stroma *(1 mark)*
B – thylakoid membrane / lamella *(1 mark)*
C – outer membrane of envelope *(1 mark)*
ii) A/stroma *(1 mark)*

b) Primary pigments are reaction centres, where electrons are excited during the light-dependent reaction *(1 mark)*. Accessory pigments make up light-harvesting systems, which surround reaction centres and transfer light energy to them to boost the energy available for electron excitement to take place *(1 mark)*.

c) i) **5-6 marks:**
A full description of all the steps in the process is given in the correct order, including an explanation of the involvement of ATP, hydrogen ions, reduced NADP and ribulose bisphosphate carboxylase (RuBisCO) in the process.
The answer has a clear and logical structure.
The information given is relevant and detailed.
3-4 marks:
Some of the steps are described and they are in the correct order, but the answer is incomplete. The answer includes an explanation of the involvement of at least one from ATP, hydrogen ions, reduced NADP and ribulose bisphosphate carboxylase (RuBisCO). The answer has some structure. Most of the information given is relevant and there is some detail involved.
1-2 marks:
A few of the steps in the process are described briefly and not necessarily in the right order.
The answer has no clear structure. The information given is basic and lacking in detail. It may not all be relevant.
0 marks:
No relevant information is given.
Here are some points your answer may include:
Carbon dioxide enters the leaf through the stomata and diffuses into the stroma of the chloroplast. Here, it's combined with ribulose bisphosphate (RuBP), a 5-carbon compound. This gives an unstable 6-carbon compound, which quickly breaks down into two molecules of glycerate 3-phosphate (GP). Ribulose bisphosphate carboxylase (RuBisCO) catalyses the reaction between carbon dioxide and RuBP. GP is then reduced to the 3-carbon compound called triose phosphate (TP), which glucose is synthesised from. ATP from the light-dependent reaction provides the energy to do this. This reaction also requires H+ ions, which come from reduced NADP.

ii) ATP is used *(1 mark)* to convert the five molecules of triose phosphate/TP/the 3-carbon compound back into ribulose bisphosphate/RuBP *(1 mark)*.

d) respiration *(1 mark)*

2 a) In tube B light energy was absorbed by photosystem I in the chloroplasts *(1 mark)* and electrons were excited to a very high energy level *(1 mark)*. Then these excited electrons were transferred to DNIP to produce reduced DNIP *(1 mark)*.

NADP is a coenzyme that can accept from or give hydrogen (and therefore electrons) to another molecule. The question says DNIP is an artificial hydrogen acceptor. This means it can accept hydrogen (and therefore electrons) from other molecules too — it works in the same way as NADP.

b) Tube A receives no light energy so the light-dependent reaction of photosynthesis can't take place *(1 mark)*. The chloroplasts in test tube C have been boiled, which will have denatured the enzymes in the chloroplast, therefore preventing photosynthesis from taking place *(1 mark)*.

c) Glycerate 3-phosphate/GP is reduced to triose phosphate/TP *(1 mark)* using hydrogen ions from reduced NADP *(1 mark)*.

3 a) No. The student hasn't taken into account the amount of oxygen that the plant has used for respiration *(1 mark)*.

b) i) In experiment 1, the rate of photosynthesis increased with increasing light intensity *(1 mark)*. However, after about 100 µmoles m^{-2} s^{-1} the rate of photosynthesis levelled off *(1 mark)* because light intensity was no longer the limiting factor *(1 mark)*.

ii) The limiting factor in experiment 2 must be temperature because the graph for experiment 3 levels off at a higher point *(1 mark)* but experiment 3 had the same light intensity and CO_2 concentration as experiment 2 *(1 mark)*.

c) The level of RuBP will have increased because there would have been less CO_2 to combine with RuBP to form GP / because RuBP is still being made but isn't being used up *(1 mark)*. The level of TP will have decreased because it's being used up to make RuBP but isn't being remade *(1 mark)*.

If you get a question like this in the exam, make sure you think of the substances before the reactant in the cycle as well as those that come after it.

Section 6 — Respiration

1. Aerobic Respiration

Page 133 — Application Questions

Q1 a) ATP
    b) reduced NAD
    c) inorganic phosphate (P_i)
    d) hexose bisphosphate
    e) triose phosphate
    f) H$^+$ ions/hydrogen ions

Q2 a) phosphorylation
    b) oxidation

Q3 The formation of hexose phosphate in the first part of the reaction and the formation of 4ATP from 4ADP + 4P_i in the second part of the reaction.

Page 135 — Application Questions

Q1 a) oxaloacetate = 4C, citrate = 6C
    b) Decarboxylation and dehydrogenation occur, producing one molecule of reduced FAD and two of reduced NAD. ATP is produced by substrate-level phosphorylation.

Q2 24
    Two molecules of carbon dioxide are produced per turn of the Krebs cycle and the Krebs cycle turns twice for each molecule of glucose. So for one molecule of glucose four molecules of carbon dioxide are produced. Therefore if six molecules of glucose were respired, 24 (6 x 4) molecules of carbon dioxide would be produced in the Krebs cycle.

Q3 Acetyl coenzyme A can enter the Krebs cycle, leading to the formation of reduced coenzymes, which are then used in oxidative phosphorylation

Page 136 — Application Questions

Q1 Carrier 1 will be in a reduced state because it has received electrons from reduced NAD but can't pass them on. Carrier 3 will be in an oxidised state because it has passed its electrons onto oxygen, but hasn't received any more from carrier 2.
    If a substance gains electrons it is reduced. If a substance loses electrons it is oxidised.

Q2 Antimycin A inhibits carrier 2 and so stops electrons moving down the electron transport chain. This means no more energy will be lost from electrons moving down the chain, so H$^+$ ions will not be transported across the inner mitochondrial membrane and the electrochemical gradient across the membrane won't be maintained. This means the synthesis of ATP by ATP synthase will stop. If a fish can't produce ATP it will die as energy from ATP is needed to fuel all biological processes.
    Don't write that H$^+$ ions/protons are prevented from moving into or out of the inner mitochondrial membrane — they're prevented from moving across it.

Page 138 — Fact Recall Questions

Q1 In the cytoplasm.

Q2 ATP is used to phosphorylate glucose, making triose phosphate.

Q3 By active transport.

Q4 In the mitochondrial matrix.

Q5 a) Pyruvate is decarboxylated — one carbon atom is removed from pyruvate in the form of carbon dioxide. Then NAD is reduced to NADH — it collects hydrogen from pyruvate, changing pyruvate into acetate.
    b) It combines with acetate to form acetyl coenzyme A.
    c) Acetyl coenzyme A enters the Krebs cycle. Reduced NAD is used in oxidative phosphorylation. Carbon dioxide is released as a waste product.

Q6 substrate-level phosphorylation

Q7 a) It is reused in the link reaction.
    b) It is regenerated for use in the next Krebs cycle.

Q8 They lose energy.

Q9 It's the process of ATP production driven by the movement of H$^+$ ions across a membrane (due to electrons moving down an electron transport chain).

Q10 oxygen

Q11 E.g. the conversion of pyruvate to acetate in the link reaction. / The conversion of citrate to the 5-carbon compound in the Krebs cycle. / The conversion of the 5-carbon compound to oxaloacetate in the Krebs cycle.
    Every time CO_2 is lost in a reaction, decarboxylation is happening.

Q12

Substance	Glycolysis	Link reaction	Krebs cycle	Oxidative phosphorylation
ATP	X		X	X
reduced NAD	X	X	X	
reduced FAD			X	
CO$_2$		X	X	

Remember, oxidative phosphorylation also produces (oxidised) NAD and FAD, and water.

2. Anaerobic Respiration

Page 140 — Application Questions
Q1 a) anaerobically
   b) two
   c)

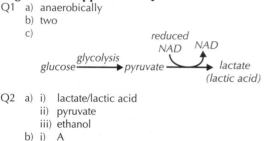

Q2 a) i) lactate/lactic acid
      ii) pyruvate
      iii) ethanol
   b) i) A
      ii) B
      iii) A
   c) two

Page 140 — Fact Recall Questions
Q1 In the cytoplasm.
Q2 E.g. both start with glycolysis. / Both produce ATP. / Both require NAD.
Q3 a) E.g. mammals / some bacteria
   b) E.g. yeast / plants
Q4 Reduced NAD (from glycolysis) transfers hydrogen to pyruvate to form lactate and NAD.
Q5 Reduced NAD (from glycolysis) transfers hydrogen to ethanal to form ethanol and NAD.
Q6 a) 30 fewer ATP
   If aerobic respiration can produce 32 molecules of ATP per molecule of glucose and anaerobic respiration produces 2 molecules of ATP, then 32 – 2 = 30 fewer.
   b) Because anaerobic respiration only includes one energy-releasing stage (glycolysis), whereas aerobic respiration includes more energy-releasing stages (Krebs cycle, oxidative phosphorylation).

3. Respiratory Substrates

Page 142 — Application Questions
Q1 a) RQ = molecules of CO$_2$ released ÷ molecules of O$_2$ consumed = 57 ÷ 80 = **0.71**
   b) A lipid because lipids have a respiratory quotient of 0.7.
   Carbohydrates have an RQ of 1 and proteins have an RQ of 0.9.
Q2 a) RQ = volume of CO$_2$ released ÷ volume of O$_2$ consumed = 180 ÷ 250 = **0.72**
   b) E.g. more carbohydrates are being respired. / Fewer fats are being respired.
   An increase or decrease in an organism's RQ doesn't mean that it is respiring more or less substrate overall — it just means that the type of substrate being respired has changed.

Page 142 — Fact Recall Questions
Q1 Any biological molecule that can be broken down in respiration to release energy.
Q2 Because lipids contain more hydrogen atoms per unit of mass than carbohydrates or proteins. Hydrogen atoms are required for the oxidative phosphorylation stage of aerobic respiration, in which most ATP is synthesised, so respiratory substrates that contain more hydrogen atoms per unit of mass will cause more ATP to be produced when respired.
Q3 carbohydrates
Q4 They can be used to determine what kind of respiratory substrates an organism is respiring and what type of respiration it's using.

4. Respiration Experiments

Pages 144-145 — Application Question
Q1 a) E.g. the scientist could have set up a test tube containing a known volume and concentration of substrate (e.g. glucose) solution and a buffer solution at specific pH. She could then have added a known mass of dried yeast of species A to the tube and stirred until the yeast dissolved. Next, she could have sealed the test tube with a bung and attached it via a tube to a gas syringe in order to catch the CO$_2$ produced by the respiring yeast. At regular intervals (e.g. every minute) for a set amount of time (e.g. 10 minutes), the scientist could have recorded the volume of gas present in the gas syringe. By repeating the experiment (e.g. three times) at this pH, she could then have calculated the mean rate of CO$_2$ production at this pH. She could then have repeated the experiment at a range of pH levels by using buffer solutions of different pH levels. She could have done the same thing for species B.
   b) Respiration is a series of reactions controlled by enzymes. The enzymes used in respiration by the different species of yeast may have different optimum pH levels, at which they are able to catalyse the reactions most effectively.
   c) Mean rate of CO$_2$ production of species A at pH 5.5 = 1.75 cm^3 min^{-1}
   Anything between 1.7 and 1.8 cm^3 would be acceptable here.
   Mean rate of CO$_2$ production of species B at pH 5.5 = 3.75 cm^3 min^{-1}
   Anything between 3.7 and 3.8 cm^3 would be acceptable here.
   Percentage change in rate from species A to species B = ((1.75 – 3.75) ÷ 1.75) × 100 = **114% faster**
   Your final answer may differ a little depending on what you got for the mean rates of CO$_2$ production for the two species.
   d) Boiled yeast won't respire as the boiling will have killed it. Therefore, it acts as a negative control to show that the CO$_2$ production is a result of the respiring yeast and not any other reactions that may be happening in the tube.

Page 146 — Fact Recall Questions
Q1 To stop oxygen getting into the yeast solution, forcing the yeast to respire anaerobically.
Q2 E.g. prepare and treat a test tube in the same way as the others in the investigation, but do not put any yeast in it.
Q3 It absorbs any CO$_2$ produced by the respiring organisms.
Q4 10 g
   You know the answer here is 10 g because the mass of the peas and the mass of the glass beads in the control tube have to be the same.

Exam-style Questions — pages 148-149

1   a) i)   A – mitochondrial matrix *(1 mark)*
            B – crista/inner mitochondrial membrane *(1 mark)*
            C – outer mitochondrial membrane *(1 mark)*
        ii) There is less folding of the inner membrane/fewer crista *(1 mark)*.
    b) i)   Because glycolysis takes place in the cytoplasm of the cell *(1 mark)*.

Because glycolysis takes place in the cytoplasm and not the mitochondria, it doesn't matter whether you have functioning mitochondria or not — glycolysis can still happen.

        ii) Any three from: Glucose is phosphorylated by adding a phosphate from a molecule of ATP *(1 mark)*. / This creates one molecule of hexose phosphate *(1 mark)*. / Hexose phosphate is phosphorylated by ATP to form hexose bisphosphate *(1 mark)*. / Two molecules of ADP are produced overall *(1 mark)*.
        iii) In the oxidation of triose phosphate to pyruvate, NAD collects the hydrogen ions from triose phosphate *(1 mark)*, forming reduced NAD *(1 mark)*.
    c) RQ = molecules of CO_2 released ÷ molecules of O_2 consumed = 6 ÷ 7 = **0.86**
        (2 marks for correct answer, otherwise 1 mark for correct working).

2   D *(1 mark)*
3   B *(1 mark)*
4   a) i)   The oxidation of triose phosphate to pyruvate produces one molecule of reduced NAD *(1 mark)*. The conversion of pyruvate to acetate produces one molecule of reduced NAD *(1 mark)*. The conversion of citrate to a 5-carbon compound in the Krebs cycle produces one molecule of reduced NAD *(1 mark)*. The conversion of this 5-carbon compound to oxaloacetate produces another two molecules of reduced NAD *(1 mark)* and one molecule of reduced FAD *(1 mark)*.
        ii) The electrons move along the electron transport chain *(1 mark)* losing energy at each electron carrier *(1 mark)*. Finally they are passed onto oxygen as it is the final electron acceptor *(1 mark)*.
    b) There would be no electrochemical gradient produced across the inner mitochondrial membrane *(1 mark)*. This means there would be no movement of ions across the mitochondrial membrane to drive ATP synthase *(1 mark)* so no ATP would be made *(1 mark)*. The cells would only get ATP from anaerobic respiration *(1 mark)*.

Even though H⁺ ions will still be pumped across the inner mitochondrial membrane into the intermembrane space, the uncoupler will be moving them back into the matrix at the same time — so no gradient would be produced.

Module 6

Section 1 — Cellular Control

1. Regulating Gene Expression

Page 153 — Application Questions

Q1 Any three from, e.g. temperature / the presence of other nutrients in the medium / the length of time the bacteria were left for / volume of culture / number of bacteria / amount of lactose/glucose added.

Q2 The normal *E. coli* have been included as a negative control. They show that any differences in the results were down to the mutations and nothing else.

Q3 a) E.g. Mutant 1 always produces mRNA and β-galactosidase, even in the absence of lactose. This may mean that Mutant 1 has a faulty lac repressor. If the repressor is faulty, it may not be able to bind to the operator and block transcription even in the absence of lactose (so mRNA and β-galactosidase are always produced).
    b) E.g. in Mutant 2, mRNA is produced in the presence of lactose, but active β-galactosidase isn't. This suggests that Mutant 2 is producing faulty β-galactosidase (e.g. because a mutation has affected its active site) / Mutant 2 isn't producing any β-galactosidase (e.g. because the mutation has affected a protein involved in translation).

Q4 They are reproducible.

Page 153 — Fact Recall Questions

Q1 a) A protein that binds to DNA and switches genes on or off by increasing or decreasing the rate of transcription.
    b) Activators — start/activate transcription. Repressors — stop/repress transcription.
    c) Specific DNA sites near the start of their target genes/the genes they control the expression of.

Q2 a) These code for useful proteins, e.g. enzymes.
    b) These include a promoter (a DNA sequence located before the structural genes that RNA polymerase binds to) and an operator (a DNA sequence that transcription factors bind to).
    c) This codes for a transcription factor.

Q3 The *lac* operon contains a regulatory gene (lacI), control elements and three structural genes (lacZ, lacY and lacA). When lactose is not present, lacI produces the lac repressor, which binds to the operator and blocks the transcription of lacZ, lacY and lacA. This means no mRNA is produced so no proteins are made.

Q4 Introns are removed / mature mRNA is produced.

Q5 Molecules like hormones can bind to cell membranes. This triggers the production of cyclic AMP (cAMP) within the cell. cAMP then activates proteins in the cell by changing their 3D structure.

2. Body Plans

Page 156 — Application Questions

Q1 a) Cells are broken down/killed.
    b) E.g. it may refine plant parts created by mitosis and differentiation by removing unwanted structures.

Q2 a) Hox genes code for proteins that control the development of the body plan. The ag-1 mutation alters the body plan (by causing petals to grow in place of stamens), so ag-1 must be a Hox gene.
    b) A homeobox sequence codes for a part of the protein called the homeodomain. The homeodomain binds to specific sites on DNA, enabling the protein to work as a transcription factor. The protein binds to DNA at the start of developmental genes, activating or repressing transcription and so altering the production of proteins involved in the development of the body plan.
    c) Because other organisms (e.g. animals and fungi) have similar Hox genes to plants, so the development of their body plans will be controlled in a similar way.

Page 156 — Fact Recall Questions

Q1 The general structure of an organism.

Q2 Hox genes.

Q3 Because it's controlled by similar Hox genes in each type of organism.

Q4 Enzymes inside the cell break down cell components, e.g. proteins and DNA. The cell shrinks and breaks up into fragments. The fragments are engulfed by phagocytes and digested.

Q5 Mitosis creates the bulk of the body parts.

Q6 Internal stimuli (e.g. DNA damage) and external stimuli (e.g. stress caused by a lack of nutrient availability).

3. Gene Mutations

Page 159 — Application Questions

Q1 a) Mutation A = a substitution mutation
The third base along is now C, not T.
Mutation B = a substitution mutation
The seventh base along is now C, not G.
Mutation C = a deletion mutation
The fourth base, C, has been deleted.
Mutation D = an insertion mutation
The second triplet, TAT, has been inserted.

b) Mutation A: Leu-His-Asp-Thr
Mutation B: Leu-His-His-Thr
Mutation C: Leu-Met-Ile
Mutation D: Leu-Tyr-His-Asp-Thr

Q2 a) Mutation A is likely to have the least serious effect on the protein's structure. CTC still codes for Leu so the amino acid sequence/primary structure of the protein won't change from the original sequence.

b) Mutation C is likely to have the most serious effect on the protein's structure as it is a frameshift mutation, and has caused all the amino acids coded for after the mutation to be different compared to the original sequence.

Page 160 — Fact Recall Questions

Q1 A change in the DNA base (nucleotide) sequence.

Q2 E.g. if the mutation changes a base in a triplet, but the amino acid the triplet codes for doesn't change. If the mutation produces a triplet that codes for a different amino acid, but the amino acid is chemically similar to the original so it functions like the original amino acid. If the mutated triplet codes for an amino acid not involved with the protein's function.

Q3 It may alter the function of the protein produced so that it increases the organism's chance of survival.

Q4 E.g. a mutation at the start of a gene could result in RNA polymerase not being able to bind to the gene, which would mean that the protein coded for by the gene wouldn't be produced.

Exam-style Questions — page 161

1 B *(1 mark)*
Remember, similar Hox genes are found in plants, animals and fungi — they are not identical.

2 a) By the order of bases in the glucagon gene *(1 mark)*.

b) E.g. glucagon could bind to cell membranes causing the production of cAMP inside the cell *(1 mark)*. cAMP would then activate the protein inside the cells by changing its three-dimensional structure *(1 mark)*.

c) Once bound to the promoter, RNA polymerase begins the transcription of the structural genes in the *lac* operon *(1 mark)*. The structural genes produce proteins/enzymes that help the bacteria to digest lactose *(1 mark)*. This means the bacteria are able to respire lactose instead of glucose *(1 mark)*.

3 a) A single-base deletion will cause a frameshift *(1 mark)* and this could cause a change in the amino acid sequence/primary structure of the protein *(1 mark)*. This could change the tertiary structure of the protein and prevent it from functioning *(1 mark)*.

b) A single-base substitution will only affect one amino acid *(1 mark)*, whereas a single-base deletion will probably alter all the amino acids after the mutation *(1 mark)*.

c) Mutations that have a neutral effect on a protein's function won't affect an organism overall *(1 mark)*. This may happen because the mutation doesn't change the amino acid coded for by a triplet *(1 mark)* or because it changes the amino acid to one that is chemically similar to the original *(1 mark)*. Alternatively, the mutation may affect an amino acid that isn't involved in the protein's function *(1 mark)*.

Section 2 — Patterns of Inheritance

1. Types and Causes of Variation

Page 164 — Application Questions

Q1 a) monogenic

b) Both. MAOA production is controlled by a gene, but it is also influenced by the environment (e.g. taking anti-depressants or smoking tobacco causes it to drop).

Q2 Environmental factors (temperature) affect mean percentage germination. All three genotypes showed variation in mean percentage germination at each temperature. For all genotypes, the highest percentage germination was at 30 °C and the lowest was at 35 °C. Genetic factors also affect mean percentage germination. The mean percentage germination was highest for genotype B at all three temperatures, and genotype C is higher than genotype A at all three temperatures.

If you're asked to give evidence from a study, make sure you quote some figures to back up what you're saying.

Page 164 — Fact Recall Questions

Q1 polygenic

Q2 When a plant grows abnormally long and spindly because it's not getting enough light.

Q3 continuous

2. Genetic Terms

Page 166 — Application Questions

Q1 A = tufted tail, B = tufted tail, C = non-tufted tail

Q2 a) yellow

b) YY

c) yy

3. Genetic Diagrams — Monogenic Crosses

Pages 169-170 — Application Questions

Q1 The only possible genotype of offspring is heterozygous, e.g. Tt. Worked example:

T — tall dominant allele
t — dwarf recessive allele

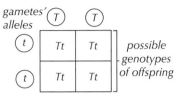

gametes' alleles

	T	T
t	Tt	Tt
t	Tt	Tt

possible genotypes of offspring

The question asked you to show your working. So even though you know that a monogenic cross with two homozygous parents always produces all heterozygous offspring, you must draw a genetic diagram of some kind to show how you would work that out.

Q2 The phenotype ratio of curly hair : smooth hair for the offspring will be 3 : 1 / 75% of offspring will have curly hair and 25% will have smooth hair.

$(8 ÷ 4) × 3 = $ **6 puppies**

Worked example:

H — curly hair allele
h — smooth hair allele

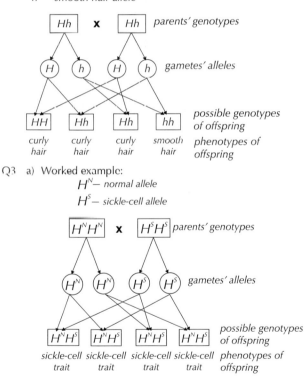

Q3 a) Worked example:

H^N— normal allele
H^S — sickle-cell allele

b) There is a 25% chance that any of these children will have sickle-cell anaemia. Worked example:

H^N— normal allele
H^S — sickle-cell allele

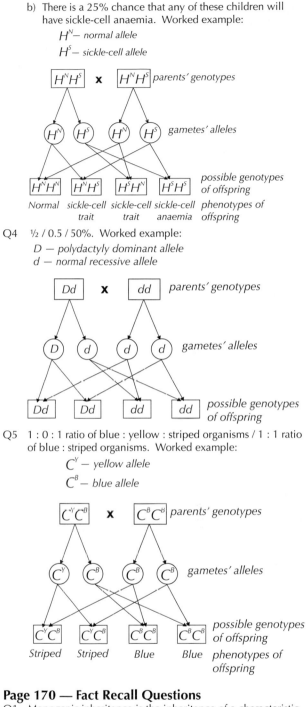

Q4 ½ / 0.5 / 50%. Worked example:

D — polydactyly dominant allele
d — normal recessive allele

Q5 1 : 0 : 1 ratio of blue : yellow : striped organisms / 1 : 1 ratio of blue : striped organisms. Worked example:

C^Y — yellow allele
C^B — blue allele

Page 170 — Fact Recall Questions

Q1 Monogenic inheritance is the inheritance of a characteristic controlled by a single gene.

Q2 The ratio of different phenotypes in the offspring.

Q3 Codominant alleles are alleles that are both expressed in the phenotype, and neither one is recessive.

Q4 a) 3 : 1 ratio of dominant : recessive characteristics
   b) 1 : 2 : 1 ratio of homozygous for one allele : heterozygous : homozygous for the other allele

The phenotypic ratios are always the same for these types of crosses, so it's well worth learning them.

4. Genetic Diagrams — Multiple Allele and Dihybrid Crosses

Page 173 — Application Questions

Q1 The possible striping patterns are Abyssinian (50%) and Mackerel (50%). Worked example:

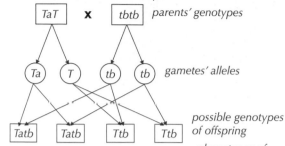

Q2 a) Melanic (M) is dominant to both of the other alleles, insularia is dominant to typical only and typical is recessive to all. / The dominance of the alleles is M > M' > m.

b) All heterozygous melanic (Mm). Worked example:

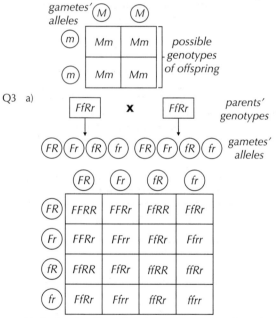

Q3 a)

b) 9 : 1 ratio of round, red tomatoes to pear-shaped, yellow tomatoes.
Round, red tomatoes = FFRR, FFRr, FfRR, FfRr
Pear-shaped, yellow tomatoes = ffrr

Q4 a) The offspring would all be heterozygous (BbPp). *The red cow with horns must have a homozygous recessive phenotype (bbpp). Dihybrid crosses between homozygous dominant and homozygous recessive parents will always produce heterozygous offspring in the F₁ generation.*

b)

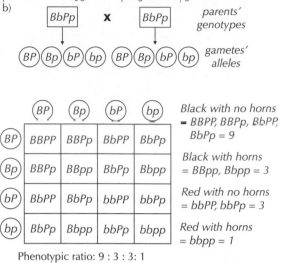

Black with no horns = BBPP, BBPp, BbPP, BbPp = 9

Black with horns = BBpp, Bbpp = 3

Red with no horns = bbPP, bbPp = 3

Red with horns = bbpp = 1

Phenotypic ratio: 9 : 3 : 3 : 1

Page 173 — Fact Recall Questions

Q1 one

Q2 Dihybrid inheritance is the inheritance of two characteristics, which are controlled by different genes.

Q3 9 : 3 : 3 : 1 ratio of dominant both : dominant first, recessive second : recessive first, dominant second : recessive both.

5. Linkage

Page 178 — Application Questions

Q1 $X^F X^f$ (affected female), $X^F Y$ (affected male), $X^f X^f$ (affected female), $X^f Y$ (unaffected male). Worked example:

$X^f Y$ — affected male
$X^F X^f$ — affected heterozygous female

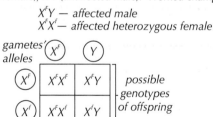

This question doesn't ask you to show your working, but it's best to always do so. Then if you write an answer down wrong for any reason, you could still pick up marks in your exam for your working.

Q2 Y-linked characteristics can only be passed on down the male (XY) line. So for a child to have a Y-linked disorder, its father must also have the disorder. So if a child has hairy ears but its dad doesn't, the dad might question if he was the father.

This is fairly tricky, but drawing a quick diagram would help you out:

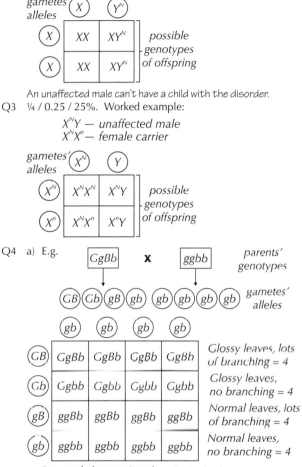

XY^N — unaffected male
XX — female

An unaffected male can't have a child with the disorder.

Q3 ¼ / 0.25 / 25%. *Worked example:*

X^NY — unaffected male
X^NX^n — female carrier

Q4 a) E.g.

| | GgBb | **X** | ggbb | *parents' genotypes* |

gametes' alleles: (GB)(Gb)(gB)(gb) (gb)(gb)(gb)(gb)

(gb) (gb) (gb) (gb)

	GgBb	GgBb	GgBb	GgBb	*Glossy leaves, lots of branching = 4*
(GB)	GgBb	GgBb	GgBb	GgBb	
(Gb)	Ggbb	Ggbb	Ggbb	Ggbb	*Glossy leaves, no branching = 4*
(gB)	ggBb	ggBb	ggBb	ggBb	*Normal leaves, lots of branching = 4*
(gb)	ggbb	ggbb	ggbb	ggbb	*Normal leaves, no branching = 4*

Expected phenotypic ratio = 1 : 1 : 1 : 1

b) Observed phenotypic ratio = 1.7 : 1.1 : 1 : 1.8

c) The GB alleles and the gb alleles in the GgBb parent may have been linked. This would mean that the GgBb parent produced mostly GB and gb gametes and would make the GgBb and ggbb genotypes more common in the offspring. As a result, a higher proportion of the offspring would have their parents' phenotypes, instead of the even split of phenotypes predicted.

Page 178 — Fact Recall Questions

Q1 ½ / 0.5 / 50%

Q2 If a characteristic is sex-linked it means that the allele that codes for it is located on a sex chromosome (X or Y).

Q3 Males are more likely than females to have X-linked disorders because males only have one X chromosome. Because they only have one copy of any alleles on the X chromosome, they express the characteristic of those alleles even if they're recessive, whereas women would need to inherit two copies to express the same characteristics.

Q4 An autosome is any chromosome that isn't a sex chromosome.

Q5 Genes on the same autosome are said to be linked because being on the same autosome usually means they'll stay together during the independent assortment of chromosomes in meiosis I. This means their alleles will be passed on to the offspring together (unless crossing over splits them up first).

6. Epistasis

Page 181 — Application Questions

Q1 a) i) EEBB, EeBB, EEBb, EeBb

For the dog to be black it must be able to express the dark pigment, so it much have at least one dominant E allele. Also, it must have at least one copy of the dominant B allele for the black pigment to be shown in the phenotype.

ii) Eebb, EEbb

For the dog to be chocolate it must be able to express the dark pigment, so it much have at least one dominant E allele. Also, it must have two copies of the recessive b allele for the chocolate pigment to be shown in the phenotype.

iii) eeBB, eeBb, eebb

For the dog to be yellow it must have two copies of the recessive e allele, so that it can't express the dark pigment. Gene 1 is epistatic over gene 2, so it doesn't matter what B or b alleles the dog has — it will still be yellow.

b) A cross between EEBB and eebb parents will give a 9 : 3 : 4 phenotypic ratio in the F_2 generation of black : chocolate : yellow. This is because gene 1 has a recessive epistatic allele (e) and two copies of the recessive epistatic allele (ee) will mask the expression of gene 2. Here's the cross to prove it:

B = black pigment, b = chocolate pigment, E = can express dark pigment, e = can't express dark pigment

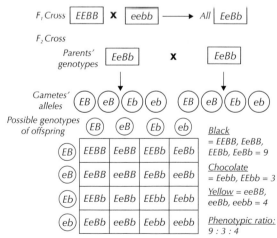

F_1 Cross: EEBB **X** eebb ⟶ All EeBb

F_2 Cross:

Parents' genotypes: EeBb **X** EeBb

Gametes' alleles: (EB)(eB)(Eb)(eb) (EB)(eB)(Eb)(eb)

Possible genotypes of offspring: (EB)(eB)(Eb)(eb)

	(EB)	(eB)	(Eb)	(eb)
(EB)	EEBB	EeBB	EEBb	EeBb
(eB)	EeBB	eeBB	EeBb	eeBb
(Eb)	EEBb	EeBb	EEbb	Eebb
(eb)	EeBb	eeBb	Eebb	eebb

Black = EEBB, EeBB, EEBb, EeBb = 9

Chocolate = Eebb, EEbb = 3

Yellow = eeBB, eeBb, eebb = 4

Phenotypic ratio: 9 : 3 : 4

In the exam, you wouldn't need to draw out the genetic cross unless the question specifically asked you to. We've just included it here to help you out.

Q2 a) dominant epistasis

b) A cross between WWPP and wwpp produces a 48 : 12 : 4 or 12 : 3 : 1 phenotypic ratio in the F_2 generation of white : purple : red. This is because gene 1 has a dominant epistatic allele (W) and one or more copies of the dominant epistatic allele (Ww or WW) will mask the expression of gene 2.

c) W = white pigment, w = red pigment, P = purple pigment, p = no purple pigment

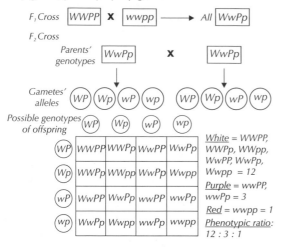

F_1 Cross WWPP **X** wwpp ⟶ All WwPp

F_2 Cross

Parents' genotypes WwPp **X** WwPp

Gametes' alleles (WP) (Wp) (wP) (wp) (WP) (Wp) (wP) (wp)

Possible genotypes of offspring (WP) (Wp) (wP) (wp)

	(WP)	(Wp)	(wP)	(wp)
(WP)	WWPP	WWPp	WwPP	WwPp
(Wp)	WWPp	WWpp	WwPp	Wwpp
(wP)	WwPP	WwPp	wwPP	wwPp
(wp)	WwPp	Wwpp	wwPp	wwpp

White = WWPP, WWPp, WWpp, WwPP, WwPp, Wwpp = 12
Purple = wwPP, wwPp = 3
Red = wwpp = 1
Phenotypic ratio: 12 : 3 : 1

7. The Chi-Squared Test

Pages 185-186 — Application Questions

Q1 a) Yes, the difference would be significant because the chi-squared value is greater than the critical value (6.20 > 5.99).

If the difference is significant it means the difference is unlikely to be due to chance and that the null hypothesis is rejected.

b) No, the difference would not be significant because the chi-squared value is smaller than the critical value (4.85 < 5.99).

If the difference is not significant it means the difference is likely to be due to chance — we're unable to reject the null hypothesis.

Q2

Phenotype	Ratio	Expected result (E)	Observed result (O)	O − E	(O − E)²	$\frac{(O - E)^2}{E}$
Grey body	3	48	45	−3	9	0.19
Ebony body	1	16	19	3	9	0.56
					$\chi^2 = \Sigma \frac{(O - E)^2}{E} =$	0.75

Therefore $\chi^2 = $ **0.75**

Q3 a)

Phenotype	Ratio	Expected result (E)	Observed result (O)	O − E	(O − E)²	$\frac{(O - E)^2}{E}$
Round, green	9	72	74	2	4	0.06
Round, yellow	3	24	21	−3	9	0.38
Wrinkled, green	3	24	26	2	4	0.17
Wrinkled, yellow	1	8	7	−1	1	0.13
					$\chi^2 = \Sigma \frac{(O - E)^2}{E} =$	0.74

Therefore $\chi^2 = $ **0.74**

b) There are 4 phenotypes which means there are $4 - 1 = 3$ degrees of freedom. From the table, the critical value for a test with 3 degrees of freedom and a 0.05 probability level is 7.82. The chi-squared value is smaller than the critical value (0.74 < 7.82) so the difference between the observed and expected results is not significant. This means we're unable to reject the null hypothesis.

Q4 a) That there is no significant difference between the observed and expected results.

b)

Phenotype	Ratio	Expected result (E)	Observed result (O)	O − E	(O − E)²	$\frac{(O - E)^2}{E}$
Tall	3	39	43	4	16	0.41
Dwarf	1	13	9	−4	16	1.23
					$\chi^2 = \Sigma \frac{(O - E)^2}{E} =$	1.64

Therefore $\chi^2 = $ **1.64**.

There are two phenotypes (tall and dwarf) which means there is $2 - 1 = 1$ degree of freedom. From the table, the critical value for a test with 1 degree of freedom and a 0.05 probability level is 3.84. The chi-squared value is smaller than the critical value (1.64 < 3.84) so the difference between the observed and expected results is not significant. This means that the null hypothesis can't be rejected, so the results from this experiment support the scientist's theory.

Q5 a)

Phenotype	Ratio	Expected result (E)	Observed result (O)	O − E	(O − E)²	$\frac{(O - E)^2}{E}$
Red	1	40	24	−16	256	6.40
Pink	2	80	92	12	144	1.80
White	1	40	44	4	16	0.40
					$\chi^2 = \Sigma \frac{(O - E)^2}{E} =$	8.60

Therefore $\chi^2 = $ **8.6**.

There are 3 phenotypes which means there are $3 - 1 = 2$ degrees of freedom. From the table, the critical value for a test with 2 degrees of freedom and a 0.05 probability level is 5.99. The chi-squared value is greater than the critical value (8.6 > 5.99) so the difference between the observed and expected results is significant. This means that the null hypothesis is rejected, so this is unlikely to be an example of codominance.

Be careful — the order that observed results are written in the question won't necessarily be the same as the order that things need to be written in the table.

b)

Phenotype	Ratio	Expected result (E)	Observed result (O)	O − E	(O − E)²	$\frac{(O - E)^2}{E}$
Pink	9	90	92	2	4	0.04
Red	3	30	24	−6	36	1.20
White	4	40	44	4	16	0.40
					$\chi^2 = \Sigma \frac{(O - E)^2}{E} =$	1.64

Therefore $\chi^2 = $ **1.64**.

The critical value is 5.99 (the same as for part a). This time the chi-squared value is smaller than the critical value (1.64 < 5.99) so the difference between the observed and expected results is not significant. This means that the null hypothesis can't be rejected and it is likely that recessive epistasis is involved.

The critical value is the same here as in part a) because the number of degrees have freedom haven't changed (there are still 3 phenotypes involved).

1 a) Number of agouti offspring = $(256 \div 4) \times 3 = \mathbf{192}$
       (1 mark)

A normal case of monogenic inheritance would give a phenotypic ratio of 3 : 1 of agouti : solid coloured. So three-quarters of the offspring would have agouti coat colour.

   b) ppAA, ppAa, ppaa *(1 mark)*

The allele for pigmentation is <u>controlled</u> by the gene (P) — you need to have a gene for coat colour <u>as well as</u> the control gene to get the albino phenotype.

   c) A cross between PPAA and ppaa parents will give a 9 : 3 : 4 phenotypic ratio in the F$_2$ generation of agouti : solid coloured : albino *(1 mark)*. This is because the P gene has a recessive epistatic allele (p) and two copies of the recessive epistatic allele (pp) will mask the expression of the pigmentation gene *(1 mark)*. A dihybrid cross will only give a phenotypic ratio of 9 : 3 : 3 : 1 in the F$_2$ generation if the two genes do not interact and are not linked *(1 mark)*.

2 a)

Genotype	Growth on substance 1
AaBb	✓
aaBb	✗
AAbb	✗
AABb	✓

(1 mark for all three correct)

   b) They must have the genotype aaBb or aaBB *(1 mark)*. They can't produce enzyme A but can produce enzyme B *(1 mark)*, so if they're given substance 2 they can convert it to substance 3 *(1 mark)*.

   c) E.g.

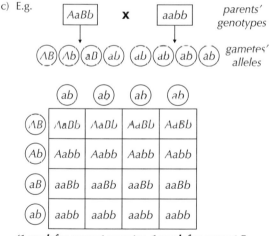

(1 mark for correct gametes, 1 mark for correct F$_1$ genotypes)

The ratio of genotypes AaBb : Aabb : aaBb : aabb is 1 : 1 : 1 : 1 *(1 mark)*.

$(12 \div 16) \times 100 = \mathbf{75\%}$ *(1 mark)*

Offspring with the genotype Aabb, aaBb and aabb would not be able to grow in medium containing substance 1.

3 a)

X^hY — haemophiliac male
X^HX^h — female carrier

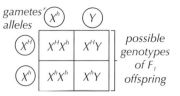

Possible phenotypes of F$_1$ offspring: carrier female (X^HX^h), unaffected male (X^HY), haemophiliac female (X^hX^h) and haemophiliac male (X^hY).

(1 mark for correct gametes, 1 mark for correct F$_1$ genotypes, 1 mark for F$_1$ phenotypes matched to correct F$_1$ genotypes.)

   b) i)

Phenotype	Ratio	E	O	O − E	(O − E)^2	$\frac{(O-E)^2}{E}$
Carrier female	1	68	72	4	16	0.24
Haemophilic female	1	68	70	2	4	0.06
Unaffected male	1	68	69	1	1	0.02
Haemophilic male	1	68	61	−7	49	0.72

$$\chi^2 = \Sigma \frac{(O-E)^2}{E} = 1.04$$

Therefore $\chi^2 = \mathbf{1.04}$.

(3 marks for correct answer, otherwise 1 mark for correct expected results, 1 mark for correct $(O - E)^2 \div E$ calculation.)

      ii) The difference between the observed and expected results is not significant at the 0.05 probability level *(1 mark)*.

This is because the critical value for this test is 7.82 and the chi-squared value (1.04) is less than this.

Section 3 — Evolution

1. Evolution by Natural Selection and Genetic Drift

Page 194 — Application Questions

Q1 a) The frequency of the three alleles in Population 1 is relatively even. However in Population 2 there is a very high frequency of the white allele and much lower frequencies of the purple and pink alleles.

   b) By chance, the white allele was passed onto offspring more than the other alleles. As a result, the number of individuals with the white allele increased and the number of individuals with purple and pink alleles fell.

   c) Population 2, because genetic drift has a much greater effect in smaller populations.

Q2 a) The peak in allele frequency in 2000 was most likely a result of the fire in 1999. The peak may be due to an increase in the number of mammals emigrating to the south from the north as a result of the fire. The northern population had a slightly higher frequency of the allele, so an influx from this population could have caused an increase in the allele frequency in the south.

b) From 1998 to 2002 there was a big increase in the dark fur allele in the northern population. In 1999, a fire destroyed a large area in the north of the forest. This would have left a large area of barren, darkened forest and blackened soil. Mammals with darker fur would have a selective advantage and so be more likely to survive, reproduce and pass on their alleles for darker fur, causing an increase in the frequency of the dark fur allele.

Page 194 — Fact Recall Questions
Q1 a) The complete range of alleles in a population.
   b) How often an allele appears in a population.
Q2 Evolution is the change in the frequency of an allele in a population over time.
Q3 Because individuals vary, it means that some organisms are better adapted to selection pressures than others. These individuals are more likely to survive, reproduce and pass on their beneficial alleles to their offspring than others so that, over many generations, these alleles become more common in a population.
Q4 It makes it more likely that individuals with alleles for characteristics towards the middle of the range will survive and reproduce. This reduces the range of possible phenotypes.
Q5 An event that causes a big reduction in the size of a population. Evolution by genetic drift has a greater effect on a population if there's a genetic bottleneck.
Q6 The founder effect describes the effect of starting a population from just a few individuals — when this happens, the number of alleles present in the new population will be much smaller than in the original population, so the frequency of these alleles will be much higher than in the original population. If, by chance, one of these alleles represents a genetic disorder, this could lead to an increased incidence of that disorder in the new population.

2. The Hardy-Weinberg Principle

Page 197 — Application Questions
Q1 a) $p + q = 1$
   $p = 1 - q$
   $p = 1 - 0.10 = \mathbf{0.90}$
   You're given one allele frequency in the table and are asked to find the other, so its the simple equation.
   b) $p = 0.9$, $q = 0.1$, so $2pq = 2 \times 0.9 \times 0.1 = \mathbf{0.18}$
   c) No, it does not apply. The frequency of the allele changes between the generations, and the Hardy-Weinberg principle is only true in cases where the allele frequency stays the same.
Q2 $q = 0.16$ and $p + q = 1$, so $p = 1 - q$
   $p = 1 - 0.16 = 0.84$
   homozygous dominant genotype frequency = p^2
   $p^2 = 0.84^2 = \mathbf{0.71}$
Q3 recessive wrinkled allele = $q^2 = 31\% \div 100 = 0.31$
   $q = \sqrt{0.31} = 0.557$
   $p + q = 1$, so $p = 1 - q$
   $p = 1 - 0.557 = 0.443$
   Heterozygous genotype = $2pq$
   $2pq = 2 \times 0.443 \times 0.557 = 0.49$
   $0.49 \times 100 = 49$, so $\mathbf{49\%}$ of the population have a heterozygous genotype.

Page 197 — Fact Recall Questions
Q1 The Hardy-Weinberg principle is a mathematical model that predicts that the frequencies of alleles in a population won't change from one generation to the next as long as the population is large, there's no immigration, emigration, mutations or natural selection, and mating is totally random.
Q2 $p + q = 1$ and $p^2 + 2pq + q^2 = 1$, where p = the frequency of the dominant allele, q = the frequency of the recessive allele, p^2 = the frequency of the homozygous dominant genotype, q^2 = the frequency of the homozygous recessive genotype and $2pq$ = the frequency of the heterozygous genotype.

3. Artificial Selection

Page 199 — Fact Recall Questions
Q1 Artificial selection is where humans select individuals in a population to breed together to get desirable traits.
Q2 a) E.g. females with large udders and males whose mothers had large udders were selected and bred together. The offspring with the largest udders were then selected and bred together. This process was continued over several generations until a cow with very large udders was produced.
   b) E.g. high milk yield / high milk quality / a long lactation period / resistance to mastitis/disease / a calm temperament
Q3 E.g. bread wheat has been selectively bred to have a high wheat yield/large ears / a high tolerance to the cold / short stalks / uniform stalk height.
Q4 E.g. selective breeding can reduce the gene pool of a species, which could lead to problems in the future with resistance to new strains of diseases. Selective breeding can also cause unforeseen health problems for the organisms involved.

4. Speciation

Pages 201-202 — Application Questions
Q1 E.g. the two elephant populations separated and became geographically isolated. The different habitats caused different selective pressures, so in each habitat elephants with different alleles were more likely to survive, reproduce and pass on their advantageous alleles. Over time this caused the frequencies of the advantageous alleles in each habitat to increase. Mutations also took place independently in each population, which also altered the allele frequencies in each habitat. Eventually the differences in allele frequencies resulted in the phenotypes of the two populations changing so much that they became reproductively isolated. Speciation had occurred.
Q2 a) Test whether they are able to breed with each other to produce fertile offspring.
   b) Sympatric speciation. The two populations occur in the same area.

Page 202 — Fact Recall Questions
Q1 a) When populations of the same species can no longer breed together to produce fertile offspring (as a result of changes in allele frequencies).
   b) When a physical barrier divides two populations of a species.
   c) The development of a new species.

Q2 In allopatric speciation the populations are geographically isolated before they become reproductively isolated. In sympatric speciation, reproductive isolation evolves between two populations without geographical isolation.

Q3 E.g. individuals could develop different flowering or mating seasons. Changes in genitalia may prevent individuals from mating successfully. A group of individuals may develop courtship rituals that aren't attractive to the main population.

Exam-style Questions — pages 204-205

1   a) stabilising selection
    b) Birds could evolve to breed earlier in the year *(1 mark)*, as sufficient food will be available to allow them to breed earlier in the year, and offspring that hatch earlier in the year are more likely to survive *(1 mark)*.

2   a) i) artificial selection / selective breeding *(1 mark)*
        ii) E.g. males and females which grew quickly, converted food into body mass efficiently and produced a high proportion of breast meat were selected and bred together. Their offspring that showed these traits most strongly were then selected and bred together *(1 mark)*. This process continued over multiple generations, to give chickens that grew quickly and efficiently to produce a high proportion of breast meat *(1 mark)*.
    b) E.g. because broiler chickens grow quickly and can be slaughtered at a younger age, producing chicken is quicker, meaning a large volume of meat can be generated easily *(1 mark)*. The fact that broiler chickens are efficient at converting food to body mass also reduces costs, and means raising broiler chickens uses fewer resources than normal chickens (which is good for the environment) *(1 mark)*. However, selective breeding appears to have increased broiler chickens' vulnerability to some health problems, such as cardiovascular problems and walking issues, and many people don't think it's fair to artificially select traits that cause the organism to suffer *(1 mark)*.

3   a) The change may be due to genetic drift *(1 mark)* or it may be due to natural selection for smaller body size in the smaller forest fragment *(1 mark)*.
    b) Genetic drift is random, but natural selection increases the frequency of traits that increase an organism's chances of survival, so the scientists could distinguish between the two possibilities by looking at whether smaller beetles in the small forest fragment have a higher chance of survival *(1 mark)*. If they do, then the change is likely to be due to natural selection *(1 mark)*.

4   a) $q^2 = 5 \div 1000 = 0.005$
       $q = \sqrt{0.005} = 0.0707$
       $p = 1 - 0.0707 = 0.9293$
       $2pq = 0.1314$
       $0.1314 \times 100 = \mathbf{13.14\%}$
       (2 marks for the correct answer, otherwise 1 mark for identifying 2pq as the frequency of heterozygotes in the population.).
    b) Genetic drift *(1 mark)*. The syndrome does not increase a person's chance of surviving, so the allele must have become more common in the population by chance *(1 mark)*.

5   a) *7-9 marks:*
       The answer gives a detailed discussion of the selection pressures on both islands, and how the population sizes on the two islands will have affected their ability to respond to the selection pressures. Scientific terminology is used correctly, and the answer demonstrates a detailed understanding of the process of evolution, including the founder effect and genetic drift. The answer has a clear and logical structure. The information given is relevant and detailed.
       4-6 marks:
       The selection pressures on both islands are discussed, but no reference is made to the effect of population size. Scientific terminology is used correctly, and the answer is mostly well-structured. Most of the information given is relevant and there is some detail involved.
       1-3 marks:
       The selection pressures on Pod Mrcaru are discussed, but no comparisons are made to Pod Kopiste. Use of scientific terminology is poor. The answer has no clear structure. The information given is basic and lacking in detail. It may not all be relevant.
       0 marks:
       No relevant information is given
       Here are some points your answer may include:
       On Pod Mrcaru, more vegetation is available to eat than on Pod Kopiste. This has acted as a selection pressure on Pod Mrcaru, favouring individuals with alleles that make them better able to eat and digest vegetation. The individuals introduced to Pod Mrcaru included some individuals who were better able to eat vegetation, due to having stronger jaws, and individuals who were better able to digest vegetation due to the structure of their gut. These individuals were more likely to survive and reproduce, and pass on their alleles, leading to an increase in the frequency of these alleles over time and a change in jaw strength and gut structure across generations. The speed of this change may have been increased by the effect of genetic drift, and also by the founder effect, as the population of Pod Mrcaru was initially very small.
       On Pod Kopiste, on the other hand, as less vegetation is present, the selection pressure to be able to eat and process vegetation will have been lower. The population of lizards on Pod Kopiste will also have initially been larger, meaning that there was less of a chance of alleles for features that would make it easier to eat and digest vegetation increasing in frequency by chance via genetic drift. This weaker selection pressure and lack of drift will have meant that the ability to eat and digest vegetation efficiently has not evolved on Pod Kopiste within the same timescale as on Pod Mrcaru.
    b) i) allopatric speciation *(1 mark)*
       ii) The two populations would need to become reproductively isolated *(1 mark)*.

Section 4 — Manipulating Genomes

1. Common Techniques

Page 210 — Application Questions
Q1 a) top strand = CGTA, bottom strand = GGTA
   b) $2 \times 2 \times 2 \times 2 \times 2 \times 2 \times 2 = \mathbf{128}$
   Remember, you start with two single stands of DNA.
   The amount of DNA then doubles with each PCR cycle.
Q2 There is a *Bam*HI site on the left-hand side of the fragment
   and an *Eco*RI site towards the right-hand side. The DNA
   sample could be incubated with *Bam*HI and *Eco*RI, which
   would cut the DNA via a hydrolysis reaction at these sites.
   This is because the shape of each recognition sequence is
   complementary to each enzyme's active site.
   Make sure you use the correct terms in the exam, e.g. the
   shape of the recognition sequence is complementary *to the*
   enzyme's active site, not *the same as the enzyme's active site.*
Q3 a) It helps the samples to sink to the bottom of the wells
      and makes them easier to see.
   b) Make sure the tip of the micropipette is in the buffer
      solution and just above the opening of the well. Be
      careful not to pierce the bottom of the well by sticking
      the tip of the micropipette too far into the well. Also, use
      a clean micropipette tip for each different sample.
   c) Put the lid on the gel box and connect the leads from
      the gel box to the power supply. Then turn on the power
      supply and set it to the required voltage so an electrical
      current will pass through the gel. Let the gel run for
      about 30 minutes before turning off the power supply.

Page 210 — Fact Recall Questions
Q1 polymerase chain reaction
Q2 A sequence of DNA that consists of antiparallel base pairs/
   base pairs that read the same in opposite directions.
Q3 Small tails of unpaired bases at the end of a DNA
   fragment. They can be used to bind/anneal the DNA
   fragment to another piece of DNA that has sticky ends with
   complementary sequences.
Q4 At the top / near the negative electrode.
Q5 You need to mix them with a chemical that denatures the
   proteins so they all have the same charge.
Q6 E.g. it could be used to identify the proteins present in urine
   or blood samples, which may help to diagnose disease.

2. DNA profiling

Page 211 — Fact Recall Question
Q1 DNA profiling can be used to compare samples of
   DNA collected from crime scenes to samples of DNA
   from possible suspects. The DNA is isolated from all
   the collected samples (from the crime scene and from
   the suspects) and PCR is used to amplify multiple areas
   containing different sequence repeats. The PCR products
   are run on an electrophoresis gel and the DNA profiles
   produced are compared to see if any match. If the samples
   match, it links a person to the crime scene.

3. Genetic Engineering

Page 213 — Application Question
Q1 a) Vector DNA was cut with the same restriction enzymes
      as the DNA fragment, so complementary sticky ends
      were produced. The DNA fragment and cut vector
      were mixed with DNA ligase, which joined together the
      sugar-phosphate backbones of the two pieces to form the
      recombinant DNA.
   b) electroporation

Page 213 — Fact Recall Questions
Q1 The manipulation of an organism's DNA.
Q2 recombinant DNA
Q3 a) It transfers the fragment of DNA containing the desired
      gene into the host cell.
   b) E.g. plasmids and bacteriophages.
Q4 It means that the sticky ends of the vector DNA are
   complementary to the sticky ends of the DNA fragment
   containing the gene (allowing them to be joined).
Q5 DNA ligase is used to join the sticky ends of the DNA
   fragment containing the desired gene to the sticky ends of
   the vector DNA. They join together the sugar-phosphate
   backbones of the two bits of DNA.

4. Genetically Modified Organisms

Pages 217 — Application Questions
Q1 a) E.g. the desired genes from the maize plant and soil
      bacterium could have been isolated using restriction
      enzymes and inserted into a plasmid from a bacterium,
      such as *A. tumefaciens*. The plasmid could then have
      been put back into *A. tumefaciens* and the rice plant
      cells infected with the transformed *A. tumefaciens*
      bacteria. The desired genes would then get inserted into
      the rice plant cells, creating the genetically modified
      rice.
   b) E.g. Golden Rice could be used to feed people in areas
      where people suffer from a vitamin A deficiency.
Q2 E.g. people with diabetes are now able to obtain human
   insulin instead of pig insulin, animals are not involved in
   the process, and the drugs can be made in large quantities,
   making them more available.
Q3 a) The DNA fragments that code for the production of
      alpha-1-antitrypsin could have been injected into a
      sheep embryo. The embryo could then have been
      implanted into a female sheep. When the offspring was
      born it could have been tested to see if it could make
      alpha-1-antitrypsin. If it could, selective breeding would
      have been used to produce more sheep that produce
      alpha-1-antitrypsin in their milk.
   b) The company may want legal protection for making the
      product so that they can control who uses the product
      and when. It also means that they will receive money for
      selling the product.

Page 217 — Fact Recall Questions
Q1 a) E.g. to prevent yields of soybean plants being greatly
      reduced by insect pests that feed on them.
   b) *Bacillus thuringiensis* (Bt)
   c) The gene codes for a protein that is toxic to some of the
      insects that feed on soybean plants.
Q2 a) Pharming is where pharmaceuticals are produced using
      genetically modified organisms.

b) There are positive ethical issues with 'pharming'— e.g. drugs made this way can be made in large quantities compared to other methods of production. This can make them more available to more people. However, the creation of genetically modified animals raises negative ethical issues, e.g. there is concern that manipulating an animal's genes could cause harmful side-effects for the animal, and that using an animal in this way is enforcing the idea that animals are merely 'assets' that can be treated however we choose.

Q3 E.g. it could lead to new treatments for disease.

Q4 The sharing of knowledge, skills and technology between scientists at different institutions.

Q5 E.g. they may not be able to afford patented genetically modified seeds. / They may not be allowed to plant and grow any of the seeds from one crop without paying again.

5. Gene Therapy

Page 219 — Application Questions

Q1 The virus is acting as a vector — it is being used to carry the normal FIX gene into the body cells of the sufferers of haemophilia.

Q2 $(2 + 2 + 3 + 4 + 8 + 12) ÷ 6 = 5.16... = \textbf{5.2\%}$ (2 s.f.)

Q3 E.g. Yes. The maximum level after gene therapy was more than 1% for all the patients, which could improve their health.

Q4 E.g. this therapy could prolong the lives of people with haemophilia B and could provide people with haemophilia B with a greater quality of life, as they may not have to receive injections for the protein multiple times a week in the future. It could save health authorities money, as the injections usually required by sufferers are expensive.

Page 219 — Fact Recall Questions

Q1 A possible treatment option for genetic disorders and some cancers that involves altering defective alleles inside cells.

Q2 Somatic gene therapy involves altering the alleles in body cells (particularly those most affected by the disorder being treated). Germ line gene therapy involves altering the alleles in sex cells.

6. Sequencing Genes and Genomes

Page 225 — Application Question

Q1 a) A single-stranded template of the bone's DNA, DNA polymerase, lots of DNA primer, free nucleotides and a fluorescently-labelled modified nucleotide (a different one for each tube).

b) The tubes undergo PCR, which produces many strands of DNA all of different lengths. The DNA fragments in each tube are separated by electrophoresis and visualised under UV light. The complementary base sequence can then be read from the gel.

c) ATAAGCCATTCG

Remember — DNA sequencing gels are read from the bottom up. This will give you a DNA sequence that is complementary to the original sequence (TATTCGGTAAGC). To get the original sequence, remember that A always pairs with T and C pairs with G.

d) Species 2, because it has the same DNA sequence as the bone.

Page 226 — Fact Recall Questions

Q1 a) You need to chop up the genome into smaller pieces because the chain termination method can only be used for DNA fragments up to about 750 bp long.

b) bacterial artificial chromosomes (BACs)

Q2 a) They are techniques that can sequence a lot faster than original methods (e.g. up to 1000 times more bases in a given time), at a fraction of the cost.

b) E.g. pyrosequencing

Q3 You can use DNA sequencing to sequence a gene and work out the sequence of amino acids that a gene codes for. From this you can predict the primary structure of a polypeptide, which allows biological molecules to be created from scratch. This has led to the development synthetic biology.

Q4 E.g. computational biology and bioinformatics.

Q5 Computerised comparisons between the genomes of people that have a disease and those that don't can be used to detect particular mutations that could be responsible for an increased risk of the disease.

Q6 Whole genomes of different species can be sequenced and then analysed using computer software to tell us how closely related different species are.

Exam-style Questions — pages 228-229

1 B *(1 mark)*

2 a) PCR is used to amplify multiple areas containing different sequence repeats in each DNA sample *(1 mark)*. The PCR products from each sample are run on an electrophoresis gel *(1 mark)*. Shorter DNA fragments move faster and travel further through the gel, so the DNA fragments separate according to length, with longer pieces nearer the top *(1 mark)*. The fragments are stained before electrophoresis so that the bands produced for each sample can be seen — these are the DNA profiles *(1 mark)*.

b) DNA profiling technology involves comparing the number of times repetitive, non-coding base sequences *(1 mark)* are repeated at a number of different, specific places (loci) in a genome *(1 mark)*. The probability of two individuals having the same DNA profile is very low because the chance of two individuals having the same number of sequence repeats at each locus tested is very low *(1 mark)*.

c) Yes. The DNA profile of the stolen horse and DNA profile of horse 3 have exactly the same band pattern, so the DNA that produced both DNA profiles must have come from the same horse *(1 mark)*.

d) It can be used in medical diagnosis to analyse the risk of genetic disorders *(1 mark)*.

3 a) A reaction mixture is set up that contains the plant DNA sample, free nucleotides, primers and DNA polymerase *(1 mark)*. The DNA mixture is heated to 95 °C to break the hydrogen bonds between the two strands of DNA *(1 mark)*. The mixture is then cooled to 50-65 °C so that the primers can bind to the strands *(1 mark)*. The reaction mixture is heated to 72 °C, so that DNA polymerase can create new DNA strands *(1 mark)*. Two new copies of the DNA fragment are formed and then the cycle of heating and cooling is repeated many times *(1 mark)*.

b) It would show a band at the same point on the gel as that for the GM soybean plant *(1 mark)*.

c) The farmer's non-GM soybean plant *(1 mark)*.
d) E.g. there may be concerns that growing a genetically modified crop could encourage monoculture *(1 mark)*. Monoculture decreases biodiversity and could leave the whole crop vulnerable to disease, because all the plants are genetically identical *(1 mark)*.

4   a) E.g. plasmids / BACs/bacterial artificial chromosomes / liposomes *(1 mark)*

Bacteriophages are vectors too, but they are a type of virus that infects bacteria, so this doesn't answer the question. Make sure you read the question carefully before and, if you've time, after you answer it.

   b) i) Nine out of the ten patients had a functional immune system after gene therapy *(1 mark)*. However, two out of the ten patients developed leukaemia within 3 years of the treatment *(1 mark)*.
      ii) Any two from: e.g. a larger sample size could be used *(1 mark)*. / The patients could be followed for longer than three years after treatment *(1 mark)*. / Indicators other than developing leukaemia could be used to check the health status of the patients *(1 mark)*.
   c) E.g. the technology could be used in ways other than for medical treatment, e.g. to reverse the cosmetic effects of aging *(1 mark)*. / There's the potential to do more harm than good by using the technology, e.g. by causing the overexpression of genes *(1 mark)*. / Gene therapy is expensive and the resources may be better spent on treatments that have already passed clinical trials *(1 mark)*.

Section 5 — Cloning and Biotechnology

1. Plant Cloning

Page 233 — Application Questions
Q1 a) Micropropagation. Clone the plant using tissue culture, then take cells from the developing clone. Subculture the cells in fresh medium to make even more clones, then repeat the process.
   b) E.g. the unusual pattern on the petals will always be passed on to the clones. / The plant could be reproduced in any season. / Less space is required by tissue culture/ micropropagation than would be needed to produce the same number of plants by conventional growing methods. / If the plant takes a long time to produce seeds it can be reproduced very quickly.
Q2 E.g. any undesirable characteristics the strawberry plant has will be passed on to all the clones. The cloned strawberry plant population will have no genetic variability and so a single disease could kill them all.

Page 233 — Fact Recall Questions
Q1 Vegetative propagation is the natural production of plant clones from non-reproductive tissues, e.g. roots, leaves and stems.
Q2 E.g. cover the whole pot with a plastic bag. / Put the pot in a propagator.
Q3 Stem, leaf and root.
Q4 Any two from: e.g. to reproduce plants that don't readily reproduce naturally. / To reproduce plants that are rare or endangered. / To grow whole plants from genetically engineered plant cells.

2. Animal Cloning

Page 237 — Application Questions
Q1 a) He could extract an egg cell from a female mouse and fertilise it in a Petri dish. He would then leave the fertilised egg to divide at least once, forming an embryo. Next, the individual cells from the embryo would be separated and each one put into a separate Petri dish. Each cell would divide and develop normally, so an embryo would form in each Petri dish. He would then implant the embryos into female mice. The embryos would continue to develop inside the surrogate mice, and eventually the offspring/cloned mice would be born.
   b) Cloned mice are all genetically identical, so the variables that come from genetic differences are removed. Controlling variables in this way will increase the validity of the results of the drug trial.
Q2 a) Somatic cell nuclear transfer/SCNT
   b) The embryo would be implanted into a surrogate mother and eventually a puppy would be born. The puppy would be a clone of the dog that the body/somatic cell nucleus came from.

Page 237 — Fact Recall Questions
Q1 During sexual reproduction, once an egg has been fertilised, it splits during the very early stages of development and develops into multiple embryos with the same genetic information. The embryos develop as normal to produce offspring that are all genetically identical — they are clones.
Q2 To increase the number of animals with desirable characteristics to breed from.
Q3 E.g. for research purposes (e.g. in medicine). / To help save endangered species from extinction. / To produce many animals that have been genetically modified to produce a useful substance.
Q4 Arguments for — any three from: e.g. desirable genetic characteristics are always passed onto the clones. / Infertile animals can be reproduced. / Animals can be cloned at any time. / Increasing the population of endangered species helps to preserve biodiversity. / Cloning can help to develop new treatments for disease.
    Arguments against — any three from: e.g. cloned animals have no genetic variability/undesirable genetic characteristics are always passed on to the clones. / Cloning is very difficult/expensive/time-consuming. / Clones may not live as long as natural offspring. / Using cloned human embryos as a source of stem cells in controversial.

3. Biotechnology — The Use of Microorganisms

Page 241 — Application Questions
Q1 Bioremediation could be used. This is the process of using organisms to remove pollutants from contaminated sites. Bioremediation could be used in this case by, e.g. providing extra nutrients and optimising growing conditions for microorganisms that occur naturally at the site and are capable of biodegrading/breaking down the pollutants. This would allow these microorganisms to thrive, so they would break down the pollutants into less harmful products more quickly, cleaning up the soil.

Q2 a) E.g. the hot climate may make it difficult to grow crops or rear livestock on a large scale and the rapid population growth means that the demand for food will be constantly increasing. Single-cell protein would be advantageous in this environment because the microorganisms cultured to produce single-cell protein have simple growth requirements so they can be cultured anywhere if the right equipment is available. Also, single-cell protein can be produced using many different organic substrates (including waste materials) and only needs a relatively small area of land to produce food on a large scale. These factors mean that once the initial equipment has been bought and installed, single-cell protein is cheap, easy and quick to produce.

b) Any two from: e.g. the food could easily get contaminated with unwanted bacteria, which could be dangerous to humans / spoil the food. / The food may not be popular, as people may not like the idea of eating food that has been grown using waste products / single-cell protein doesn't have the same texture or flavour as real meat. / If single-cell protein is consumed in high quantities, health problems could be caused due to the high levels of uric acid released when the large amounts of amino acids are broken down.

Page 241 — Fact Recall Questions
Q1 The industrial use of living organisms to produce food, drugs and other products.

Q2 Any three from: e.g. their ideal growth conditions can be easily created. / They have a short life-cycle, so they grow rapidly under the right conditions, meaning products can be made quickly. / They can grow on a range of inexpensive materials, so they're economical. / They can be grown at any time of the year.

Q3 a) Brewing uses yeast to produce alcohol/ethanol by fermenting glucose from the grain.

b) Yeast is used in baking to produce CO_2 to make bread rise.

c) The enzyme chymosin, which is required to clot the milk, can be obtained from yeast cells that have been genetically modified to produce the enzyme. Cheese making also involves lactic acid bacteria, which convert the lactose in milk into lactic acid, making it turn sour and contribute to its solidifying. The production of blue cheeses also involves the addition of fungi to make the characteristic blue veins.

d) Yoghurt production uses lactic acid bacteria to clot the milk and cause it to thicken.

e) *Penicillium* fungi are grown under stress in industrial fermenters to produce penicillin on a massive scale.

f) Insulin is made by genetically modified bacteria, which have had the gene for human insulin production inserted into their DNA. These bacteria are grown in an industrial fermenter on a massive scale.

4. Biotechnology — Culturing Microorganisms

Page 248 — Application Questions
Q1 a) E.g. the turbidity of a sample of broth that doesn't have any bacteria added should be measured over time at room temperature. It should be used to make sure that the bacteria are responsible for the increasing turbidity rather than anything else in the broth.

b) Any two from: e.g. tie long hair back to prevent it from falling into anything. / Work near a Bunsen flame. / Regularly disinfect work surfaces to minimise contamination. / Sterilise the instrument used to transfer cultures. / Briefly flame the neck of the container of broth just after it's opened and just before it's closed. / Sterilise all glassware before and after use, e.g. in an autoclave.

c) Aseptic techniques are important because they prevent contamination of cultures by unwanted microorganisms, which may affect the growth of the microorganism being cultured. Contaminated cultures in laboratory experiments give imprecise results and may be hazardous to health.

d) E.g. turbidity increased more quickly for species 1 and species 1 spent more time in the exponential growth phase/took longer to reach the stationary phase. This is likely to be because the growing conditions were more favourable for species 1 than for species 2.

Q2 E.g. prepare separate samples of the bacteria in broth, each mixed in with a buffer solution at each of the pH levels under investigation. Next, apply the same volume of one of the bacterial broth samples to three separate agar plates and spread the broth across the entire surface of the agar using a sterile plastic spreader. Repeat this step for the other two bacterial broth samples. Put the lids on the plates and tape them shut. Put the plates upside down either in an incubator or leave them at room temperature, in a place where the temperature will remain constant. Also put another lidded agar plate, which has broth without any bacteria added to it, in the same place. This will act as a negative control. Leave all the plates for the same amount of time, then count the number of colonies that have formed on each plate and record the results in a table. Work out the mean number of colonies formed at each pH level.

Page 248 — Fact Recall Questions
Q1 A population of one type of microorganism that's been grown under controlled conditions.

Q2 Any three from: e.g. pH / temperature / oxygen supply / contamination / nutrient concentration.

Q3 When growth of microorganisms takes place in a vessel that's isolated from the external environment.

Q4 a) Lag phase, exponential/log phase, stationary phase and decline phase.

b) Lag phase — the population size increases very slowly because the microorganisms have to make enzymes and other molecules before they can reproduce. This means the reproduction rate is low.
Exponential/log phase — the population size increases quickly because the culture conditions are at their most favourable for reproduction. The number of microorganisms doubles at regular intervals.
Stationary phase — the population size stays level because the death rate of the microorganisms equals their reproductive rate. Microorganisms die because there's not enough food and poisonous waste products build up.
Decline phase — the population size falls because the death rate is greater than the reproductive rate. This is because food is very scarce and waste products are at toxic levels.

5. Immobilised Enzymes

Page 251 — Application Questions

Q1 By immobilising the enzyme (attaching the enzyme to an insoluble material so it can't become mixed with the products).

Q2 a) Columns of immobilised enzymes can be washed and reused, which reduces the cost of running the reaction on an industrial scale because the company doesn't have to keep buying new enzymes. Also, because the desired product won't be mixed in with the enzyme, no time and money has to be spent separating them.

b) Extra equipment is required, compared to using free enzymes, which can be expensive to buy. Immobilised enzymes are also more expensive to buy than free enzymes, so may not be economical if they aren't going to be used a lot.

Page 251 — Fact Recall Questions

Q1 Encapsulation in jelly-like alginate beads, which act as a semi-permeable membrane. Trapping in a silica gel matrix. Covalent bonding to cellulose or collagen fibres.

Q2 The substrate solution is run through the column, where it binds to the active sites of the enzymes, which catalyse the reaction. The solution that flows out of the column contains the desired product.

Q3 Any three from: e.g. immobilised lactase — used in the breakdown of lactose in the production of lactose-free dairy products. / Immobilised penicillin acylase — used in the production of semi-synthetic penicillins. / Immobilised glucoamylase — used in the production of glucose and glucose syrup. / Immobilised glucose isomerase — used to convert glucose to fructose. / Immobilised aminoacylase — used to separate L and D amino acids. / Immobilised nitrilase — used to convert acrylonitrile to acrylamide.
This isn't a comprehensive list of immobilised enzymes and their uses. There are loads more examples that aren't listed here, but would be acceptable.

Exam-style Questions — pages 253-254

1 a) i) Any three from: e.g. pH probe — monitors the pH and keeps it at an optimum level so enzymes work more efficiently *(1 mark)*. / Water jacket — keeps the temperature at an optimum level so enzymes work more efficiently *(1 mark)*. / Paddles — circulate the medium around the vessel so the bacteria can always access the nutrients needed for growth *(1 mark)*. / Sterile air-in pipe — pumps oxygen into the vessel when needed, so the microorganisms can always respire to provide energy for growth *(1 mark)*.
The question asks you to identify three features of the fermentation vessel in Fig. 1.1., so make sure you only write about features shown on the vessel in the diagram or you won't get the marks.

ii) It prevents unwanted microorganisms from entering the vessel and contaminating the culture *(1 mark)*. If the culture is contaminated, it may mean that product yield will be reduced as the bacteria will be competing for nutrients / the whole batch will have to be thrown away, which will be very costly *(1 mark)*.

b) i) 25 minutes *(1 mark)*. *(Accept answers in range 22 minutes – 28 minutes.)*
To answer this question, the first thing you need to do is identify the exponential growth phase. Then you pick a number of cells during this phase and read the time at which there are this many cells (e.g. 500 cells). Next, read off the time at which this number of cells has doubled. The difference between these two times gives you the answer.

ii) E.g. because the bacteria have to make enzymes and other molecules before they can reproduce *(1 mark)*.

iii) E.g.

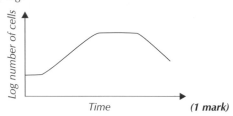

Time   *(1 mark)*

(y-axis: *Log number of cells*)

iv) In a closed culture, no extra nutrients are added and waste products aren't removed, so after a time, there's not enough food and waste products start to build up *(1 mark)*. This causes the bacteria to reproduce more slowly and die faster *(1 mark)*. The graph levels off when death rate equals reproduction rate and decreases when death rate is higher than reproduction rate *(1 mark)*. In a culture like the one in Fig. 1.2, this doesn't happen because the constant addition of nutrients and removal of waste products keep conditions favourable for growth *(1 mark)*.

c) A somatic/body cell could be taken from a patient with diabetes and its nucleus removed *(1 mark)*. This nucleus could then be inserted into an enucleated egg cell/ oocyte *(1 mark)*. These would then be fused together and stimulated to divide *(1 mark)*, which would produce an embryo from which embryonic stem cells could be harvested *(1 mark)*.

2 a) Any two from: e.g. rhizomes are stem structures that grow horizontally underground away from the parent plant. They have 'nodes' from which new shoots and roots can develop *(1 mark)*. / Stolons/runners are stem structures that grow above the ground, on the surface of the soil. New shoots and roots can either develop from nodes or form at the end of the stolon *(1 mark)*. / Suckers are shoots that grow from sucker buds/undeveloped shoots present on the shallow roots of a parent plant *(1 mark)*. / Tubers are large underground plant structures that act as a food store for the plant. They're covered in 'eyes', each of which is able to sprout and form a new plant *(1 mark)*. / Bulbs are underground food stores. New bulbs are able to develop from the original bulb and form new individual plants *(1 mark)*.

b) He should remove any leaves from the lower end of the cutting and dip it in rooting powder *(1 mark)*. He should then plant the cutting in a pot of suitable growth medium *(1 mark)* and place the pot in a propagator / cover it completely with a plastic bag *(1 mark)*. Once the cutting has developed its own roots, he should plant it in a suitable place to continue growing *(1 mark)*. *(Maximum of 3 marks available.)*

c) i) These cells are stem cells *(1 mark)*, so they can develop into any of the cell types needed to produce a new plant *(1 mark)*.

ii) Any two from: e.g. desirable characteristics will always be passed onto the clones **(1 mark)**. / Less space is required by tissue culture than would be needed to produce the same number of plants by conventional growing methods **(1 mark)**. / Plants that take a long time to produce seeds can be reproduced quickly **(1 mark)**.

d) i) The clones are all genetically identical, so they will all be susceptible to the bacterial infection **(1 mark)**.

ii) Any two from: e.g. their ideal growth conditions can be easily created **(1 mark)**. / Due to their short life-cycle they grow rapidly, so products can be made very quickly **(1 mark)**. / They can grow on a range of inexpensive materials, so are economical to use **(1 mark)**. / They can be grown at any time of year **(1 mark)**.

Section 6 — Ecosystems

1. Ecosystems and Energy Flow

Page 261 — Application Questions

Q1 a) net productivity = gross productivity – respiratory loss
net productivity = 22 861 – 17 000 = **5861 kJm^{-2}yr^{-1}**

b) % efficiency of energy transfer =
(net productivity of trophic level ÷ net productivity of previous trophic level) × 100
= (627 ÷ 5861) × 100 = **10.7%**

Q2 a) respiratory loss = gross productivity – net productivity
respiratory loss = 8072 – 2073 = **5999 kJm^{-2}yr^{-1}**
The total amount of energy taken in is the gross productivity. Once you have identified this you can plug the numbers into the equation to work out the respiratory loss (you already know the net productivity from the diagram).

b) gross productivity = net productivity + respiratory loss
gross productivity = 119 + 450 = **569 kJm^{-2}yr^{-1}**
converting m^{-2} to km^{-2} gives:
569 × 1 000 000 = **5.69 × 10^8 kJkm^{-2}yr^{-1}**
There are 1000 m in 1 km so (1000 × 1000 =)
1 000 000 m^2 in 1 km^2.

c) E.g. because some parts of the small fish aren't eaten so the energy isn't taken in. / Because some parts of the small fish are indigestible and will pass through the large fish and come out as waste.
Some questions like this are tricky to work out — you need to think about what the key phrases, like gross productivity and net productivity, actually mean. Here the question is actually asking you 'Why is the energy absorbed by the large fish less than the energy available to them from the small fish?'

d) % efficiency of energy transfer =
(net productivity of trophic level ÷ net productivity of previous trophic level) × 100
Between plant plankton and animal plankton =
(8105 ÷ 31 023) × 100 = **26.1%**
Between animal plankton and small fish=
(2073 ÷ 8105) × 100 = **25.6%**
Between small fish and large fish =
(119 ÷ 2073) × 100 = **5.7%**
This example of a food chain is a bit different — the efficiency of energy transfer decreases as you go up it. But you don't need to worry about this when you're doing the calculations — just use the equation as normal.

Page 261 — Fact Recall Questions

Q1 Biotic factors are the living features of an ecosystem (e.g. the presence of predators or food).

Q2 a) E.g. tides (affecting pH, salinity, temperature).
b) E.g. rainfall making the soil waterlogged / sunlight affecting growth.
c) E.g. drought conditions.

Q3 a) An organism that produces organic molecules using sunlight energy.
b) An organism that eats other organisms.

Q4 photosynthesis

Q5 gross productivity

Q6 Carnivores, because more of the food they eat is digestible.
Remember, herbivores only eat plants, which contain a lot of indigestible material. This means lots of the available energy is lost as waste, e.g. in faeces.

Q7 Measure the dry mass/biomass of the organisms.

Q8 Any two from: e.g. herbicides — these kill weeds that compete with crops for energy. Reducing competition means crops receive more energy, so they grow faster and become larger. / Fungicides — these kill fungal infections, so the crops use more energy for growth and less for fighting infection. / Insecticides — these kill insect pests so less biomass is lost from crops. / Natural predators are introduced to the ecosystem. These eat the pest species so crops lose less energy and biomass. / Fertilisers — these replace minerals in the soil, so more energy from the ecosystem can be used to grow. / Intensive rearing of livestock — this controls the conditions animals live in and when they're slaughtered, so more of their energy is used for growth and less is used for other activities, so more energy is transferred to their biomass.

2. Recycling in Ecosystems

Page 264 — Fact Recall Questions

Q1 E.g. carbon is absorbed by plants when they carry out photosynthesis — it becomes carbon compounds in plant tissues. Carbon is passed on through the food chain by feeding. All living organisms die and are broken down by microorganisms called decomposers. Decomposers secrete enzymes onto dead organic material to digest the carbon compounds in them. They then absorb the products of digestion. Carbon is returned to the air (and water) as all living organisms (including the decomposers) carry out respiration, which produces CO_2.

Q2 The carbon comes from fossil fuels, such as oil and coal. These are formed when dead organic matter ends up in places where there aren't any decomposers (e.g. deep oceans or bogs), and then is subject to heat and pressure over millions of years.

Q3 Rock, such as limestone, can be weathered chemically by rainwater and physically, e.g. by plant roots, animals, etc. Chemical weathering causes mineral ions and bicarbonate ions to be released from the rock into solution and enter groundwater, from where they are transported into rivers and the oceans. There they combine to form carbon-containing compounds such as $CaCO_3$.

Q4 CO_2 dissolves directly into the oceans from the atmosphere.

Q5 To make proteins/nucleic acids. / For growth.

Name of process	Bacteria responsible
Nitrogen fixation	*Rhizobium* and *Azotobacter*
Ammonification	Decomposers
Nitrification	*Nitrosomonas* and *Nitrobacter*
Denitrification	Denitrifying bacteria

Q7 Nitrogen compounds from dead organisms and animal waste are turned into ammonia by decomposers, which goes on to form ammonium ions.

Q8 denitrification

3. Succession

Page 267 — Application Questions

Q1 Primary succession, because there is no soil present in 1800.

Remember, the key difference between primary and secondary succession is soil — it's present in secondary succession, but not in primary succession. If you have a good look at the graph you'll see that there's no soil moisture in 1800. That's a pretty good sign that there's no soil, either.

Q2 The dominant plant species would have been adapted to survive without much water/in a soil with low moisture content and fluctuating ground temperatures. They would have had seeds that could remain viable for long periods of time. They would have been species of small plants / they would not have been tree species.

There's a lot going on in the graph with all the different lines — and you could get something like this in the exam. Don't let the graph's complexity put you off though. Take your time and make sure you really understand what the graph is showing, and read the questions carefully so you pick out the right bits from the graph for your answers.

Q3 E.g. the average length of time dominant plant seeds remained viable for was relatively high between 1800 and 1860. This might have been because seeds that remained viable for a long time could lie dormant until conditions were favourable enough to germinate. Between about 1860 and 1880 the average length of time fell sharply, and then continued to fall more slowly until levelling off at around 1960. This may have been because the plants that were dominant between 1800 and 1860 were succeeded by other plant species which were more suited to the changed conditions, e.g. a higher soil moisture content, so they no longer needed to be viable for long periods of time.

Q4 Between 1800 and 1920 because there were no tree species present during this time, so there would have been more light / less shade cast by the trees.

Q5 The soil moisture content is 0 between 1800 and 1820 because there is no soil. The soil moisture content increased gradually from 1820 until 1940 as the soil developed, then it increased more rapidly between 1940 and 2000 because the addition of decomposed organic material helped to increase soil moisture content and the deeper soil was able to retain more water.

Page 268 — Fact Recall Questions

Q1 The process by which an ecosystem changes over time.

Q2 primary succession

Q3 pioneer species

Q4 The largest and most complex community of plants and animals that an ecosystem can support.

Q5 E.g. deforestation / volcanic eruption / fire

Q6 The climax community for a particular climate.

Q7 The climax community that exists when succession is stopped artificially by human activities.

4. Investigating Ecosystems

Page 272 — Application Questions

Q1 a) She could place the quadrat on the ground at random locations across the field and count how much of the quadrat is covered by daisies. A square should be counted if it's more than half-covered.

 b) E.g. the student could divide the field into a grid and use a random number generator to select coordinates. The quadrat could then be placed at these coordinates and the number of daisies in each quadrat counted.

Q2 a) The kite diagram shows that species A is present between 20 and 45 m from the road with a low percentage cover. It's also present between 80-140 m, and is most abundant between 130-140 m. Species B is present between 55-130 m from the road, and is most abundant between 60-85 m. Species C is present between 0-50 m from the road and is most abundant between 0-20 m. The graph shows that soil salinity is high between 0-30 m from the road, falls sharply between 30-40 m, continues to fall until around 50 m and then remains low.

 b) Species C, as it is present between 0-50 m from the road and is the most abundant species between 0-30 m from the road, where soil salinity is highest.

 c) The data shows that at a high soil salinity there is an absence of species B, but this doesn't prove that salt spray from the road is the cause. Species B might be absent for other reasons, e.g. because it is out-competed by species C.

Page 272 — Fact Recall Questions

Q1 a) The number of individuals of one species in a particular area.

 b) Where a particular species is in the area being investigated.

Q2 a) Because it would be too time-consuming to measure the abundance of the entire species in the area being investigated.

 b) To avoid biased results.

Q3 It would be put on the ground at random points within the field. Pins would be dropped through the holes in the frame and every plant that each pin touched would be recorded.

In the exam, if you're asked to describe a method you could use to investigate a population, don't forget to say that you would use random samples of the area you are investigating.

Q4 For a line transect, a tape measure is placed along the transect and the species that touch the tape measure are recorded. For a belt transect, data is collected along the transect using frame quadrats placed next to each other.

Q5 To capture ground insects.

1 B *(1 mark)*
2 D *(1 mark)*
3 a) i) E.g. they could set up a belt transect / place quadrats next to each other along a transect *(1 mark)* leading from the edge of the field that's next to the stream into the middle of the field *(1 mark)*.
      ii) E.g. they could count how many squares of each quadrat are covered by marsh marigolds by counting a square if it's more than half-covered *(1 mark)*. Measuring percentage cover is a quick way to investigate the abundance of marsh marigolds *(1 mark)* and they wouldn't have to count all the individual marsh marigolds *(1 mark)*.
   b) The non-living features of an ecosystem *(1 mark)*.
   c) Regular grazing would prevent the normal climax community from developing *(1 mark)*, so succession would be deflected from its natural course *(1 mark)*.
4 a) Light / the Sun *(1 mark)*
   b) gross productivity (secondary consumer 1)
      = net productivity (primary consumer 1) – energy lost
      = 2619 – 476 = 2143 kJm^{-2}yr^{-1}
      net productivity = gross productivity – respiratory loss
      net productivity = 2143 – 1571 = **572 kJm^{-2}yr^{-1}**
      (1 mark for correct working only, 2 marks for correct answer)
   c) E.g. because some parts of food, e.g. roots or bones, aren't eaten by organisms so the energy isn't taken in *(1 mark)*. Also, some parts of food are indigestible so pass through organisms and come out as waste, e.g. faeces *(1 mark)*.
   d) percentage efficiency of energy transfer =
      (net productivity of trophic level ÷ net productivity of previous trophic level) × 100
      between the producer and primary consumer 1 =
      (2619 ÷ 38750) × 100 = 6.76%
      between the producer and primary consumer 2 =
      (1265 : 38750) × 100 – 3.26%
      6.76 – 3.26 = **3.5%**
      (1 mark for each correct percentage efficiency of energy transfer or 3 marks for correct answer)
   e) Nitrogen compounds from dead organisms and animal waste are turned into ammonia by decomposers (e.g. bacteria or fungi), which goes on to form ammonium ions (ammonification) *(1 mark)*. *Nitrosomonas* change ammonium ions into nitrites *(1 mark)*. *Nitrobacter* change nitrites into nitrates (nitrification) *(1 mark)*. Nitrates are converted into nitrogen gas by denitrifying bacteria (denitrification) *(1 mark)*.

Section 7 — Populations and Sustainability

1. Variation in Population Size

Page 279 — Application Questions
Q1 the number of mice
    Remember, biotic factors are the living things in an ecosystem.
Q2 As the temperature fell, the size of the mouse population decreased. This could have been because the cold weather caused the temperature of the surroundings to fall below the body temperature of the mice. Mice are mammals, so if that had happened the mice would have used up more energy maintaining their body temperature. This would have meant less energy was available for growth and reproduction, causing their population size to fall.
Q3 As the mouse population size increased, there was more food for the owls and so the owl population grew. As the owl population increased, more mice were eaten and so the mice population began to fall. This meant there was less food for the owls, so their population decreased — and so this cycle continued.

Page 279 — Fact Recall Questions
Q1 All organisms of one species in a habitat.
Q2 a) Interspecific competition is when organisms of different species compete with each other for the same resources.
    b) i) The population size of both of the species competing will be lowered. This is because there are fewer resources available to both populations, so they will both be less likely to reproduce.
       ii) The less well adapted species will be outcompeted and won't be able to exist alongside the better adapted species.
    c) E.g. grey squirrels and red squirrels in the UK compete for the same food sources and habitats. In areas where they both live, both populations are smaller than they would be if only one species lived there. The red squirrel has also disappeared from large areas as the grey squirrel is better adapted to the surroundings.
Q3 a) Intraspecific competition is when organisms of the same species compete with each other for the same resources.
    b) The population of a species increases when resources are plentiful. As the population increases, there'll be more organisms competing for the same amount of space and food. Eventually, resources such as food and space become limiting, so the population begins to decline. A smaller population then means that there's less competition for space and food, which is better for growth and reproduction, so the population starts to grow again.
Q4 It is the maximum stable population size of a species that an ecosystem can support.
Q5 It will cause the predator population to increase as well because there is more food available for the predators.
Q6 limiting factor

2. Conservation of Ecosystems

Page 283 — Fact Recall Questions

Q1   Ecosystems provide resources for lots of things that humans need and these are traded on a local and global scale. If the ecosystems aren't conserved, the resources that we use now will be lost, so there will be less trade in the future.

Q2   E.g. because people use them for activities such as walking.

Q3   Any two from, e.g. trees are cleared in strips or patches rather than over large areas, as this allows trees to grow back more quickly and reduces soil erosion. / Trees can be coppiced rather than cut down, which allows the same tree to grow back, rather than requiring a new one to be planted. / Native trees are preferentially planted, which are considered better for biodiversity due to their long-established interactions with other native species. / Young trees are surrounded by protective tubes which prevents them from being damaged by grazing animals. / Young trees are attached to posts, which provide support and make them more likely to grow successfully. / Trees are spaced out when they are planted, reducing competition between them for light and other resources, and making it more likely that they'll survive and grow successfully.

Q4   Restricting mesh sizes can reduce the number of unwanted fish of the wrong species that are caught and can allow younger fish to escape the net, meaning they are more likely to reach breeding age and maintain the population.

Q5   Many plants and animals live in the forests in the Terai Arc, but the forest is being put at risk by local populations who need wood from the forests for fuel and from people who want to clear areas of the forest to make way for housing and other developments. Elephants and tigers can come into conflict with farmers as they can eat and trample crops and kill livestock.

Q6   Ecotourism projects have been developed in the Maasai Mara, which allow people to make money from the environment without damaging it. This alternative source of income reduces the reliance of the local population on farming, and therefore reduces damage to the grasslands caused by overgrazing.

3. Human Impact on Ecosystems

Page 286 — Fact Recall Questions

Q1   Any two from: e.g. explorers and sailors many years ago ate some of the animals which directly affected their populations. / Non-native animals have been introduced to the islands by humans. The non-native animals eat some native species, causing a decrease in the populations of native species. / Non-native plants have been introduced to the islands by humans. The non-native species compete with native plant species, causing a decrease in their populations. / Fishing has caused a decrease in the populations of some of the sea life. / An increase in tourism has caused damage to the ecosystems as more land is cleared and pollution is increased.

Q2   E.g. commercial whaling has been banned from the ocean surrounding Antarctica, and seal hunting has also been banned. Fishing limits have been set. Many research stations treat their sewage before releasing it, to reduce its effect on the environment, and all waste other than food and sewage is removed by ship for disposal in other countries, in order to reduce pollution. There are tourists restrictions to prevent them from causing damage to the ecosystems of the area. Ships that use thick oil as a fuel have been banned from the area, as heavy oil spills are likely to cause more damage and be harder to clean up than spills of lighter fuels.

Q3   E.g. erosion of footpaths can cause soil to be washed into lakes and rivers, altering the pH of the water and negatively affecting organisms living in aquatic environments. Erosion of footpaths can also cause people to walk on the vegetation on either side of the path, destroying vegetation. / Phosphates in fertilisers, in detergents and in the water released by local sewage works have accumulated in some of the lakes. These can contribute to algal blooms, which deoxygenate the water and can kill fish.

Exam-style Questions — pages 288-289

1   B *(1 mark)*

visitor numbers in 2015: 280 000
visitor numbers in 2009: 220 000
280 000 – 220 000 = 60 000
(60 000 ÷ 220 000) × 100 = 27.27... = 27%

2   a)   The population sizes of species A and B rise and fall cyclically over the 20 year period *(1 mark)*. The population sizes increase when resources are plentiful but decrease when resources become limited *(1 mark)*. This is because of intraspecific competition / organisms of species A are competing with each other for the same resources, and organisms of species B are competing with each other for the same resources *(1 mark)*.

   b)   (biotic) limiting factor *(1 mark)*

   c)   The carrying capacity of the ecosystem *(1 mark)*.

3   a)   E.g. mangrove swamps are a unique ecosystem, and some people believe we have an ethical duty to protect them *(1 mark)*. People may also believe it is important to preserve mangrove swamps because of the protection they give the coastline, which could protect other ecosystems and people *(1 mark)*.

   You don't actually need to know anything about mangrove swamps to answer this question — the command word 'suggest' means that you're expected to use your scientific knowledge of the benefits of conservation to come up with possible reasons. So your answer could include any sensible economic, social, ethical or ecological reasons that people may have for supporting conservation.

   b)   *7-9 marks:*
   The answer gives a detailed discussion of all three methods for protecting the mangrove habitat, giving well-explained disadvantages and advantages of each. Scientific terminology is used correctly, and the answer demonstrates a detailed understanding of the conservation of ecosystems.
   The answer has a clear and logical structure.
   The information given is relevant and detailed.
   4-6 marks:
   The answer includes a discussion of each of the three methods for protecting the habitat, but it may not include both advantages and disadvantages for all three, so the comparison of the methods is limited. Scientific terminology is used correctly, and the answer is mostly well-structured.
   Most of the information given is relevant and there is some detail involved.
   1-3 marks:
   The answer doesn't consider all of the habitat protection methods mentioned, and the discussion of the advantages and disadvantages of any of the methods is very limited. Use of scientific terminology is poor.
   The answer has no clear structure. The information given is basic and lacking in detail. It may not all be relevant.
   0 marks:
   No relevant information is given.

Here are some points your answer may include:
Creating a nature reserve and heavily restricting access would be an effective way of preserving the mangrove swamp, as it would prevent any further damage to the ecosystem by local populations. However, this suggestion doesn't take the needs of the local population into account, so doesn't represent an ethical solution to the problem. In addition, maintaining restrictions to access in the long term will require continued investment from the charity, so the solution isn't economically sustainable.

On the other hand, paying local people to limit their use of the mangrove swamp to sustainable levels may represent an effective way of conserving the ecosystem whilst taking the needs of the local population into account. It allows them to continue using resources from the swamp, but at a reduced level, and offers them financial compensation. However, like the nature reserve suggestion, this solution requires a continued investment from the charity, so doesn't represent an economically sustainable solution. It may also be hard to enforce, as it requires constant monitoring of what is being taken from the swamp.

The final suggestion, of developing ecotourism in the area, may be an effective way of protecting the mangrove swamp. By providing an alternative income for local populations it could reduce their need to take wood from the swamp to make charcoal, and gives the local population an incentive to conserve the swamp effectively. Unlike the other two suggestions, it may not require long-term investment from the conservation charity, so may be self-sustaining. It would, however, require careful management to make sure that tourists did not damage the ecosystem. Of these suggestions, ecotourism therefore seems like the best long-term solution for conserving the mangrove swamp, as it takes the needs of local people into account and doesn't require indefinite investment from the charity.

c) i) Preservation keeps ecosystems exactly as they are, so nothing is removed, and human activity is limited. Conservation, on the other hand, does allow the removal of resources from ecosystems *(1 mark)*.

   ii) Creating a nature reserve and restricting access *(1 mark)*.

4 a) E.g. it's the right thing to do, especially if the ecosystem is at risk because of human activity. / There is a moral responsibility to conserve ecosystems for future generations, so they can enjoy and use them. *(1 mark)*

If the question tells you to 'outline' a reason for something (like this one), you need to give a bit more than a one word answer — make sure you include a little bit of detail.

b) It means taking enough resources from the woodland to meet the needs of people today without reducing the ability of people in the future to meet their own needs *(1 mark)*.

c) Any two from: e.g.

Method	Explanation
Trees cleared in strips or patches.	Woodland grows back more quickly in smaller areas between bits of existing woodland than it does in larger, open areas.
Cleared strips or patches of woodland aren't too large or exposed.	Lots of soil erosion can occur on large areas of bare ground. If the soil is eroded, newly planted trees won't be able to grow.
Timber is harvested by coppicing/cut down in a way that lets them grow back.	New trees don't need to be planted.
Native species are preferentially planted.	Native species are better for biodiversity.
Planted trees are attached to posts / grown in plastic tubes.	This makes it more likely the trees will survive to become mature adults as they're supported/protected.
Trees aren't planted too close together.	The trees aren't competing with each other for space or resources, so they're more likely to survive.

(Maximum of 4 marks available — 1 mark for each correct method up to a maximum of 2 marks and 1 mark for each correctly matched explanation of how the method works).

Glossary

A

Abiotic factor
A non-living feature of an ecosystem.

Abiotic stress
Something that's potentially harmful to a plant that's natural but non-living, e.g. a drought (water stress).

Abscisic acid (ABA)
A plant hormone that can trigger stomatal closure.

Abscission layer
A layer of cells at the bottom of a leaf stalk, which expand when stimulated by ethene, breaking the cell walls and causing the leaf to fall off.

Abundance
The number of individuals of one species in a particular area.

Accurate result
A result that is really close to the true answer.

Acetylcholine (ACh)
A type of neurotransmitter that binds to cholinergic receptors.

Actin
The thin myofilament protein in muscle fibres.

Actin-myosin cross bridge
The bond formed when a myosin head binds to an actin filament.

Activator
A transcription factor that starts transcription.

ADP (adenosine diphosphate)
A molecule made up of adenine, a ribose sugar and two phosphate groups. ATP is synthesised from ADP and a phosphate group.

Adrenal gland
An endocrine gland that secretes hormones including cortisol, aldosterone, adrenaline and noradrenaline.

Adrenaline
A hormone secreted from the adrenal glands that has many effects, including increasing the blood glucose concentration.

Aerobic respiration
Process where energy is released from glucose using oxygen.

Alcoholic fermentation
A type of anaerobic respiration that occurs in yeast (and plants). Ethanol is the final product.

Alkaloid
A nitrogen-containing chemical produced by plants, which may have a bitter taste, noxious smell or poisonous characteristics to protect against herbivory.

Allele
One or more alternative versions of the same gene.

Allele frequency
How often an allele occurs in a population.

Allopatric speciation
When populations become reproductively isolated through a combination of geographical isolation and natural selection.

Alpha (α) cell
A type of cell found in the islets of Langerhans, which secretes glucagon.

Ammonification
The process in which nitrogen compounds from dead organisms or waste material are turned into ammonia by decomposers. This ammonia then goes on to form ammonium ions.

Anaerobic respiration
Process where energy is released from glucose without oxygen.

Antidiuretic hormone (ADH)
A hormone which regulates the water potential of the blood by controlling the permeability of the cells of the distal convoluted tubule and the collecting duct in the kidney.

Apical dominance
When the apical bud (tip of a plant shoot) grows more than the side shoots.

Apoptosis
A highly controlled process by which cells are broken down.

Artificial embryo twinning
A technique for cloning animals. The technique involves manually separating embryos into individual cells, which each develop into further embryos that are implanted into surrogate animals.

Artificial selection
When humans select individuals in a population to breed together to get desirable traits.

Aseptic technique
A technique used to prevent the unwanted growth or transfer of microorganisms.

ATP (adenosine triphosphate)
A molecule made up of adenine, a ribose sugar and three phosphate groups. It is the immediate source of energy in a cell.

ATPase
An enzyme which catalyses the hydrolysis of ATP into ADP and a phosphate group.

ATP-creatine phosphate (CP) system
A system that generates ATP very quickly by phosphorylating ADP using a phosphate group from creatine phosphate.

ATP synthase
An enzyme which catalyses the synthesis of ATP from ADP and a phosphate group.

Autonomic nervous system
A division of the peripheral nervous system that controls unconscious activities, e.g. heart rate.

Autosomal linkage
When alleles on the same chromosome end up in the same daughter cell and so are inherited together.

Autosome
A chromosome that isn't a sex chromosome.

Auxin
A type of plant growth hormone produced in the tips of shoots, which stimulates cell elongation.

B

BAC (Bacterial artificial chromosome)
A man-made plasmid used in gene technology.

Batch fermentation
Where microorganisms are grown in individual batches in a fermentation vessel — when one culture ends it's removed and a different batch of microorganisms is grown.

Beta (β) cell
A type of cell found in the islets of Langerhans, which secretes insulin.

Bioinformatics
Developing and using computer software that can analyse, organise and store biological data.

Biomass
The mass of living material in an organism.

Bioremediation
A process that uses organisms (usually microorganisms) to remove pollutants from contaminated sites.

Biotechnology
The industrial use of living organisms (or parts of living organisms) to produce food, drugs and other products.

Biotic factor
A living feature of an ecosystem.

Body plan
The general structure of an organism.

Bowman's capsule
A hollow ball at the start of a nephron, which contains the glomerulus where ultrafiltration takes place.

C

Calvin cycle
Another name for the light-independent reaction of photosynthesis (see that entry).

Carbon cycle
The movement of carbon through living organisms and the non-living environment.

Carrier
A person carrying an allele which is not expressed in the phenotype but that can be passed on to offspring.

Carrying capacity
The maximum stable population size of a species that an ecosystem can support.

Central nervous system (CNS)
Part of the nervous system made up of the brain and spinal cord.

Cerebellum
Part of the brain, which plays an important role in muscle coordination, posture and coordination of balance.

Cerebrum
The largest part of the brain, which plays an important role in vision, hearing, learning and thinking.

Chain termination method
A technique used to sequence DNA.

Chemiosmosis
The movement of protons (H+ ions) across a membrane which generates ATP.

Chi-squared test
A statistical test that that's used to see if the results of an experiment support a theory.

Chlorophyll
A photosynthetic pigment found in chloroplasts. There are different types of this pigment, e.g. chlorophyll a.

Chloroplast
A small, flattened organelle found in plant cells. It is the site of photosynthesis.

Chlorosis
Where a plant doesn't produce enough chlorophyll and turns yellow.

Cholinergic synapse
A synapse that uses the neurotransmitter acetylcholine.

Climax community
The largest and most complex community of plants and animals an ecosystem can support.

Cloning
The process of producing genetically identical cells or organisms from the cells of an existing organism.

Closed culture
A culture which has been grown in a vessel that's isolated from the external environment.

Codominant allele
An allele whose characteristic appears together with another allele in the phenotype because neither allele is recessive.

Coenzyme
A molecule that aids the function of an enzyme. They work by transferring a chemical group from one molecule to another.

Coenzyme A (CoA)
A type of coenzyme involved in respiration. It transfers acetate from one molecule to another.

Compensation point (for light intensity)
The level of light intensity at which the rate of photosynthesis exactly matches the rate of respiration.

Computational biology
Using computers to study biology, e.g. to create computer simulations and mathematical models.

Conservation (of ecosystems)
A dynamic process that involves the protection, management and sometimes the reclamation of ecosystems.

Consumer
An organism that eats other organisms.

Continuous fermentation
Where microorganisms are continually grown in a fermentation vessel without stopping.

Continuous variation
When the individuals in a population vary within a range — there are no distinct categories.

Control variable
A variable you keep constant throughout an experiment.

Convergence (at a synapse)
When many neurones connect to one neurone.

Correlation
A relationship between two variables.

Culture (microorganisms)
A population of one type of microorganism that's been grown under controlled conditions.

Cutting (plant)
A section of a plant (e.g. from a stem, root or leaf) that can be used to produce new plants via vegetative propagation.

Cyclic AMP (cAMP)
A molecule that activates proteins inside cells by altering their 3D structures.

Deamination
The process by which nitrogen-containing amino groups are removed from amino acids, forming ammonia and organic acids.

Decarboxylation
The removal of carbon dioxide from a molecule.

Deciduous plant
A plant that loses its leaves in winter.

Decomposer
An organism that breaks down dead or undigested organic material.

Dehydrogenation
The removal of hydrogen from a molecule.

Denitrification
The process in which nitrates in the soil are converted into nitrogen gas by denitrifying bacteria.

Dependent variable
The variable you measure in an experiment.

Depolarisation
A decrease in the potential difference across a cell's membrane, making it less negative (i.e. more positive) than the resting potential.

Detoxification
The process by which harmful substances are broken down by the liver into less harmful compounds, which can then be excreted from the body.

Diabetes mellitus (Type I)
A condition in which blood glucose concentration can't be controlled properly because the body doesn't produce any insulin.

Diabetes mellitus (Type II)
A condition in which blood glucose concentration can't be controlled properly because the body doesn't produce enough insulin or the body's cells don't respond properly to insulin.

Dihybrid inheritance
The inheritance of two characteristics which are controlled by different genes.

Directional selection
Where individuals with alleles for characteristics of an extreme type are more likely to survive, reproduce and pass on their alleles.

Discontinuous variation
When an individual falls into only one of two or more distinct categories — there are no intermediates.

Distribution
Where a particular species is within an area being investigated.

Divergence (at a synapse)
When one neurone connects to many neurones.

DNA ligase
An enzyme that joins together the sticky ends of DNA fragments by joining up their sugar-phosphate backbones.

DNA polymerase
An enzyme that joins together the nucleotides on a new strand of DNA during DNA replication.

DNA profile
A DNA gel that shows the number of times repetitive, non-coding base sequences are repeated at different loci in an individual.

DNA sequencing
A technique used to determine the order of bases in a section of DNA.

Dominant allele
An allele whose characteristic appears in the phenotype even when there's only one copy.

E

Ecosystem
All the organisms living in a particular area and all the non-living (abiotic) conditions found there.

Ectotherm
An animal that can't control its body temperature internally.

Effector
A cell that brings about a response to a stimulus, to produce an effect.

Electron carrier
A protein that transfers electrons from one molecule to another.

Electron transport chain
A chain of proteins through which excited electrons flow.

Electroporation
A technique that uses an electric field to increase the permeability of cell membranes, which allows the cells to take up biological material, e.g. plasmids.

Embryonic stem cell
A stem cell harvested from an embryo, which can differentiate into any of the cell types in the body.

Endocrine gland
A group of cells specialised to secrete hormones directly into the blood.

Endotherm
An animal that can control its body temperature internally by homeostasis.

Enucleated cell
A cell which has had the nucleus removed.

Epidemiology
The study of health and disease within a population.

Epistasis
When an allele of one gene masks (blocks) the expression of the alleles of other genes.

Ethene (in plants)
A plant hormone produced by ageing leaves, which stimulates leaf loss. It also stimulates enzymes which promote ripening.

Etiolation
Where a plant grows abnormally long and spindly because it's not getting enough light.

Evolution
The change in allele frequency in a population over time.

Excretion
The removal of the waste products of metabolism from the body.

Exon
A section of DNA that codes for amino acids.

F

FAD
A type of coenzyme involved in respiration. It transfers hydrogen from one molecule to another.

Fermentation vessel
A large container in which microorganisms can be grown on an industrial scale.

'Fight or flight' response
A response involving the sympathetic nervous system and adrenaline, which prepares the body for action in reaction to a threat.

Filtrate
The liquid and small molecules present in the kidney tubules following ultrafiltration of the blood. Also called the tubular fluid.

Final electron acceptor
A molecule which accepts an electron at the end of an electron transport chain. E.g. oxygen in respiration.

First messenger
A chemical involved in cell signalling (e.g. a hormone) that binds to a receptor in a cell membrane and triggers activity inside the cell.

Founder effect
The reduction in genetic diversity that occurs when just a few organisms from a population start a new colony.

Frame quadrat
A square frame, divided into a grid of 100 smaller squares, which can be used to investigate the abundance and distribution of organisms in an area.

G

Gamete
A sex cell — e.g. the sperm cell in males or the egg cell in females.

Gel electrophoresis
A technique that allows DNA fragments, RNA fragments or proteins to be separated on a gel according to size (length).

Gene
A section of DNA that codes for a protein (polypeptide) which results in a characteristic.

Gene pool
The complete range of alleles present in a population.

Generator potential
The change in potential difference across a cell membrane due to the presence of a stimulus.

Gene therapy
Possible treatment option for genetic disorders and some cancers that involves altering defective alleles inside cells.

Genetic bottleneck
An event that causes a big reduction in the size of a population.

Genetic disorder
An inherited disorder caused by an abnormal gene or chromosome.

Genetic drift
The process whereby an allele becomes more common in a population due to chance.

Genetic engineering
The manipulation of an organism's DNA.

Genome
All the genetic material in an organism.

Genotype
The alleles an organism has.

Geographical isolation
When a physical barrier, e.g. a flood, divides a population of a species, causing some individuals to become separated from the main population.

Geotropism
The growth of a plant in response to gravity.

Germ line gene therapy
A possible cure for genetic disorders and some cancers that involves altering defective genes inside sex cells.

Gibberellin
A type of plant growth hormone that is produced in young leaves and in seeds. It stimulates seed germination, stem elongation, side shoot formation and flowering.

Glomerular filtration rate
The rate at which blood is filtered from the glomerulus into the Bowman's capsule.

Glomerulus
A bundle of capillaries that loop inside the Bowman's capsule of a nephron. Where ultrafiltration takes place.

Glucagon
A hormone secreted by the pancreas that has an important role in raising blood glucose concentration.

Gluconeogenesis
The conversion of fatty acids or amino acids to glucose, activated by glucagon.

Glycogenesis
The conversion of glucose to glycogen, activated by insulin.

Glycogenolysis
The conversion of glycogen to glucose, activated by glucagon.

Glycolysis
The first stage of aerobic respiration — here glucose is converted into pyruvate.

Gross productivity
The energy available to organisms that is absorbed by them.

H

Habitat
The place where an organism lives.

Haploid
When a cell contains one copy of each chromosome.

Hardy-Weinberg principle
A mathematical model that predicts that the frequency of alleles in a population won't change from one generation to the next provided that certain conditions are met.

Herbivory
When plants are eaten by animals (including insects).

Heterozygous
When an organism carries two different alleles for the same characteristic.

Hexose sugar
A monosaccharide that has six carbon atoms, e.g. glucose.

High-throughput sequencing
DNA sequencing techniques that can sequence up to 1000 times more bases in a given time compared to original methods.

Homeobox sequence
A sequence in a homeotic gene that codes for the homeodomain (part of the protein that binds to DNA, allowing the protein to act as a transcription factor).

Homeostasis
The maintenance of a constant internal environment.

Homozygous
When an organism carries two copies of the same allele.

Hormone
A chemical messenger secreted from an endocrine gland.

Host cell
A cell that is used to carry recombinant DNA.

Hox genes
Genes that encode proteins which control body plan development.

Human chorionic gonadotropin (hCG)
A hormone that is only found in the urine of pregnant women, which allows it to be used in pregnancy testing.

Hydrolysis
The splitting (lysis) of a molecule using water (hydro).

Hyperpolarisation
An increase in the potential difference across a cell's membrane, making it more negative than the resting potential.

Hypothalamus
A part of the brain that controls body temperature and monitors water potential of the blood.

Hypothesis
A specific testable statement, based on a theory, about what will happen in a test situation.

I

Immobilised enzyme
An enzyme that is attached to an insoluble material so it can't become mixed with the products of a reaction.

Independent variable
The variable you change in an experiment.

Indoleacetic acid (IAA)
A type of auxin produced in the tips of shoots and roots in flowering plants.

Insulin
A hormone secreted by the pancreas that has an important role in lowering blood glucose concentration.

Interspecific competition
Competition between organisms of different species for the same resources.

Intraspecific competition
Competition between organisms of the same species for the same resources.

Intron
A section of DNA that doesn't code for amino acids.

Islet of Langerhans
An area of endocrine tissue in the pancreas, containing α and β cells.

Isolated enzyme
An enzyme not contained within the cells of organisms.

K

Krebs cycle
The third stage of aerobic respiration. It is a series of oxidation-reduction reactions that produces reduced coenzymes and ATP.

L

Lac operon
An operon containing the genes responsible for producing the enzymes needed to respire lactose in E. coli.

Lactate fermentation
A type of anaerobic respiration that occurs in mammals (and some bacteria). Lactate is the final product.

Light-dependent reaction
The first stage of photosynthesis. Light energy is absorbed by photosynthetic pigments and converted to ATP and reduced NADP.

Light harvesting system
A complex of proteins that surrounds a reaction centre and transfers light to it to boost the energy available for electron excitement to take place.

Light-independent reaction
The second stage of photosynthesis. Here ATP and reduced NADP (from the light-dependent reaction) are used to make glucose from carbon dioxide.

Limiting factor of photosynthesis
A variable that can slow down the rate of photosynthesis.

Limiting factor of population
A biotic or abiotic factor that stops the population size of a species increasing.

Link reaction
The second stage of aerobic respiration where pyruvate is converted into acetyl coenzyme A.

Locus
The position on a chromosome where a particular allele is found.

Loop of Henle
Part of the kidney nephron responsible for establishing the water potential gradient, which allows water to be reabsorbed by the kidney.

M

Mature mRNA
mRNA strands containing only exons — the introns have been removed.

Medulla oblongata
Part of the brain which automatically controls breathing rate and heart rate.

Metabolism
All the chemical reactions that occur within a living organism, which are essential for life.

Micropropagation
A technique where tissue culture is used to produce lots of cloned plants very quickly.

Mitochondrion
An oval shaped organelle found in plant and animal cells. It is the site of respiration.

Model (scientific)
A simplified picture of what's physically going on.

Monogenic characteristic
A characteristic influenced by one gene.

Monogenic inheritance
The inheritance of a single characteristic (gene) controlled by different alleles.

Mutation
Any change in the DNA base (nucleotide) sequence.

Myelin sheath (in the peripheral nervous system)
A layer of Schwann cells around a neurone that acts as an electrical insulator and speeds up conduction of nervous impulses.

Myofibril
A long, cylindrical organelle within a muscle fibre that's highly specialised for contraction.

Myosin
The protein that makes up the thick myofilaments in myofibrils.

N

NAD
A type of coenzyme involved in respiration. It transfers hydrogen from one molecule to another.

NADP
A coenzyme involved in photosynthesis. It transfers hydrogen from one molecule to another.

Natural selection
The process whereby an allele becomes more common in a population because it codes for an adaptation that makes an organism more likely to survive, reproduce and pass on its alleles to the next generation.

Negative feedback mechanism
When a system reacts to a change in a way that pushes it back towards a stable state.

Nephron
One of the filtering units of the kidney, responsible for removing waste substances such as urea from the blood.

Net productivity
The amount of energy that's available to the next trophic level in a food chain.

Neuromuscular junction
A specialised cholinergic synapse between a motor neurone and a muscle cell.

Neurotransmitter
A chemical that transmits a nerve impulse from one nerve cell to another nerve cell or to a muscle cell.

Nitrification
The process in which ammonium ions in the soil are changed into nitrogen compounds by nitrifying bacteria called *Nitrosomonas* and *Nitrobacter*.

Nitrogen cycle
The conversion of nitrogen into a usable form and its movement through living organisms and the non-living environment.

Nitrogen fixation
The process in which nitrogen gas in the atmosphere is turned into ammonia by bacteria such as called *Rhizobium* and *Azotobacter*.

O

Oocyte
An immature egg cell.

Operator
A DNA sequence that transcription factors bind to.

Operon
A section of DNA that contains structural genes that are all transcribed together, control elements and sometimes a regulatory gene.

Ornithine cycle
A cycle of biochemical reactions in which ammonia is combined with carbon dioxide to create urea and water.

Osmoreceptor
A cell in the hypothalamus which monitors the water potential of the blood.

Oxidation
A chemical reaction where a molecule loses electrons, and may have lost hydrogen or gained oxygen.

Oxidative phosphorylation
The final stage in aerobic respiration. Energy carried by electrons, from reduced coenzymes, is used to make ATP.

P

Pacinian corpuscle
A type of mechanoreceptor found in your skin.

Palindromic sequence
A sequence of DNA bases that consists of antiparallel base pairs (base pairs that read the same in opposite directions).

Parasympathetic nervous system
A division of the autonomic nervous system which calms the body down. It's the 'rest and digest' system.

PCR (polymerase chain reaction)
A technique used to make millions of identical copies of a DNA fragment in a few hours.

Peer review
Where a scientific report is sent out to peers (other scientists) who examine the data and results, and if they think that the conclusion is reasonable it's published.

Peripheral nervous system
Part of the nervous system that connects the CNS to the rest of the body. It consists of the somatic and autonomic nervous systems.

Pharming
Producing pharmaceuticals using genetically modified organisms, such as animals.

Phenotype
The characteristics an organism's alleles produce.

Phenotypic ratio
The ratio of different phenotypes in the offspring.

Pheromone
A signalling chemical, released by an organism, that produces a response in other organisms.

Phosphorylation
The process of adding phosphate to a molecule.

Photolysis
The splitting (lysis) of a molecule using light (photo) energy.

Photophosphorylation
The process of adding phosphate to a molecule using light energy.

Photosynthesis
The process where energy from light is used to make glucose from carbon dioxide and water.

Photosynthetic pigment
A coloured substance (e.g. chlorophyll a) that absorbs the light energy needed for photosynthesis.

Photosystem
A protein and photosynthetic pigment structure found in the thylakoid membranes of chloroplasts in plants and algae.

Phototropism
The growth of a plant in response to light.

Pioneer species
The first species to colonise an area during succession.

Pituitary gland
A gland located beneath the hypothalamus in the brain, which releases hormones and stimulates other glands to release hormones.

Plagioclimax
The climax community produced when succession is artificially stopped by human activities.

Plant growth hormone
A chemical that speeds up or slows down plant growth.

Point quadrat
A horizontal bar on two legs with a series of holes set at intervals along its length, through which pins are dropped. Can be used to investigate the abundance and distribution of organisms in an area.

Polygenic characteristic
A characteristic influenced by many genes.

Population
All the organisms of one species in a habitat.

Positive feedback mechanism
When a system reacts to a change in a way that amplifies it away from a stable state.

Potential difference
The voltage across a cell membrane.

Precise result
A result that is really close to the mean.

Predation
Where an organism (the predator) kills and eats another organism (the prey).

Prediction
See hypothesis.

Preservation (of ecosystems)
The protection of ecosystems so they're kept exactly as they are.

Primary mRNA
mRNA strand that contains both introns and exons.

Primary succession
Succession which happens on newly formed or exposed land with no soil.

Primer
A short piece of single stranded DNA that is complementary to the bases at the start of the DNA fragment you want.

Probability
How likely something is to happen.

Producer
An organism that produces organic molecules using sunlight energy.

Promoter
A DNA sequence (located before the structural genes in an operon) that RNA polymerase binds to.

Phylogenetics
The study of the evolutionary history of organisms.

R

Reaction centre
A site where electrons are excited during the light-dependent reaction of photosynthesis.

Receptor
A cell, or protein on a cell surface membrane, that detects a specific stimulus.

Recessive allele
An allele whose characteristic only appears in the phenotype if there are two copies present.

Recognition sequence
A specific palindromic sequence in DNA recognised by a restriction enzyme.

Recombinant DNA
The name for DNA formed by joining together DNA from different sources.

Redox reaction
A chemical reaction that involves oxidation and reduction.

Reduction
A chemical reaction where a molecule gains electrons, and may have gained hydrogen or lost oxygen.

Reflex action
An automatic nervous response to a stimulus.

Regulatory gene
A gene that codes for a transcription factor (either an activator or repressor).

Repolarisation
The return of a cell membrane to its resting potential.

Repressor
A transcription factor that stops transcription.

Reproductive isolation
When two populations of the same species are unable to breed together to produce fertile offspring.

Respiratory loss
The amount of energy lost to the environment when organisms use energy produced from respiration for movement or body heat.

Respiratory quotient
The volume of carbon dioxide produced when a substrate is respired, divided by the volume of oxygen consumed, in a set period of time.

Respiratory substrate
Any biological molecule that can be broken down in respiration to release energy.

Respirometer
A device that can be used to measure the rate of oxygen being taken up by an organism.

Resting potential
The potential difference across a cell membrane when the cell is at rest.

Restriction enzymes
Enzymes that recognise specific recognition sequences and cut DNA at these places.

Reverse transcriptase
An enzyme that makes a DNA copy of RNA.

R_f value
The distance a substance moves through the stationary phase during thin-layer chromatography, relative to the solvent.

Ribulose bisphosphate carboxylase (rubisco)
An enzyme which catalyses the formation of glycerate 3-phosphate from carbon dioxide and ribulose bisphosphate (RuBP) in the light-independent reaction of photosynthesis.

S

Saltatory conduction
The process in myelinated neurones by which a nervous impulse travels between nodes of Ranvier.

Saprobiontic nutrition
The process of feeding on dead organic matter used by decomposers.

Sarcomere
A short contractile unit that's part of a myofibril, made up of overlapping myosin and actin filaments.

Saturation point (in photosynthesis)
The point at which a particular factor no longer limits the rate of reaction. Here another factor has begun to limit the rate of reaction.

Schwann cell
The type of cell that makes up the myelin sheath around neurones in the peripheral nervous system.

Secondary succession
Succession which happens on land cleared of all plants but where the soil remains, e.g. after a forest fire.

Second messenger
A chemical that's produced inside a cell in response to a signal outside the cell. The chemical relays the signal to the inside of the cell.

Selection pressure
Anything that affects an organism's chance of survival and reproduction.

Selective reabsorption (kidneys)
The reabsorption of useful substances along the kidney nephron back into the blood.

Sex-linked characteristic
When the allele that codes for the characteristic is located on a sex chromosome (X or Y).

Sliding filament model
The model that explains muscle contraction, in which myosin and actin filaments slide over one another to make sarcomeres contract.

Somatic cell
Any cell of a multicellular organism that isn't a reproductive cell.

Somatic cell nuclear transfer (SCNT)
A technique for cloning animals which involves taking a nucleus from a somatic cell and inserting it into an enucleated oocyte.

Somatic gene therapy
A possible treatment option for genetic disorders and some cancers that involves altering defective genes inside body cells.

Somatic nervous system
A division of the peripheral nervous system that controls conscious activities, e.g. running.

Spatial summation
Where two or more neurones release their neurotransmitters onto the same postsynaptic neurone at the same time, so the effect of their neurotransmitters is added together.

Speciation
The development of a new species.

Species
A group of similar organisms that can reproduce to give fertile offspring.

Stabilising selection
Where individuals with alleles for characteristics towards the middle of the range are more likely to survive, reproduce and pass on their alleles.

Standard growth curve (for microorganisms)
A curve with four phases that represents the growth of a population of microorganisms grown in a closed culture.

Stem cell
An unspecialised cell that can differentiate into different types of cell.

Sticky end
A small tail of unpaired DNA bases at each end of a DNA fragment.

Stimulus
A change in an organism's internal or external environment.

Structural gene
A gene that codes for a useful protein, e.g. an enzyme.

Substrate-level phosphorylation
When a phosphate group is directly transferred from one molecule to another.

Succession
The process by which an ecosystem changes over time.

Sympathetic nervous system
A division of the autonomic nervous system which gets the body ready for action. It's the 'fight or flight' system.

Sympatric speciation
When a new species develops without geographical isolation.

Synapse
A junction between a neurone and another neurone, or between a neurone and an effector cell.

Synthetic biology
A large field of biology that includes building biological systems from artificially-made molecules, redesigning biological systems to perform better, and designing new biological systems and molecules that don't exist in the natural world.

Tannin
A bitter tasting chemical released by plants to protect against herbivory.

Target cell (or target tissue)
A cell (or tissue) that has specific receptors for a particular type of chemical, such as a hormone or a neurotransmitter.

Technology transfer
The sharing of knowledge, skills and technology.

Temporal summation
Where one neurone is stimulated a lot in quick succession and the effects of all the neurotransmitters released onto the postsynaptic membrane are added together.

Theory
A possible explanation for something.

Threshold level
The level a generator potential needs to reach for an action potential to be generated.

Tissue culture (of plants)
A technique for cloning plants which involves taking stem cells from the stem or root tips of a plant and growing them in culture.

Transcription factor
A protein that binds to DNA and switches a gene on or off by increasing or decreasing the rate of transcription.

Transducer
Something that converts one form of energy into another.

Transect
A line used to help measure how plants are distributed across an area, e.g. how species change from a hedge towards the middle of a field.

Transformed cell
A host cell that has taken up recombinant DNA.

Transformed organism
A organism that has had its genes altered by genetic engineering.

Transgenic organism
An organism that has been genetically engineered to include a gene from a different species.

Trophic level
A stage in a food chain that's occupied by a particular group of organisms.

Tropism
The response of a plant to a directional stimulus.

Ultrafiltration (kidneys)
The filtering of the blood that takes place under high pressure, as blood passes from the glomerulus into the Bowman's capsule.

Valid conclusion
A conclusion that answers the original question.

Variable
A quantity that has the potential to change, e.g. weight, temperature, concentration.

Vasoconstriction
Constriction (narrowing) of a blood vessel.

Vasodilation
Dilation (widening) of a blood vessel.

Vector (in gene technology)
Something used to transfer DNA into a cell, e.g. a plasmid or a bacteriophage.

Vegetative propagation
The natural production of plant clones from non-reproductive tissues, e.g. roots, leaves and stems.

Acknowledgements

OCR Specification reference points and practical activity requirements are adapted and reproduced by permission of OCR.

Data acknowledgements

Data used to create graph on page 164 from Figure 1 of the following study Nascimento WM; Huber DJ; Cantliffe DJ. 2013. Carrot seed germination and ethylene production at high temperature in response to seed osmopriming. Horticultura Brasileira 31: 554-558

Information used in question 2 on page 205 from A. Herrel et al. 2008. Rapid large-scale evolutionary divergence in morphology and performance associated with exploitation of a different dietary resource. PNAS 105: 4792-4795. Copyright (2008) National Academy of Sciences, U.S.A.

Data used to produce the table on page 219 from A.C. Nathwani et al., Adenovirus-Associated Virus Vector–Mediated Gene Transfer in Hemophilia B: N Engl J Med 2011; 365:2357-2365

Data used to construct the graphs on page 229 from S. Hacein-Bey-Abina et al. SCIENCE 302: 415-419 (2003)

Photograph acknowledgements

Cover photo **Power and Syred**/Science Photo Library, p 1 **National Library of Medicine**/Science Photo Library, p 4 © **stevanovicigor**/iStockphoto.com, p 8 © **Ecelop**/iStockphoto.com, p 9 **Andrew Lambert Photography**/Science Photo Library, p 15 **Steve Gschmeissner**/Science Photo Library, p 17 **Ray Simons**/Science Photo Library, p 22 **Dr David Furness, Keele University**/Science Photo Library, p 24 **Don Fawcett**/Science Photo Library, p 30 **Ramon Andrade 3DCiencia**/Science Photo Library, p 32 **CNRI**/Science Photo Library, p 33 **Steve Gschmeissner**/Science Photo Library, p 35 **CNRI**/Science Photo Library, p 37 (middle) **Adam Jones**/Science Photo Library, p 37 (bottom) **Edward Kinsman**/Science Photo Library, p 44 **Dr P. Marazzi**/Science Photo Library, p 52 (top) **Prof. P. Motta/Dept. of Anatomy/University "La Sapienza", Rome**/Science Photo Library, p 52 (bottom) **Thomas Deerinck, NCMIR**/Science Photo Library, p 53 **CNRI**/Science Photo Library, p 54 **Science Photo Library**, p 55 **Biophoto Associates**/Science Photo Library, p 56 **Dr Keith Wheeler**/Science Photo Library, p 57 **Steve Gschmeissner**/Science Photo Library, p 58 (top) **ISM**/Science Photo Library, p 58 (bottom) **CNRI**/Science Photo Library, p 59 **Ralph Hutchings/Visuals Unlimited, Inc.**/Science Photo Library, p 60 **Science Photo Library**, p 62 (top) **Anthony Mercieca**/Science Photo Library, p 62 (middle) **Tom McHugh**/Science Photo Library, p 65 **Life In View**/Science Photo Library, p 66 **Life In View**/Science Photo Library, p 67 **Life In View**/Science Photo Library, p 68 **Mark Sykes**/Science Photo Library, p 70 **Steve Gschmeissner**/Science Photo Library, p 73 **Alfred Pasieka**/Science Photo Library, p 74 **Astrid & Hanns-Frieder Michler**/Science Photo Library, p 75 **PH. Gerbier**/Science Photo Library, p 79 © **dulezidar**/iStockphoto.com, p 82 **Steve Gschmeissner**/Science Photo Library, p 83 **Thomas Deerinck, NCMIR**/Science Photo Library, p 88 (top) **Eric Grave**/Science Photo Library, p 88 (bottom) **Science Photo Library**, p 89 **CNRI**/Science Photo Library, p 90 **Kent Wood**/Science Photo Library, p 94 **Dr Colin Chumbley**/Science Photo Library, p 97 (top, middle and bottom) **Martin Shields**/Science Photo Library, p 102 **David R. Frazier Photolibrary, Inc.**/Science Photo Library, p 103 **Scott Sinklier/AGStockUSA**/Science Photo Library, p 105 (top) **Dr Keith Wheeler**/Science Photo Library, p 105 (middle) © **lepas2004**/iStockphoto.com, p 105 (bottom) © **alphacell**/iStockphoto.com, p 106 **Andrew Lambert Photography**/Science Photo Library, p 114 **Dr Kari Lounatmaa**/Science Photo Library, p 120 **Biophoto Associates**/Science Photo Library, p 123 © **Arie J. Jager**/iStockphoto.com, p 126 **Sinclair Stammers**/Science Photo Library, p 130 **Dr. Jeremy Burgess**/Science Photo Library, p 132 **Dr David Furness, Keele University**/Science Photo Library, p 139 **Power And Syred**/Science Photo Library, p 142 **Philippe Psaila**/Science Photo Library, p 145 **Martin Shields**/Science Photo Library, p 151 **Mitchell Lewis, University Of Pennsylvania Medical Center**/Science Photo Library, p 154 **Eye of Science**/Science Photo Library, p 155 (top) **Dr Gopal Murti**/Science Photo Library, p 155 (middle) **Dr Keith Wheeler**/Science Photo Library, p 155 (bottom) **Claude Nuridsany & Marie Perennou**/Science Photo Library, p 156 **Dr Jeremy Burgess**/Science Photo Library, p 162 **Herve Conge, ISM**/Science Photo Library, p 163 **Geoff Kidd**/Science Photo Library, p 166 © **anakondasp**/iStockphoto.com, p 167 (top) **Wim van Egmond, Visuals Unlimited**/Science Photo Library, p 167 (bottom) **J. C. Revy, ISM**/Science Photo Library, p 169 **Eye Of Science**/Science Photo Library, p 172 **Wally Eberhart, Visuals Unlimited**/Science Photo Library, p 180 **Ed Young/AGStockUSA**/Science Photo Library, p 182 **Science Photo Library**, p 198 **Dr. John Brackenbury**/Science Photo Library, p 200 **Paul D Stewart**/Science Photo Library, p 207 **Robert Longuehaye, NIBSC**/Science Photo Library, p 209 **Tek Image**/Science Photo Library, p 213 (top) **J. C. Revy, ISM**/Science Photo Library, p 213 (middle) **Biozentrum, University Of Basel**/Science Photo Library, p 215 **Philippe Psaila**/Science Photo Library, p 216 **Bill Barksdale/AGStockUSA**/Science Photo Library, p 217 **International Rice Research Institute**, p 221 **Geoff Tompkinson**/Science Photo Library, p 222 **James King-Holmes**/Science Photo Library, p 223 **Volker Steger**/Science Photo Library, p 225 **Martin Krzywinski**/Science Photo Library, p 230 **Michael P. Gadomski**/Science Photo Library, p 231 **Cordelia Molloy**/Science Photo Library, p 232 (top) **Tony Craddock**/Science Photo Library, p 232 (bottom) **Rosenfeld Images Ltd**/Science Photo Library, p 235 **James King-Holmes**/Science Photo Library, p 236 **Reinhard Dirscherl, Visuals Unlimited**/Science Photo Library, p 237 **Philippe Plailly**/Science Photo Library, p 239 (top) **Rosenfeld Images Ltd**/Science Photo Library, p 239 (bottom) **Andrew McClenaghan**/Science Photo Library, p 240 **Cordelia Molloy**/Science Photo Library, p 242 **Ed Young**/Science Photo Library, p 246 (top) **Trevor Clifford Photography**/Science Photo Library, p 246 (bottom) **Martyn F. Chillmaid**/Science Photo Library, p 262 **Cordelia Molloy**/Science Photo Library, p 263 **Simon Fraser**/Science Photo Library, p 264 (top) **Dr. Jeremy Burgess**/Science Photo Library, p 264 (bottom) **Alfred Pasieka**/Science Photo Library, p 265 **Annie Haycock**/Science Photo Library, p 266 **Simon Fraser**/Science Photo Library, p 267 (top) **Andrea Balogh**/Science Photo Library, p 267 (middle) **Simon Fraser**/Science Photo Library, p 267 (bottom) **Simon Fraser**/Science Photo Library, p 268 **Colin Varndell**/Science Photo Library, p 270 **Martyn F. Chillmaid**/Science Photo Library, p 278 **Jeff Lepore**/Science Photo Library, p 281 (top) © **Volodymyr Goinyk**/iStockphoto.com, p 281 (bottom) **Geoff Kidd**/Science Photo Library, p 282 (top) **Angel Fitor**/Science Photo Library, p 282 (bottom) © **Utopia_88**/iStockphoto.com, p 284 (top) **David Fleetham/Visuals Unlimited, Inc.**/Science Photo Library, p 284 (bottom) **PlanetObserver**/Science Photo Library, p 285 **Frans Lanting, Mint Images**/Science Photo Library, p 286 **Charlotte Whiteley**

Every effort has been made to locate copyright holders and obtain permission to reproduce sources. For those sources where it has been difficult to trace the originator of the work, we would be grateful for information. If any copyright holder would like us to make an amendment to the acknowledgements, please notify us and we will gladly update the book at the next reprint. Thank you.

Index

A

abiotic factors 255, 256, 276
abiotic stress 96
abscisic acid (ABA) 105
abundance 269
acetylcholine (ACh) 24, 77, 90
acetylcholinesterase (AChE)
    25, 90
acetyl coenzyme A (acetyl CoA)
    134
actin filaments 82-86
actin-myosin cross bridges
    85, 86
action potentials 17, 20, 21
    factors affecting speed
        of conduction 22
adenylyl cyclase 31
ADP (adenosine diphosphate)
    111
adrenal glands 31, 32, 76
adrenaline 31, 76
aerobic respiration 132-137
    measuring the rate of 143, 145
agar plates 246, 247
alcoholic fermentation 139
alkaloids 96
allele frequencies 190
    calculations of 195, 196
alleles 163, 165, 166
allopatric speciation 200
all-or-nothing principle
        (of action potentials) 21
alpha (α) cells 32, 41, 42
amino acids
    breakdown of 53, 54
ammonia 53, 54
ammonification 263, 264
anabolic steroids 67
    testing for 68
anaerobic respiration 139, 140
    measuring the rate of 144
animal cloning 234-237
Antarctica 285
antidiuretic hormone (ADH)
    62, 63

B

apical dominance 102, 103
apoptosis 155
aquaporins 62
artificial embryo twinning 234
artificial selection 198, 199
aseptic techniques 246
ATP (adenosine triphosphate)
    110, 111
    in muscle contraction 87
    from aerobic respiration 137
    from anaerobic respiration 140
ATPase 85, 111
ATP-creatine phosphate (ATP-CP)
    system 87
ATP synthase 111, 116, 136
autonomic nervous system 72
autosomal linkage 176, 177
auxins 98, 102, 103, 105, 106
Azotobacter 264

bacteria 46, 239, 240, 247, 248
bacterial artificial chromosomes
        (BACs) 221
bacteriophages 212, 213
baking 239
baroreceptors 77
batch fermentation 242
beta (β) cells 32, 41-43
bile duct 51
bioinformatics 224
biomass 256-260
bioremediation 239
biotechnology 238-250
biotic factors 255, 276, 277
blinking reflex 74, 75
blood glucose concentration
    41, 42
body plans 154, 155
body temperature 37-40
    control by hypothalamus
        39, 40
    control mechanisms 38, 39
Bowman's capsule 56, 57
brain 73
brewing 239

C

calcium ion channels 43
Calvin cycle 114, 118-120
    limiting factors 123, 124
cAMP (cyclic AMP) 31, 152
capturing motile organisms 271
carbon cycle 262, 263
cardiac muscle 88, 89
carriers (inheritance) 166
carrying capacity 277, 279
cell signalling 14
central nervous system (CNS) 72
cerebellum 73
cerebrum 73
cheese making 239
chemiosmotic theory 116, 136
chemoreceptors 77
chi-squared test 182-184
chloroplasts 113
chlorosis 163
cholinergic synapses 24
chromatography 126, 127
citations 11
climax communities 266, 267
cloning
    animals 234-237
    plants 230-233
closed cultures 243
codominant alleles 166
    inheritance of 169, 172
coenzyme A 132, 134
coenzymes
    in photosynthesis 114
    in respiration 132
collecting ducts 57, 62, 63
command words 292
communication systems 14
compensation points 111, 112
computational biology 224
conclusions 7
conservation 280-283
consumers 256
continuous fermentation 242
continuous variation 162
control elements 151
correlations 7

H

habitats 255
Hardy-Weinberg principle 195-197
hazards 8, 9
heart rate
control of 76-78
investigating 78, 79
monitors 79
herbivory 96
heterozygotes 165
high-throughput sequencing 223
histology
kidney 58
liver 53
pancreas 32
homeobox sequences 154
homeostasis 34, 35
homozygotes 165
hormonal systems 30-32
hormones 30-32
in plants 98, 102-106
host cells 213
Hox genes 154
human chorionic gonadotropin (hCG) 67
hypothalamus 39, 62, 73, 76
hypotheses 1

I

immobilised enzymes 249
uses of 250
indoleacetic acid (IAA) 98
inheritance 167-181
insect resistance 214
insertion mutations 157
insulin 41, 42
from genetically modified bacteria 46, 239
production 46, 239
secretion 43
therapy 44
interspecific competition 277
intraspecific competition 277, 278
introns 152
involuntary muscle 88
islets of Langerhans 32, 41
isolated enzymes 238, 249

K

kidney failure 64-66
kidney transplants 66
kidneys 56-59, 61-63
dissection of 59
histology 58
knee-jerk reflex 75
Krebs cycle 134, 135

L

lac operon 151
lactate fermentation 139
Lake District 286
leaf loss 104, 105
ligation 212
light-dependent reaction 114-116
light-harvesting systems 113
light-independent reaction 114, 118-120
limiting factors
of photosynthesis 122-124
of population sizes 279
linkage 174-177
link reaction 134
liver 41, 42, 51-53
histology 52, 53
loci 165
logarithmic scales 245
logarithms 244
loop of Henle 57, 61, 62

M

Maasai Mara 283
manometers 145
mature mRNA 152
medulla oblongata 73, 77
metabolic waste products 51
microorganisms
culturing 242, 243, 246
investigating factors affecting growth 247, 248
standard growth curves 243-245
use in biotechnology 238-240
micropropagation 232
Mimosa pudica 97
mitochondria 132
mitosis 155

models (scientific) 1

monoclonal antibodies (in pregnancy tests) 67
monoculture 214
monogenic characteristics 163
monogenic inheritance 167-169
motor neurones 15
mRNA editing 152
multiple allele crosses 171
muscle contraction 82-87
energy for 87
investigating 91
nervous control of 90
sliding filament model of 83
muscle fibres (structure of) 82, 83
muscle types 88, 89
mutations 157-159
myelinated neurones 22
myelin sheaths 22
myofibrils 82, 83
myosin filaments 82-86

N

NAD 132-137, 139
NADP 114, 116
natural selection 190
negative feedback 20, 34, 35, 42, 278
nephrons 56-58, 61, 62
nervous impulses 19-22
nervous system 15-17, 72
control of heart rate 76, 77
net productivity 257, 258
neuromuscular junctions 90
neurones 15
neurotransmitters 24, 90
nitrification 263, 264
Nitrobacter 264
nitrogen cycle 263, 264
nitrogen fixation 263, 264
Nitrosomonas 264
nodes of Ranvier 22
non-cyclic photophosphorylation 115
noradrenaline 77
null hypotheses 79, 182

O

operons 151
ornithine cycle 53, 54
osmoreceptors 62, 63
oxaloacetate 135
oxidative phosphorylation 136

P

Pacinian corpuscles 17
palindromic sequences 207
pancreas 32
parasympathetic nervous system 72
patents 216
pathogens (in genetic engineering) 215, 216
peat bogs 283
pedigree dogs 199
peer reviews 2
penicillin production 239
peripheral nervous system 72
peripheral temperature receptors 39
'pharming' 215
phenotypes 165
phenotypic ratios 168
    with epistasis 179, 180
    with linkage 177
phenotypic variation 162, 163
pheromones 96, 97
phosphorylation 111
photolysis 115
photophosphorylation 115, 116
photosynthesis 110-128
    experiments 126-128
    factors affecting 121, 122
    in energy transfer 256
    in the carbon cycle 262
    light-dependent reaction 114-116
    light-independent reaction 114, 118-120
    limiting factors of 122-124
photosynthetic pigments 113, 121
    separation of 126, 127
photosystems 113
phototropism 97, 98
    investigating 99

pioneer species 265
pituitary gland 62, 73
plagioclimaxes 268
plant cloning 230-233
plant hormones 98, 102-106
    commercial uses of 105, 106
plants 96-106
plasmids 212
polygenic characteristics 163
polymerase chain reaction (PCR) 206, 207
populations (size of) 276
    investigating 269-271
positive feedback 20, 35
potassium ion channels 19, 43
practical activity groups (PAGs) 5, 12
Practical Endorsement 5
predation 278
predator-prey relationships 278
predictions 1
pregnancy tests 67
presenting data 6
preservation 281, 283
primary mRNA 152
primers 206
problem solving 5
processing data 6
producers 256
programmed cell death 155
protein activation 152
proximal convoluted tubule (PCT) 57
pulse rate measurements 78, 79
Punnett squares 168
pyrosequencing 223
pyruvate 133, 134

Q

quadrats 269-271

R

random sampling 269
rearing livestock 260
receptors 14, 34, 72
recessive alleles 166
recognition sequences 207
recombinant DNA 212, 213
recording data 6

recording experiments 10
recreational drugs
    testing for 68
recycling (in ecosystems) 262-264
redox reactions 114
reduced NADP 114, 116
references 11
reflex actions 74, 75
refractory periods 21
regulatory genes 151
relay neurones 15
renal dialysis 65, 66
reproductive isolation 200, 201
research skills 10, 11
respiration 110, 132-146
    aerobic 132-137
    anaerobic 139, 140
    experiments 143-146
    in the carbon cycle 262
respiratory loss 257
respiratory quotients (RQs) 141
    uses of 142
respiratory substrates 141
respirometers 145, 146
resting potential
    of neurones 19
    of sensory receptors 16
restriction enzymes 207, 208, 212
R_f values 127
Rhizobium 264
ribulose bisphosphate (RuBP) 118, 119, 124
ribulose bisphosphate carboxylase (RuBisCO) 118, 119
risk assessments 8, 9
rooting powders 106

S

saltatory conduction 22
sampling 269
saprobiontic nutrition 262
sarcomeres 83
Schwann cells 22
scientific journals 2
second messengers 30
seed germination 103, 104
selective reabsorption (in the kidneys) 57, 58
sensory neurones 15